1959

FIRST PRINCIPLES

BY

HERBERT SPENCER

THE DE WITT REVOLVING FUND, INC.

NEW YORK

1958

PUBLISHER'S NOTE

The DeWitt Revolving Fund, Inc., a corporation organized for educational and charitable purposes and not for profit, has arranged for the reprinting of this book and the free distribution of copies thereof to the libraries of all the institutions of higher education in the United States, including those sometimes designated as senior and junior colleges; and in so far as practicable, for the placing of copies in other public libraries.

The reasons for this project are set forth in the following statement by Macdonald DeWitt, President of the above named organization. Mr. DeWitt says:

Some years ago when I was a young man I read the book written by Herbert Spencer entitled "First Principles." I felt then—and having since read it again several times, I feel now—that this is one of the greatest books ever written. To me as a young man it caused (as the author himself suggested it might) "a revolution of thought," determined my "conception of the universe, of life, of human nature," and influenced my ideas of right and wrong.

This book is now out of print and in several of the public libraries where I have endeavored to consult it from time to time I have either not been able to find it at all or have found the volume in such a bad state of repair as to render it practically unreadable.

My project now is to arrange for a reprinting of this book and the free distribution of copies thereof in the libraries of this country where it may be readily consulted by the young men of this current generation who may be interested in the questions so superbly presented therein.

I have been assured by competent authority that while

some, or perhaps many, of the statements made by Mr. Spencer in this book by way of illustration are no longer scientifically valid, the theory of evolution as developed by Herbert Spencer and set forth in this book has not been disproved in any substantial way by the discoveries of science made since the book was first written and published, and that the author's fundamental philosophy is as valid now as it was in his own time.

Spencer was an original thinker who presented his ideas in a manner somewhat unorthodox, and there were in his time and are now many who disagree with him, especially among professional scholars and scientists.

I believe that "First Principles" is a work which should not be allowed to get out of print and thus become unavailable to the young men of current generations who might be interested in the questions presented therein and who might therefore wish to consult the book.

"First Principles" was and is now an influence in my life, both powerful and beneficial, and if I could, by taking the trouble and incurring the expense involved in causing it to be reprinted and distributed, bring some measure of a similar influence into the life of another or other young men, I would feel that I had repaid to some small extent my great debt to Herbert Spencer and his work.

FIRST PRINCIPLES

PREFACE TO THE FOURTH EDITION

To THE first edition of this work there should have been prefixed a definite indication of its origin; and the misapprehensions that have arisen in the absence of such indication ought before now to have shown me the need of supplying it.

Though reference was made, in a note on the first page of the original preface, to certain Essays entitled "Progress: its Law and Cause," and "Transcendental Physiology," as containing generalizations which were to be elaborated in the "System of Philosophy" there set forth in programme, yet the dates of these Essays were not given; nor was there any indication of their cardinal importance as containing, in a brief form, the general Theory of Evolution. No clear evidence to the contrary standing in the way, there has been very generally uttered and accepted the belief that this work, and the works following it, originated after, and resulted from, the special doctrine contained in Mr. Darwin's "Origin of Species."

The Essay on "Progress: its Law and Cause," coextensive in the theory it contains with Chapters XV., XVI., XVII. and XX., in Part II. of this work, was first published in the "Westminster Review" for April, 1857; and the Essay in which is briefly set forth the general truth elaborated in Chapter XIX. originally appeared, under the title of "The Ultimate Laws of Physiology," in the "National Review" for October, 1857. Further I may point out that in the first edition of "The Principles of Psychology," published in July, 1855, mental phenomena are interpreted entirely from the evolution point of view; and the words used in the titles of sundry chapters imply the presence, at that date, of ideas more widely applied in the Essays just named. As the first edition of "The Origin of Species" did not make its appearance till October, 1859, it is manifest that the theory set forth in this work and its successors had an origin independent of, and prior to, that which is commonly assumed to have initiated it.

The distinctness of origin might, indeed, have been inferred from the work itself, which deals with Evolution at large—Inorganic, Organic, and Super-organic—in terms of Matter and Motion; and touches but briefly on those particular processes so luminously exhibited by Mr. Darwin. In § 159 only (p. 447), when illustrating the law of "The Multiplication of Effects," as universally displayed, have I had occasion to refer to the doctrine set forth in the "Origin of Species": pointing out that the general cause I had previously assigned for the production of divergent varieties of organisms would not suffice to account for all the facts without that special cause disclosed by Mr. Darwin. The absence of this passage would, of course, leave a serious gap in the general argument; but the remainder of the work would stand exactly as it now does.

I do not make this explanation in the belief that the prevailing misapprehension will thereby soon be rectified; for I am conscious that, once having become current, wrong beliefs of this kind long persist—all disproofs notwithstanding. Nevertheless, I yield to the suggestion that, unless I state the facts as they stand, I shall continue to countenance the misapprehension, and cannot expect it to cease.

With the exception of unimportant changes in one of the notes, and some typographical corrections, the text of this edition is identical with that of the last. I have, however, added an Appendix dealing with certain criticisms that have been passed upon the general formula of Evolution, and upon the philosophical doctrine which precedes it.

May, 1880.

PREFACE TO THE AMERICAN EDITION

THE present volume is the first of a series designed to unfold the principles of a new philosophy. It is divided into two parts: the aim of the first being to determine the true sphere of all rational investigation, and of the second, to elucidate those fundamental and universal principles which science has established within that sphere, and which are to constitute the basis of the system. The scheme of truth developed in these First Principles is complete in itself, and has its independent value; but it is designed by the author to serve for guidance and verification in the construction of the succeeding and larger portions of his philosophic plan.

Having presented in his introductory volume so much of the general principles of Physics as is essential to the development of his method, Mr. Spencer enters upon the subject of Organic Nature. The second work of the series is to be the Principles of Biology—a systematic statement of the facts and laws which constitute the Science of Life. It is not to be an encyclopedic and exhaustive treatise upon this vast subject, but such a compendious presentation of its data and general principles as shall interpret the method of nature, afford a clear understanding of the question involved, and prepare for further inquiries. This work is now published in quarterly numbers, of from 80 to 96 pages. Four of these parts have already appeared, and some idea of the course and character of the discussion may be formed by observing the titles to the chapters, which are as follows:

PART FIRST: I. Organic Matter; II. The Actions of Forces on Organic Matter; III. The Reactions of Organic

(7)

Matter on Forces; IV. Proximate Definition of Life; V. The Correspondence between Life and its Circumstances; VI. The Degree of Life varies with the Degree of Correspondence; VII. Scope of Biology. PART SECOND: I. Growth; II. Development; III. Function; IV. Waste and Repair; V. Adaptation; VI. Individuality; VII. Genesis; VIII. Heredity; IX. Variation; X. Genesis, Heredity, and Variation; XI. Classification; XII. Distribution.

The Principles of Biology will be followed by the Principles of Psychology; that is, Mr. Spencer will pass from the consideration of Life to the study of Mind. This subject will be regarded in the light of the great truths of Biology previously established; the connections of life and mind will be traced; the evolution of the intellectual faculties in their due succession, and in correspondence with the conditions of the environment, will be unfolded, and the whole subject of mind will be treated, not by the narrow metaphysical methods, but in its broadest aspect, as a phase of nature's order which can only be comprehended in the light of her universal plan.

The fourth work of the series is Sociology, or the science of human relations. As a multitude is but an assemblage of units, and as the characteristics of a multitude result from the properties of its units, so social phenomena are consequences of the natures of individual men. Biology and Psychology are the two great keys to the knowledge of human nature; and hence from these Mr. Spencer naturally passes to the subject of Social Science. The growth of society, the conditions of its intellectual and moral progress, the development of its various activities and organizations, will be here described, and a statement made of those principles which are essential to the successful regulation of social affairs.

Lastly, in Part Fifth, Mr. Spencer proposes to consider the principles of Morality. The truths furnished by Biology, Psychology, and Sociology will be here brought to bear, to determine correct rules of human action, the principles of private and public justice, and to form a true theory of right living.

The reader will obtain a more just idea of the extent and proportions of Mr. Spencer's philosophic plan, by consulting his prospectus at the close of the volume. It will be seen to embrace a wide range of topics, but in the present work, and in his profound and original volumes on the "Principles of Psychology" and "Social Statics," as also throughout his numerous Essays and Discussions, we discover that he has already traversed almost the entire field, while to elaborate the whole into one connected and organized philosophical scheme is a work well suited to his bold and comprehensive genius. With a metaphysical acuteness equalled only by his immense grasp of the results of physical science—alike remarkable for his profound analysis, constructive ability, and power of lucid and forcible statement, Mr. Spencer has rare endowments for the task he has undertaken, and can hardly fail to embody in his system the largest scientific and philosophical tendencies of the age.

As the present volume is a working-out of universal principles to be subsequently applied, it is probably of a more abstract character than will be the subsequent works of the series. The discussions strike down to the profoundest basis of human thought, and involve the deepest questions upon which the intellect of man has entered. Those unaccustomed to close metaphysical reasoning may therefore find parts of the argument not easy to follow, although it is here presented with a distinctness and a vigor to be found perhaps in no other author. Still, the chief portions of the book may be read by all with ease and pleasure, while no one can fail to be repaid for the persistent effort that may be required to master the entire argument. All who have sufficient earnestness of nature to take interest in those transcendent questions which are now occupying the most advanced minds of the age will find them here considered with unsurpassed clearness, originality, and power.

The invigorating influence of philosophical studies upon

the mind, and their consequent educational value, have been long recognized.   In this point of view the system here presented has high claims upon the young men of our country—embodying as it does the latest and largest results of positive science; organizing its facts and principles upon a natural method, which places them most perfectly in command of memory; and converging all its lines of inquiry to the end of a high practical beneficence—the unfolding of those laws of nature and human nature which determine personal welfare and the social polity.   Earnest and reverent in temper, cautious in statement, severly logical and yet presenting his views in a transparent and attractive style which combines the precision of science with many of the graces of light composition, it is believed that the thorough study of Spencer's philosophical scheme would combine, in an unrivalled degree, those prime requisites of the highest education, a knowledge of the truths which it is most important for man to know, and that salutary discipline of the mental faculties which results from their systematic acquisition.

We say the young men of *our country,* for, if we are not mistaken, it is here that Mr. Spencer is to find his largest and fittest audience.   There is something in the bold handling of his questions, in his earnest and fearless appeal to first principles, and in the practical availability of his conclusions, which is eminently suited to the genius of our people.   It has been so in a marked sense with his work on Education, and there is no reason why it should not be so in an equal degree with his other writings.   They betray a profound sympathy with the best spirit of our institutions, and that noble aspiration for the welfare and improvement of society which can hardly fail to commend them to the more liberal and enlightened portions of the American public.

PREFACE TO THE SECOND EDITION

WHEN the First Edition of this work was published, I supposed that the general theory set forth in its Second Part was presented in something like a finished form; but subsequent thought led me to further developments of much importance, and disclosed the fact that the component parts of the theory had been wrongly put together. Even in the absence of a more special reason, I had decided that, on the completion of the "Principles of Biology," it would be proper to suspend for a few months the series I am issuing, that I might make the required reorganization. And when the time had arrived, there had arisen a more special reason, which forbade hesitation. Translations into the French and Russian languages were about to be made—had, in fact, been commenced; and had I deferred the reorganization the work would have been reproduced with all its original imperfections. This will be a sufficient explanation to those who have complained of the delay in the issue of the "Principles of Psychology."

The First Part remains almost untouched: two verbal alterations only, on pp. 43 and 99, having been made to prevent misconceptions. Part II., however, is wholly transformed. Its first chapter, on "Laws in General," is omitted with a view to the inclusion of it in one of the later volumes of the series. Two minor chapters disappear. Most of the rest are transposed, in groups or singly. And there are nine new chapters embodying the further developments, and serving to combine the pre-existing chapters into a

changed whole.   The following scheme, in which the new
chapters are marked by italics, will give an idea of the
transformation:

<table>
<tr><td align="center">FIRST EDITION.</td><td align="center">SECOND EDITION.</td></tr>
<tr><td>Laws in General.</td><td>*Philosophy Defined.*</td></tr>
<tr><td>The Law of Evolution.</td><td>*The Data of Philosophy.*</td></tr>
<tr><td>The Law of Evolution (continued).</td><td></td></tr>
<tr><td>The Causes of Evolution.</td><td></td></tr>
<tr><td>Space, Time, Matter, Motion, and Force.</td><td>Space, Time, Matter, Motion, and Force.</td></tr>
<tr><td>The Indestructibility of Matter.</td><td>The Indestructibility of Matter.</td></tr>
<tr><td>The Continuity of Motion.</td><td>The Continuity of Motion.</td></tr>
<tr><td>The Persistence of Force.</td><td>The Persistence of Force.</td></tr>
<tr><td></td><td>*The Persistence of Relations among Forces.*</td></tr>
<tr><td>The Correlation and Equivalence of Forces.</td><td>The Transformation and Equivalence of Forces.</td></tr>
<tr><td>The Direction of Motion.</td><td>The Direction of Motion.</td></tr>
<tr><td>The Rhythm of Motion.</td><td>The Rhythm of Motion.</td></tr>
<tr><td></td><td>*Recapitulation, Criticism, and Recommencement.*</td></tr>
<tr><td>The Conditions essential to Evolution.</td><td>*Evolution and Dissolution.*</td></tr>
<tr><td></td><td>*Simple and Compound Evolution.*</td></tr>
<tr><td></td><td>The Law of Evolution.</td></tr>
<tr><td></td><td>The Law of Evolution (continued).</td></tr>
<tr><td></td><td>The Law of Evolution (continued).</td></tr>
<tr><td></td><td>*The Law of Evolution concluded.*</td></tr>
<tr><td></td><td>*The Interpretation of Evolution.*</td></tr>
<tr><td>The Instability of the Homogeneous.</td><td>The Instability of the Homogeneous.</td></tr>
<tr><td>The Multiplication of Effects.</td><td>The Multiplication of Effects.</td></tr>
<tr><td>Differentiation and Integration.</td><td>Segregation.</td></tr>
<tr><td>Equilibration.</td><td>Equilibration.</td></tr>
<tr><td></td><td>*Dissolution.*</td></tr>
<tr><td>Summary and Conclusion.</td><td>Summary and Conclusion (Rewritten).</td></tr>
</table>

(The Law of Evolution, The Law of Evolution (continued), and The Law of Evolution (continued) are bracketed with the note: Re-arranged with additions.)

Of course throughout this reorganized Second Part the
numbers of the sections have been changed, and hence
those who possess the "Principles of Biology," in which
many references are made to passages in "First Principles,"

would be inconvenienced by the want of correspondence between the numbers of the sections in the original edition and in the new edition, were they without any means of identifying the sections as now numbered. The annexed list, showing which section answers to which in the two editions, will meet the requirement:

First Edit.	Second Edit.	First Edit.	Second Edit.	First Edit.	Second Edit.	First Edit.	Second Edit.	First Edit.	Second Edit.
§43	§119		107	§72	§58	§92	§81	§121	§161
44	117		108	73	59	93	82	122	162
45	118		109	74	60	94	83	123	163
46	120		110	75	61	95	84	124	164
47	121	§56 {	111	76	62	96	85	125	165
48	122		112	77	66	97	86	126	166
49	123		113	78	67	98	87	127	167
50	124		114	79	68	99	88	128	168
51	125		115	80	69	109	149	129	169
52	126	61	46	81	70	110	150	130	170
53	128	62	47	82	71	111	151	131	171
54	129	63	48	83	72	112	152	132	172
55 {	130	64	49	84	73	113	153	133	173
	131	65	50	85	74	114	154	134	174
	132	66	52	86	75	115	155	135	175
	133	67	53	87	76	116	156	136	176
	134	68	54	88	77	117	157	137 {	177
	135	69	55	89	78	118	158		183
	136	70	56	90	79	119	159	144	193
	137	71	57	91	80	120	160	145	194

The original stereotype plates have been used wherever it was possible: and hence the exact correspondence between the two editions in many places, even where adjacent pages are altered.[1]

London, November, 1867.

---

[1] This refers to the London editions only.—EDITOR.

would be inconvenienced by the want of correspondence between the numbers of the sections in the original edition and in the new edition, were they without any means of identifying the sections as now numbered. The annexed list, showing which section answers to which in the two editions, will meet the requirement.

London, November, 1862.

The original stereotype plates have been used wherever it was possible, and hence the exact correspondence between the two editions in many places, even where adjacent pages are altered.

CONTENTS

PART I.—THE UNKNOWABLE

PART II.—THE KNOWABLE

FIRST PRINCIPLES

THE UNKNOWABLE

CHAPTER I

RELIGION AND SCIENCE

§ 1. WE TOO often forget that not only is there "a soul of goodness in things evil," but very generally also a soul of truth in things erroneous. While many admit the abstract probability that a falsity has usually a nucleus of reality, few bear this abstract probability in mind, when passing judgment on the opinions of others. A belief that is finally proved to be grossly at variance with fact is cast aside with indignation or contempt; and in the heat of antagonism scarcely any one inquires what there was in this belief which commended it to men's minds. Yet there must have been something. And there is reason to suspect that this something was its correspondence with certain of their experiences: an extremely limited or vague correspondence perhaps; but still, a correspondence. Even the absurdest report may in nearly every instance be traced to an actual occurrence; and had there been no such actual occurrence, this preposterous misrepresentation of it would never have existed. Though the distorted or magnified image transmitted to us through the refracting medium of rumor, is utterly unlike the reality; yet in the absence of the reality there would have been no distorted or magnified image. And thus it is with human beliefs in general. Entirely

(17)

wrong as they may appear, the implication is that they germinated out of actual experiences—originally contained, and perhaps still contain, some small amount of verity.

More especially may we safely assume this, in the case of beliefs that have long existed and are widely diffused; and most of all so in the case of beliefs that are perennial and nearly or quite universal. The presumption that any current opinion is not wholly false gains in strength according to the number of its adherents. Admitting, as we must, that life is impossible unless through a certain agreement between internal convictions and external circumstances; admitting therefore that the probabilities are always in favor of the truth, or at least the partial truth, of a conviction; we must admit that the convictions entertained by many minds in common are the most likely to have some foundation. The elimination of individual errors of thought must give to the resulting judgment a certain additional value. It may indeed be urged that many widely-spread beliefs are received on authority; that those entertaining them make no attempts at verification; and hence it may be inferred that the multitude of adherents adds but little to the probability of a belief. But this is not true. For a belief which gains extensive reception without critical examination, is thereby proved to have a general congruity with the various other beliefs of those who receive it; and in so far as these various other beliefs are based upon personal observation and judgment, they give an indirect warrant to one with which they harmonize. It may be that this warrant is of small value; but still it is of some value.

Could we reach definite views on this matter, they would be extremely useful to us. It is important that we should, if possible, form something like a general theory of current opinions; so that we may neither overestimate nor underestimate their worth. Arriving at correct judgments on disputed questions, much depends on the attitude of mind we preserve while listening to, or taking part in, the controversy; and for the preservation of a right attitude, it is needful that we should learn how true, and yet how untrue, are average human beliefs. On the one hand, we must keep free from that bias in favor of received ideas which expresses itself in such dogmas as "What every one says must be true," or "The voice of the people is the voice of God." On the other hand, the fact disclosed by a survey of the past, that majorities have usually been wrong, must not blind us to the complementary fact, that majorities have usually not been *entirely* wrong. And the avoidance of these extremes being a prerequisite to catholic thinking, we shall do well to provide ourselves with a safeguard against them, by making a valuation of opinions in the abstract. To this end we must contemplate the kind of relation that ordinarily subsists between opinions and facts. Let us do so with one of those beliefs which under various forms has prevailed among all nations in all times.

§ 2. The earliest traditions represent rulers as gods or demigods. By their subjects, primitive kings were regarded as superhuman in origin, and superhuman in power. They possessed divine titles; received obeisances like those made before the altars of deities; and were in some cases actually worshipped. If there needs proof that the divine and half-divine characters originally ascribed to monarchs were ascribed literally, we have it in the fact that there are still existing savage races, among whom it is held that the chiefs and their kindred are of celestial origin, or, as elsewhere, that only the chiefs have souls. And of course along with beliefs of this kind, there existed a belief in the unlimited power of the ruler over his subjects—an absolute possession of them, extending even to the taking of their lives at will; as even still in Fiji, where a victim stands unbound to be killed at the word of his chief; himself declaring, "whatever the king says must be done."

In times and among races somewhat less barbarous, we find these beliefs a little modified. The monarch, instead of being literally thought god or demigod, is conceived to be a man having divine authority, with perhaps more or less of divine nature. He retains, however, as in the East to the present day, titles expressing his heavenly descent or relationships; and is still saluted in forms and words as humble as those addressed to the Deity. While the lives and properties of his people, if not practically so completely at his mercy, are still in theory supposed to be his.

Later in the progress of civilization, as during the Middle Ages in Europe, the current opinions respecting the relationship of rulers and ruled are further changed. For the theory of divine origin, there is substituted that of divine right. No longer god or demigod, or even god-descended, the king is now regarded as simply God's vicegerent. The obeisances made to him are not so extreme in their humility; and his sacred titles lose much of their meaning. Moreover, his authority ceases to be unlimited. Subjects deny his right to dispose at will of their lives and properties; and yield allegiance only in the shape of obedience to his commands.

With advancing political opinion has come still greater restriction of imperial power. Belief in the supernatural character of the ruler, long ago repudiated by ourselves, for example, has left behind it nothing more than the popular tendency to ascribe unusual goodness, wisdom, and beauty to the monarch. Loyalty, which originally meant implicit submission to the king's will, now means a merely nominal profession of subordination, and the fulfilment of certain forms of respect. Our political practice, and our political theory, alike utterly reject those regal prerogatives which once passed unquestioned. By deposing some, and putting others in their places, we have not only denied the divine rights of certain men to rule; but we have denied that they have any rights beyond those originating in the assent of the nation. Though our forms of speech and our state-documents still assert the subjection of the citizens to the ruler, our actual beliefs and our daily proceedings implicitly assert the contrary. We obey no laws save those of our own making. We have entirely divested the monarch of legislative power; and should immediately rebel against his or her exercise of such power, even in matters of the smallest concern. In brief the aboriginal doctrine is all but extinct among us.

Nor has the rejection of primitive political beliefs resulted only in transferring the authority of an autocrat to a representative body. The views entertained respecting governments in general, of whatever form, are now widely different from those once entertained. Whether popular or despotic, governments were in ancient times supposed to have unlimited authority over their subjects. Individuals existed for the benefit of the State; not the State for the benefit of individuals. In our days, however, not only has the national will been in many cases substituted for the will of the king; but the exercise of this national will has been restricted to a much smaller sphere. In England, for instance, though there has been established no definite theory setting bounds to governmental authority, yet, in practice, sundry bounds have been set to it which are tacitly recognized by all. There is no organic law formally declaring that the legislature may not freely dispose of the citizens' lives, as early kings did when they sacrificed hecatombs of victims; but were it possible for our legislature to attempt such a thing, its own destruction would be the consequence, rather than the destruction of citizens. How entirely we have established the personal liberties of the subject against the invasions of State power, would be quickly demonstrated, were it proposed by Act of Parliament forcibly to take possession of the nation, or of any class, and turn its services to public ends; as the services of the people were turned by primitive rulers. And should any statesman suggest a redistribution of property such as was sometimes made in ancient democratic communities, he would be met by a thousand-tongued denial of imperial power over individual possessions. Not only in our day have these fundamental claims of the citizen been thus made good against the State, but sundry minor claims likewise. Ages ago, laws regulating dress and mode of living fell into disuse; and any attempt to revive them would prove the current opinion to be, that such matters lie beyond the sphere of legal control. For some centuries we have been asserting in practice, and have now established in theory, the right of every man to choose his own religious beliefs, instead of receiving such beliefs on State authority. Within the last few generations we have inaugurated complete liberty of speech, in spite of all legislative attempts to suppress or limit it. And still more recently we have claimed and finally obtained, under a few exceptional restrictions, freedom to trade with whomsoever we please. Thus our political beliefs are widely different from ancient ones, not only as to the proper depositary of power to be exercised over a nation, but also as to the extent of that power.

Not even here has the change ended. Besides the average opinions which we have just described as current among ourselves, there exists a less widely diffused opinion going still further in the same direction. There are to be found men who contend that the sphere of government should be narrowed even more than it is in England. The modern doctrine that the State exists for the benefit of citizens, which has now in a great measure supplanted the ancient doctrine that the citizens exist for the benefit of the State, they would push to its logical results. They hold that the freedom of the individual, limited only by the like freedom of other individuals, is sacred; and that the legislature cannot equitably put further restrictions upon it, either by forbidding any actions which the law of equal freedom permits, or taking away any property save that required to pay the cost of enforcing this law itself. They assert that the sole function of the State is the protection of persons against each other, and against a foreign foe. They urge that as, throughout civilization, the manifest tendency has been continually to extend the liberties of the subject, and restrict the functions of the State, there is reason to believe that the ultimate political condition must be one in which personal freedom is the greatest possible and governmental power the least possible; that, namely, in which the freedom of each has no limit but the like freedom of all; while the sole governmental duty is the maintenance of this limit.

Here, then, in different times and places we find concerning the origin, authority, and functions of government a great variety of opinions—opinions of which the leading genera above indicated subdivide into countless species. What now must be said about the truth or falsity of these opinions? Save among a few barbarous tribes the notion that a monarch is a god or demigod is regarded throughout the world as an absurdity almost passing the bounds of human credulity. In but few places does there survive a vague notion that the ruler possesses any supernatural attributes. Most civilized communities which still admit the divine right of governments have long since repudiated the divine right of kings. Elsewhere the belief that there is anything sacred in legislative regulations is dying out; laws are coming to be considered as conventional only. While the extreme school holds that governments have neither intrinsic authority, nor can have authority given to them by convention, but can possess authority only as the administrators of those moral principles deducible from the conditions essential to social life. Of these various beliefs, with their innumerable modifications, must we then say that some one alone is wholly right and all the rest wholly wrong; or must we say that each of them contains truth more or less completely disguised by errors? The latter alternative is the one which analysis will force upon us. Ridiculous as they may severally appear to those not educated under them, every one of these doctrines has for its vital element the recognition of an unquestionable fact. Directly or by implication, each of them insists on a certain subordination of individual actions to social requirements. There are wide differences as to the power to which this subordination is due; there are wide differences as to the motive for this subordination; there are wide differences as to its extent, but that there must be *some* subordination all are agreed. From the oldest and rudest idea of allegiance, down to the most advanced political theory of our own day, there is on this point complete unanimity. Though, between the savage who conceives his life and property to be at the absolute disposal of his chief, and the anarchist who denies the right of any government, autocratic or democratic, to trench upon his individual freedom, there seems at first sight an entire and irreconcilable antagonism; yet ultimate analysis discloses in them this fundamental community of opinion; that there are limits which individual actions may not transgress —limits which the one regards as originating in the king's will, and which the other regards as deducible from the equal claims of fellow citizens.

It may perhaps at first sight seem that we here reach a very unimportant conclusion: namely, that a certain tacit assumption is equally implied in all these conflicting political creeds—an assumption which is indeed of self-evident validity. The question, however, is not the value or novelty of the particular truth in this case arrived at. My aim has been to exhibit the more general truth, which we are apt to overlook, that between the most opposite beliefs there is usually something in common—something taken for granted by each; and that this something, if not to be set down as an unquestionable verity, may yet be considered to have the highest degree of probability. A postulate which, like the one above instanced, is not consciously asserted but unconsciously involved; and which is unconsciously involved not by one man or body of men, but by numerous bodies of men who diverge in countless ways and degrees in the rest of their beliefs—has a warrant far transcending any that can be usually shown. And when, as in this case, the postulate is abstract—is not based on some one concrete experience common to all mankind, but implies an induction from a great variety of experiences, we may say that it ranks next in certainty to the postulates of exact science.

Do we not thus arrive at a generalization which may habitually guide us when seeking for the soul of truth in things erroneous? While the foregoing illustration brings clearly home the fact, that in opinions seeming to be absolutely and supremely wrong something right is yet to be found, it also indicates the method we should pursue in seeking the something right. This method is to compare all opinions of the same genus; to set aside as more or less discrediting one another those various special and concrete elements in which such opinions disagree; to observe what remains after the discordant constituents have been eliminated; and to find for this remaining constituent that abstract expression which holds true throughout its divergent modifications.

§ 3. A candid acceptance of this general principle, and an adoption of the course it indicates, will greatly aid us in dealing with those chronic antagonisms by which men are divided. Applying it not only to current ideas with which we are personally unconcerned, but also to our own ideas and those of our opponents, we shall be led to form far more correct judgments. We shall be ever ready to suspect that the convictions we entertain are not wholly right, and that the adverse convictions are not wholly wrong. On the one hand, we shall not, in common with the great mass of the unthinking, let our beliefs be determined by the mere accident of birth in a particular age on a particular part of the Earth's surface; and, on the other hand, we shall be saved from that error of entire and contemptuous negation which is fallen into by most who take up an attitude of independent criticism.

Of all antagonisms of belief, the oldest, the widest, the most profound, and the most important, is that between Religion and Science. It commenced when the recognition of the simplest uniformities in surrounding things set a limit to the once universal superstition. It shows itself everywhere throughout the domain of human knowledge, affecting men's interpretations alike of the simplest mechanical accidents and of the most complicated events in the histories of nations. It has its roots deep down in the diverse habits of thought of different orders of minds. And the conflicting conceptions of nature and life which these diverse habits of thought severally generate influence for good or ill the tone of feeling and the daily conduct.

An unceasing battle of opinion like this, which has been carried on throughout all ages under the banners of Religion and Science, has of course generated an animosity fatal to a just estimate of either party by the other. On a larger scale, and more intensely than any other controversy, has it illustrated that perennially significant fable concerning the knights who fought about the color of a shield of which neither looked at more than one face. Each combatant, seeing clearly his own aspect of the question, has charged his opponent with stupidity or dishonesty in not seeing the same aspect of it; while each has wanted the candor to go over to his opponent's side and find out how it was that he saw everything so differently.

Happily the times display an increasing catholicity of feeling, which we shall do well in carrying as far as our natures permit. In proportion as we love truth more and victory less, we shall become anxious to know what it is which leads our opponents to think as they do. We shall begin to suspect that the pertinacity of belief exhibited by them must result from a perception of something we have not perceived. And we shall aim to supplement the portion of truth we have found with the portion found by them. Making a more rational estimate of human authority, we shall avoid alike the extremes of undue submission and undue rebellion —shall not regard some men's judgments as wholly good and others as wholly bad; but shall rather lean to the more defensible position that none are completely right and none are completely wrong.

Preserving, as far as may be, this impartial attitude, let us then contemplate the two sides of this great controversy.

Keeping guard against the bias of education and shutting out the whisperings of sectarian feeling, let us consider what are the *à priori* probabilities in favor of each party.

§ 4. When duly realized, the general principle above illustrated must lead us to anticipate that the diverse forms of religious belief which have existed, and which still exist, have all a basis in some ultimate fact. Judging by analogy the implication is, not that any one of them is altogether right; but that in each there is something right more or less disguised by other things wrong. It may be that the soul of truth contained in erroneous creeds is very unlike most, if not all, of its several embodiments; and indeed if, as we have good reason to expect, it is much more abstract than any of them, its unlikeness necessarily follows. But however different from its concrete expressions, some essential verity must be looked for. To suppose that these multiform conceptions should be one and all *absolutely* groundless, discredits too profoundly that average human intelligence from which all our individual intelligences are inherited.

This most general reason we shall find enforced by other more special ones. To the presumption that a number of diverse beliefs of the same class have some common foundation in fact, must in this case be added a further presumption derived from the omnipresence of the beliefs. Religious ideas of one kind or other are almost universal. Admitting that in many places there are tribes who have no theory of creation, no word for a deity, no propitiatory acts, no idea of another life; admitting that only when a certain phase of intelligence is reached do the most rudimentary of such theories make their appearance—the implication is practically the same. Grant that among all races who have passed a certain stage of intellectual development there are found vague notions concerning the origin and hidden nature of surrounding things, and there arises the inference that such notions are necessary products of progressing intelligence. Their endless variety serves but to strengthen this conclusion: showing as it does a more or less independent genesis—showing how, in different places and times, like conditions have led to similar trains of thought, ending in analogous results. That these countless different, and yet allied, phenomena presented by all religions are accidental or factitious, is an untenable supposition. A candid examination of the evidence quite negatives the doctrine maintained by some, that creeds are priestly inventions. Even as a mere question of probabilities it cannot rationally be concluded that in every society, past and present, savage and civilized, certain members of the community have combined to delude the rest in ways so analogous. To any who may allege that some primitive fiction was devised by some primitive priesthood before yet mankind had diverged from a common centre, a reply is furnished by philology; for philology proves the dispersion of mankind to have commenced before there existed a language sufficiently organized to express religious ideas. Moreover, were it otherwise tenable, the hypothesis of artificial origin fails to account for the facts. It does not explain why, under all changes of form, certain elements of religious belief remain constant. It does not show us how it happens that while adverse criticism has from age to age gone on destroying particular theological dogmas, it has not destroyed the fundamental conception underlying these dogmas. It leaves us without any solution of the striking circumstance that when, from the absurdities and corruptions accumulated around them, national creeds have fallen into general discredit, ending in indifferentism or positive denial, there has always by and by arisen a reassertion of them; if not the same in form, still the same in essence. Thus the universality of religious ideas, their independent evolution among different primitive races, and their great vitality, unite in showing that their source must be deep-seated instead of superficial. In other words, we are obliged to admit that, if not supernaturally derived as the majority contend, they must be derived out of human experiences, slowly accumulated and organized.

Should it be asserted that religious ideas are products of the religious sentiment, which, to satisfy itself, prompts imaginations that it afterward projects into the external world, and by and by mistakes for realities; the problem is not solved, but only removed further back. Whether the wish is father to the thought, or whether sentiment and idea have a common genesis, there equally arises the question—Whence comes the sentiment? That it is a constituent in man's nature is implied by the hypothesis; and cannot indeed be denied by those who prefer other hypotheses. And if the religious sentiment, displayed habitually by the majority of mankind, and occasionally aroused even in those seemingly devoid of it, must be classed among human emotions, we cannot rationally ignore it. We are bound to ask its origin and its function. Here is an attribute which, to say the least, has had an enormous influence—which has played a conspicuous part throughout the entire past as far back as history records, and is at present the life of numerous institutions, the stimulus to perpetual controversies, and the prompter of countless daily actions. Any Theory of Things which takes no account of this attribute, must, then, be extremely defective. If with no other view, still as a question in philosophy we are called on to say what this attribute means; and we cannot decline the task without confessing our philosophy to be incompetent.

Two suppositions only are open to us: the one that the feeling which responds to religious ideas resulted, along with all other human faculties, from an act of special creation; the other that it, in common with the rest, arose by a process of evolution. If we adopt the first of these alternatives, universally accepted by our ancestors and by the immense majority of our contemporaries, the matter is at once settled: man is directly endowed with the religious feeling by a creator; and to that creator it designedly responds. If we adopt the second alternative, then we are met by the questions—What are the circumstances to which the genesis of the religious feeling is due? and—What is its office?

We are bound to entertain these questions; and we are bound to find answers to them. Considering all faculties, as we must on this supposition, to result from accumulated modifications caused by the intercourse of the organism with its environment, we are obliged to admit that there exist in the environment certain phenomena or conditions which have determined the growth of the feeling in question; and so are obliged to admit that it is as normal as any other faculty. Add to which that as, on the hypothesis of a development of lower forms into higher, the end toward which the progressive changes directly or indirectly tend must be adaptation to the requirements of existence; we are also forced to infer that this feeling is in some way conducive to human welfare. Thus both alternatives contain the same ultimate implication. We must conclude that the religious sentiment is either directly created, or is created by the slow action of natural causes; and whichever of these conclusions we adopt requires us to treat the religious sentiment with respect.

One other consideration should not be overlooked—a consideration which students of Science more especially need to have pointed out. Occupied as such are with established truths, and accustomed to regard things not already known as things to be hereafter discovered, they are liable to forget that information, however extensive it may become, can never satisfy inquiry. Positive knowledge does not, and never can, fill the whole region of possible thought. At the uttermost reach of discovery there arises, and must ever arise, the question—What lies beyond? As it is impossible to think of a limit to space so as to exclude the idea of space lying outside that limit; so we cannot conceive of any explanation profound enough to exclude the question—What is the explanation of that explanation? Regarding Science as a gradually increasing sphere, we may say that every addition to its surface does but bring it into wider contact with surrounding nescience. There must ever remain, therefore, two antithetical modes of mental action. Throughout all future time, as now, the human mind may occupy itself, not only with ascertained phenomena and their relations, but also with that unascertained something which phenomena and their relations imply. Hence if knowledge cannot monopolize consciousness—if it must always continue possible for the mind to dwell upon that which transcends knowledge; then there can never cease to be a place for something of the nature of Religion; since Religion under all its forms is distinguished from everything else in this, that its subject-matter is that which passes the sphere of experience.

Thus, however untenable may be any or all the existing religious creeds, however gross the absurdities associated with them, however irrational the arguments set forth in their defence, we must not ignore the verity which in all likelihood lies hidden within them. The general probability that widely-spread beliefs are not absolutely baseless is in this case enforced by a further probability due to the omnipresence of the beliefs. In the existence of a religious sentiment, whatever be its origin, we have a second evidence of great significance. And as in that nescience which must ever remain the antithesis to science, there is a sphere for the exercise of this sentiment, we find a third general fact of like implication. We may be sure, therefore, that religions, though even none of them be actually true, are yet all adumbrations of a truth.

§ 5. As, to the religious, it will seem absurd to set forth any justification for Religion; so, to the scientific, will it seem absurd to defend Science. Yet to do the last is certainly as needful as to do the first. If there exists a class who, in contempt of its follies and disgust at its corruptions, have contracted toward Religion a repugnance which makes them overlook the fundamental verity contained in it—so, too, is there a class offended to such a degree by the destructive criticisms men of science make on the religious tenets they regard as essential, that they have acquired a strong prejudice against Science in general. They are not prepared with any avowed reasons for their dislike. They have simply a remembrance of the rude shakes which Science has given to many of their cherished convictions, and a suspicion that it may perhaps eventually uproot all they regard as sacred; and hence it produces in them a certain inarticulate dread.

What is Science. To see the absurdity of the prejudice against it, we need only remark that Science is simply a higher development of common knowledge; and that if Science is repudiated, all knowledge must be repudiated along with it. The extremest bigot will not suspect any harm in the observation that the sun rises earlier and sets later in the summer than in the winter; but will rather consider such an observation as a useful aid in fulfilling the duties of life. Well, Astronomy is an organized body of similar observations, made with greater nicety, extended to a larger number of objects, and so analyzed as to disclose the real arrangements of the heavens, and to dispel our false conceptions of them. That iron will rust in water, that wood will burn, that long-kept viands become putrid, the most timid sectarian will teach without alarm, as things useful to be known. But these are chemical truths: Chemistry is a systematized collection of such facts, ascertained with precision, and so classified and generalized as to enable us to say with certainty, concerning each simple or compound substance, what change will occur in it under given conditions. And thus is it with all the sciences. They severally germinate out of the experiences of daily life; insensibly as they grow they draw in remoter, more numerous, and more complex experiences; and among these, they ascertain laws of dependence like those which make up our knowledge of the most familiar objects. Nowhere is it possible to draw a line and say— here Science begins. And as it is the function of common observation to serve for the guidance of conduct; so, too, is the guidance of conduct the office of the most recondite and abstract inquiries of Science. Through the countless industrial processes and the various modes of locomotion which it

has given to us, Physics regulates more completely our social
life than does his acquaintance with the properties of surrounding bodies regulate the life of the savage. Anatomy
and Physiology, through their effects on the practice of
medicine and hygiene, modify our actions almost as much
as does our acquaintance with the evils and benefits which
common environing agencies may produce on our bodies.
All Science is prevision; and all prevision ultimately aids
us in greater or less degree to achieve the good and avoid
the bad. As certainly as the perception of an object lying
in our path warns us against stumbling over it; so certainly
do those more complicated and subtle perceptions which constitute Science warn us against stumbling over intervening
obstacles in the pursuit of our distant ends. Thus being
one in origin and function, the simplest forms of cognition
and the most complex must be dealt with alike. We are
bound in consistency to receive the widest knowledge which
our faculties can reach, or to reject along with it that narrow
knowledge possessed by all. There is no logical alternative
between accepting our intelligence in its entirety, or repu-
diating even that lowest intelligence which we possess in
common with brutes.

   To ask the question which more immediately concerns
our argument—whether Science is substantially true?—is
much like asking whether the sun gives light. And it is
because they are conscious how undeniably valid are most
of its propositions, that the theological party regard Science
with so much secret alarm. They know that during the two
thousand years of its growth some of its larger divisions—
mathematics, physics, astronomy—have been subject to the
rigorous criticism of successive generations; and have notwithstanding become ever more firmly established. They
know that, unlike many of their own doctrines, which were
once universally received but have age by age been more
frequently called in question, the doctrines of Science, at
first confined to a few scattered inquirers, have been slowly
growing into general acceptance, and are now in great part

admitted as beyond dispute. They know that men of science throughout the world subject each other's results to the most searching examination; and that error is mercilessly exposed and rejected as soon as discovered. And, finally, they know that still more conclusive testimony is to be found in the daily verification of scientific predictions, and in the never-ceasing triumphs of those arts which Science guides.

To regard with alienation that which has such high credentials is a folly. Though in the tone which many of the scientific adopt toward them the defenders of Religion may find some excuse for this alienation; yet the excuse is a very insufficient one. On the side of Science, as on their own side, they must admit that shortcomings in the advocates do not tell essentially against that which is advocated. Science must be judged by itself; and so judged, only the most perverted intellect can fail to see that it is worthy of all reverence. Be there or be there not any other revelation, we have a veritable revelation in Science—a continuous disclosure, through the intelligence with which we are endowed, of the established order of the Universe. This disclosure it is the duty of everyone to verify as far as in him lies; and, having verified, to receive with all humility.

§ 6. On both sides of this great controversy, then, truth must exist. An unbiased consideration of its general aspects forces us to conclude that Religion, everywhere present as a weft running through the warp of human history, expresses some eternal fact; while it is almost a truism to say of Science that it is an organized mass of facts, ever growing, and ever being more completely purified from errors. And if both have bases in the reality of things, then between them there must be a fundamental harmony. It is an incredible hypothesis that there are two orders of truth, in absolute and everlasting opposition. Only on some Manichean theory, which among ourselves no one dares openly avow, however much his beliefs may be tainted by it, is such a supposition even conceivable. That Religion is divine and Science diabolical, is a proposition which, though implied in many a clerical declamation, not the most vehement fanatic can bring himself distinctly to assert. And whoever does not assert this must admit that under their seeming antagonism lies hidden an entire agreement.

Each side, therefore, has to recognize the claims of the other as standing for truths that are not to be ignored. He who contemplates the Universe from the religious point of view must learn to see that this which we call Science is one constituent of the great whole; and as such ought to be regarded with a sentiment like that which the remainder excites. While he who contemplates the universe from the scientific point of view must learn to see that this which we call Religion is similarly a constituent of the great whole; and being such, must be treated as a subject of science with no more prejudice than any other reality. It behooves each party to strive to understand the other, with the conviction that the other has something worthy to be understood; and with the conviction that when mutually recognized this something will be the basis of a complete reconciliation.

How to find this something—how to reconcile them, thus becomes the problem which we should perseveringly try to solve. Not to reconcile them in any makeshift way—not to find one of those compromises we hear from time to time proposed, which their proposers must secretly feel are artificial and temporary; but to arrive at the terms of a real and permanent peace between them. The thing we have to seek out, is that ultimate truth which both will avow with absolute sincerity—with not the remotest mental reservation. There shall be no concession—no yielding on either side of something that will by and by be reasserted; but the common ground on which they meet shall be one which each will maintain for itself. We have to discover some fundamental verity which Religion will assert, with all possible emphasis, in the absence of Science; and which Science, with all possible emphasis, will assert in the absence of Religion—some fundamental verity in the defence of which each will find the other its ally.

Or, changing the point of view, our aim must be to co-ordinate the seemingly opposed convictions which Religion and Science embody. From the coalescence of antagonist ideas, each containing its portion of truth, there always arises a higher development. As in Geology when the igneous and aqueous hypotheses were united, a rapid advance took place; as in Biology we are beginning to progress through the fusion of the doctrine of types with the doctrine of adaptations; as in Psychology the arrested growth recommences now that the disciples of Kant and those of Locke have both their views recognized in the theory that organized experiences produce forms of thought; as in Sociology, now that it is beginning to assume a positive character, we find a recognition of both the party of progress and the party of order, as each holding a truth which forms a needful complement to that held by the other; so must it be on a grander scale with Religion and Science. Here, too, we must look for a conception which combines the conclusions of both; and here, too, we may expect important results from their combination. To understand how Science and Religion express opposite sides of the same fact—the one its near or visible side, and the other its remote or invisible side—this it is which we must attempt; and to achieve this must profoundly modify our general Theory of Things.

Already in the foregoing pages the method of seeking such a reconciliation has been vaguely foreshadowed. Before proceeding further, however, it will be well to treat the question of method more definitely. To find that truth in which Religion and Science coalesce, we must know in what direction to look for it, and what kind of truth it is likely to be.

§ 7. We have found *à priori* reason for believing that in all religions, even the rudest, there lies hidden a fundamen-

tal verity. We have inferred that this fundamental verity is that element common to all religions, which remains after their discordant peculiarities have been mutually cancelled. And we have further inferred that this element is almost certain to be more abstract than any current religious doctrine. Now it is manifest that only in some highly abstract proposition can Religion and Science find a common ground. Neither such dogmas as those of the trinitarian and unitarian, nor any such idea as that of propitiation, common though it may be to all religions, can serve as the desired basis of agreement; for Science cannot recognize beliefs like these: they lie beyond its sphere. Hence we see not only that, judging by analogy, the essential truth contained in Religion is that most abstract element pervading all its forms; but also that this most abstract element is the only one in which Religion is likely to agree with Science.

Similarly if we begin at the other end, and inquire what scientific truth can unite Science and Religion. It is at once manifest that Religion can take no cognizance of special scientific doctrines, any more than Science can take cognizance of special religious doctrines. The truth which Science asserts and Religion indorses cannot be one furnished by mathematics; nor can it be a physical truth; nor can it be a truth in chemistry; it cannot be a truth belonging to any particular science. No generalization of the phenomena of space, of time, of matter, or of force, can become a Religious conception. Such a conception, if it anywhere exists in Science, must be more general than any of these—must be one underlying all of them. If there be a fact which Science recognizes in common with Religion, it must be that fact from which the several branches of Science diverge, as from their common root.

Assuming, then, that since these two great realities are constituents of the same mind, and respond to different aspects of the same Universe, there must be a fundamental harmony between them, we see good reason to conclude that the most abstract truth contained in Religion and the most abstract truth contained in Science must be the one in which the two coalesce. The largest fact to be found within our mental range must be the one of which we are in search. Uniting these positive and negative poles of human thought, it must be the ultimate fact in our intelligence.

§ 8. Before proceeding in the search for this common datum let me bespeak a little patience. The next three chapters, setting out from different points and converging to the same conclusion, will be comparatively unattractive. Students of philosophy will find in them much that is more or less familiar; and to most of those who are unacquainted with the literature of modern metaphysics, they may prove somewhat difficult to follow.

Our argument, however, cannot dispense with these chapters; and the greatness of the question at issue justifies even a heavier tax on the reader's attention. The matter is one which concerns each and all of us more than any other matter whatever. Though it affects us little in a direct way, the view we arrive at must indirectly affect us in all our relations—must determine our conception of the Universe, of Life, of Human Nature—must influence our ideas of right and wrong, and so modify our conduct. To reach that point of view from which the seeming discordance of Religion and Science disappears, and the two merge into one, must cause a revolution of thought fruitful in beneficial consequences, and must surely be worth an effort.

Here ending preliminaries, let us now address ourselves to this all-important inquiry.

CHAPTER II

ULTIMATE RELIGIOUS IDEAS

§ 9. WHEN, on the sea-shore, we note how the hulls of distant vessels are hidden below the horizon, and how, of still remoter vessels, only the uppermost sails are visible, we realize with tolerable clearness the slight curvature of that portion of the sea's surface which lies before us. But when we seek in imagination to follow out this curved surface as it actually exists, slowly bending round until all its meridians meet in a point eight thousand miles below our feet, we find ourselves utterly baffled. We cannot conceive in its real form and magnitude even that small segment of our globe which extends a hundred miles on every side of us; much less the globe as a whole. The piece of rock on which we stand can be mentally represented with something like completeness: we find ourselves able to think of its top, its sides, and its under surface at the same time; or so nearly at the same time that they seem all present in consciousness together; and so we can form what we call a conception of the rock. But to do the like with the Earth we find impossible. If even to imagine the antipodes as at that distant place in space which it actually occupies, is beyond our power; much more beyond our power must it be at the same time to imagine all other remote points on the Earth's surface as in their actual places. Yet we habitually speak as though we had an idea of the Earth—as though we could think of it in the same way that we think of minor objects.

What conception, then, do we form of it? the reader may ask. That its name calls up in us some state of consciousness is unquestionable; and if this state of consciousness is not a conception, properly so called, what is it? The answer seems to be this:—We have learned by indirect methods that the Earth is a sphere; we have formed models approximately representing its shape and the distribution of its parts; generally when the Earth is referred to, we either think of an indefinitely extended mass beneath our feet, or else, leaving out the actual Earth, we think of a body like a terrestrial globe; but when we seek to imagine the Earth as it really is, we join these two ideas as well as we can—such perception as our eyes give us of the Earth's surface we couple with the conception of a sphere. And thus we form of the Earth, not a conception properly so called, but only a symbolic conception.[1]

A large proportion of our conceptions, including all those of much generality, are of this order. Great magnitudes, great durations, great numbers, are none of them actually conceived, but are all of them conceived more or less symbolically; and so, too, are all those classes of objects of which we predicate some common fact. When mention is made of any individual man, a tolerably complete idea of him is formed. If the family he belongs to be spoken of, probably but a part of it will be represented in thought; under the necessity of attending to that which is said about the family, we realize in imagination only its most important or familiar members, and pass over the rest with a nascent consciousness which we know could, if requisite, be made complete. Should something be remarked of the class, say farmers, to which this family belongs, we neither enumerate in thought all the individuals contained in the class, nor believe that we could do so if required; but we are content with taking some few samples of it, and remembering that these could be indefinitely multiplied. Supposing the subject of which something is predicated be Englishmen, the answering state of consciousness is a still more inadequate representative of the reality. Yet more remote is the likeness of the thought to the thing, if reference be made to Europeans or to human beings. And when we come to propositions concerning the mammalia, or concerning the whole of the vertebrata, or concerning animals in general, or concerning all organic beings, the unlikeness of our conceptions to the objects named reaches its extreme. Throughout which series of instances we see, that as the number of objects grouped together in thought increases, the concept, formed of a few typical samples joined with the notion of multiplicity, becomes more and more a mere symbol; not

---

[1] Those who may have before met with this term will perceive that it is here used in quite a different sense.

only because it gradually ceases to represent the size of the group, but also because, as the group grows more heterogeneous, the typical samples thought of are less like the average objects which the group contains.

This formation of symbolic conceptions, which inevitably arises as we pass from small and concrete objects to large and to discrete ones, is mostly a very useful, and indeed necessary, process. When, instead of things whose attributes can be tolerably well united in a single state of consciousness, we have to deal with things whose attributes are too vast or numerous to be so united, we must either drop in thought part of their attributes, or else not think of them at all—either form a more or less symbolic conception, or no conception. We must predicate nothing of objects too great or too multitudinous to be mentally represented; or we must make our predications by the help of extremely inadequate representations of such objects—mere symbols of them.

But while by this process alone we are enabled to form general propositions, and so to reach general conclusions, we are by this process perpetually led into danger, and very often into error. We habitually mistake our symbolic conceptions for real ones; and so are betrayed into countless false inferences. Not only is it that in proportion as the concept we form of any thing or class of things, misrepresents the reality, we are apt to be wrong in any assertion we make respecting the reality; but it is that we are led to suppose we have truly conceived a great variety of things which we have conceived only in this fictitious way; and further to confound with these certain things which cannot be conceived in any way. How almost unavoidably we fall into this error it will be needful here to observe.

From objects readily representable in their totality, to those of which we cannot form even an approximate representation, there is an insensible transition. Between a pebble and the entire Earth a series of magnitudes might be introduced, each of which differed from the adjacent ones so slightly that it would be impossible to say at what point in the series our conceptions of them became inadequate. Similarly, there is a gradual progression from those groups of a few individuals which we can think of as groups with tolerable completeness, to those larger and larger groups of which we can form nothing like true ideas. Whence it is manifest that we pass from actual conceptions to symbolic ones by infinitesimal steps. Note next that we are led to deal with our symbolic conceptions as though they were actual ones, not only because we cannot clearly separate the two, but also because, in the great majority of cases, the first serve our purposes nearly or quite as well as the last— are simply the abbreviated signs we substitute for those more elaborate signs which are our equivalents for real objects. Those very imperfect representations of ordinary things which we habitually make in thinking we know can be developed into adequate ones if needful. Those concepts of larger magnitudes and more extensive classes which we cannot make adequate, we still find can be verified by some indirect process of measurement or enumeration. And even in the case of such an utterly inconceivable object as the Solar System, we yet, through the fulfilment of predictions founded on our symbolic conception of it, gain the conviction that this symbolic conception stands for an actual existence, and, in a sense, truly expresses certain of its constituent relations. Thus our symbolic conceptions being in the majority of cases capable of development into complete ones, and in most other cases serving as steps to conclusions which are proved valid by their correspondence with observation, we acquire a confirmed habit of dealing with them as true conceptions—as real representations of actualities. Learning by long experience that they can, if needful, be verified, we are led habitually to accept them without verification. And thus we open the door to some which profess to stand for known things, but which really stand for things that cannot be known in any way.

To sum up, we must say of conceptions in general, that they are complete only when the attributes of the object conceived are of such number and kind that they can be represented in consciousness so nearly at the same time as to seem all present together; that as the objects conceived become larger and more complex, some of the attributes first thought of fade from consciousness before the rest have been represented, and the conception thus becomes imperfect; that when the size, complexity, or discreteness of the object conceived becomes very great, only a small portion of its attributes can be thought of at once, and the conception formed of it thus becomes so inadequate as to be a mere symbol; that nevertheless such symbolic conceptions, which are indispensable in general thinking, are legitimate, provided that by some cumulative or indirect process of thought, or by the fulfilment of predictions based on them, we can assure ourselves that they stand for actualities; but that when our symbolic conceptions are such that no cumulative or indirect processes of thought can enable us to ascertain that there are corresponding actualities, nor any predictions be made whose fulfilment can prove this, then they are altogether vicious and illusive, and in no way distinguishable from pure fictions.

§ 10. And now to consider the bearings of this general truth on our immediate topic—Ultimate Religious Ideas.

To the primitive man sometimes happen things which are out of the ordinary course—diseases, storms, earthquakes, echoes, eclipses. From dreams arises the idea of a wandering double; whence follows the belief that the double, departing permanently at death, is then a ghost. Ghosts thus become assignable causes for strange occurrences. The greater ghosts are presently supposed to have extended spheres of action. As men grow intelligent the conceptions of these minor invisible agencies merge into the conception of a universal invisible agency; and there result hypotheses concerning the origin, not of special incidents only, but of things in general.

A critical examination, however, will prove not only that

no current hypothesis is tenable, but also that no tenable hypothesis can be framed.

§ 11. Respecting the origin of the Universe three verbally intelligible suppositions may be made. We may assert that it is self-existent; or that it is self-created; or that it is created by an external agency. Which of these suppositions is most credible it is not needful here to inquire. The deeper question, into which this finally merges is, whether any one of them is even conceivable in the true sense of the word. Let us successively test them.

When we speak of a man as self-supporting, of an apparatus as self-acting, or of a tree as self-developed, our expressions, however inexact, stand for things that can be realized in thought with tolerable completeness. Our conception of the self-development of a tree is doubtless symbolic. But though we cannot really represent in consciousness the entire series of complex changes through which the tree passes, yet we can thus represent the leading features of the series; and general experience teaches us that by long continued observation we could gain the power to realize in thought a series of changes more fully representing the actual series; that is, we know that our symbolic conception of self-development can be expanded into something like a real conception; and that it expresses, however inaccurately, an actual process in nature. But when we speak of self-existence, and, helped by the above analogies, form some vague symbolic conception of it, we delude ourselves in supposing that this symbolic conception is of the same order as the others. On joining the word *self* to the word *existence,* the force of association makes us believe we have a thought like that suggested by the compound word self-acting. An endeavor to expand this symbolic conception, however, will undeceive us. In the first place, it is clear that by self-existence we especially mean an existence independent of any other—not produced by any other: the assertion of self-existence is simply an indirect denial of creation. In thus excluding the idea of any antecedent cause, we necessarily exclude the idea of a beginning; for to admit the idea of a beginning—to admit that there was a time when the existence had not commenced—is to admit that its commencement was determined by something, or was caused; which is a contradiction. Self-existence, therefore, necessarily means existence without a beginning; and to form a conception of self-existence is to form a conception of existence without a beginning. Now by no mental effort can we do this. To conceive existence through infinite past-time implies the conception of infinite past-time, which is an impossibility. To this let us add that, even were self-existence conceivable, it would not in any sense be an explanation of the Universe. No one will say that the existence of an object at the present moment is made easier to understand by the discovery that it existed an hour ago, or a day ago, or a year ago; and if its existence now is not made in the least degree more comprehensible by its existence during some previous finite period of time, then no accumulation of such finite periods, even could we extend them to an infinite period, would make it more comprehensible. Thus the Atheistic theory is not only absolutely unthinkable, but, even if it were thinkable, would not be a solution. The assertion that the Universe is self-existent does not really carry us a step beyond the cognition of its present existence; and so leaves us with a mere restatement of the mystery.

The hypothesis of self-creation, which practically amounts to what is called Pantheism, is similarly incapable of being represented in thought. Certain phenomena, such as the precipitation of invisible vapor into cloud, aid us in forming a symbolic conception of a self-evolved Universe; and there are not wanting indications in the heavens, and on the earth, which help us to render this conception tolerably definite. But while the succession of phases through which the Universe has passed in reaching its present form may perhaps be comprehended as in a sense self-determined; yet the impossibility of expanding our symbolic conception of self-creation into a real conception, remains as complete as ever. Really to conceive self-creation is to conceive potential existence passing into actual existence by some inherent necessity; which we cannot do. We cannot form any idea of a potential existence of the universe, as distinguished from its actual existence. If represented in thought at all, potential existence must be represented as *something*, that is as an actual existence; to suppose that it can be represented as nothing, involves two absurdities—that nothing is more than a negation, and can be positively represented in thought; and that one nothing is distinguished from all other nothings by its power to develop into something. Nor is this all. We have no state of consciousness answering to the words—an inherent necessity by which potential existence became actual existence. To render them into thought, existence, having for an indefinite period remained in one form, must be conceived as passing, without any external or additional impulse, into another form; and this involves the idea of a change without a cause—a thing of which no idea is possible. Thus the terms of this hypothesis do not stand for real thoughts; but merely suggest the vaguest symbols, incapable of any interpretation. Moreover, even were it true that potential existence is conceivable as a different thing from actual existence, and that the transition from the one to the other can be mentally realized as a self-determined change, we should still be no forwarder; the problem would simply be removed a step back. For whence the potential existence? This would just as much require accounting for as actual existence; and just the same difficulties would meet us. Respecting the origin of such a latent power, no other suppositions could be made than those above named—self-existence, self-creation, creation by external agency. The self-existence of a potential universe is no more conceivable than we have found the self-existence of the actual universe to be. The self-creation of such a potential universe would involve over again the difficulties here stated—would imply behind this potential universe a more remote potentiality; and so on in an infinite series, leaving us at last no forwarder than at first. While to assign as the source of this potential universe an external agency, would be to introduce the notion of a potential universe for no purpose whatever.

There remains to be examined the commonly-received or theistic hypothesis—creation by external agency. Alike in the rudest creeds and in the cosmogony long current among ourselves, it is assumed that the genesis of the Heavens and the Earth is effected somewhat after the manner in which a workman shapes a piece of furniture. And this assumption is made not by theologians only, but by the immense majority of philosophers, past and present. Equally in the writings of Plato, and in those of not a few living men of science, we find it taken for granted that there is an analogy between the process of creation and the process of manufacture. Now in the first place, not only is this conception one that cannot by any cumulative process of thought, or the fulfilment of predictions based on it, be shown to answer to anything actual; and not only is it that, in the absence of all evidence respecting the process of creation, we have no proof of correspondence even between this limited conception and some limited portion of the fact; but it is that the conception is not even consistent with itself—cannot be realized in thought, when all its assumptions are granted. Though it is true that the proceedings of a human artificer may vaguely symbolize to us a method after which the Universe might be shaped, yet they do not help us to comprehend the real mystery; namely, the origin of the material of which the Universe consists. The artisan does not make the iron, wood, or stone he uses; but merely fashions and combines them. If we suppose suns, and planets, and satellites, and all they contain, to have been similarly formed by a "Great Artificer," we suppose merely that certain pre-existing elements were thus put into their present arrangement. But whence the pre-existing elements? The comparison helps us not in the least to understand that; and unless it helps us to understand that, it is worthless. The production of matter out of nothing is the real mystery, which neither this simile nor any other enables us to conceive; and a simile which does not enable us to conceive this may just as well be dispensed with. Still more manifest does the insufficiency of this theory of creation become, when we turn from material objects to that which contains them—when instead of matter we contemplate space. Did there exist nothing but an immeasurable void, explanation would be needed as much as now. There would still arise the question—how came it so? If the theory of creation by external agency were an adequate one, it would supply an answer; and its answer would be—space was made in the same manner that matter was made. But the impossibility of conceiving this is so manifest, that no one dares to assert it. For if space was created, it must have been previously non-existent. The non-existence of space cannot, however, by any mental effort be imagined. It is one of the most familiar truths that the idea of space as surrounding us on all sides, is not for a moment to be got rid of—not only are we compelled to think of space as now everywhere present, but we are unable to conceive its absence either in the past or the future. And if the non-existence of space is absolutely inconceivable, then, necessarily, its creation is absolutely inconceivable. Lastly, even supposing that the genesis of the Universe could really be represented in thought as the result of an external agency, the mystery would be as great as ever; for there would still arise the question—How came there to be an external agency? To account for this only the same three hypotheses are possible—self-existence, self-creation, and creation by external agency. Of these the last is useless: it commits us to an infinite series of such agencies, and even then leaves us where we were. By the second we are practically involved in the same predicament; since, as already shown, self-creation implies an infinite series of potential existences.

We are obliged, therefore, to fall back upon the first, which is the one commonly accepted and commonly supposed to be satisfactory. Those who cannot conceive a self-existent universe, and who therefore assume a creator as the source of the universe, take for granted that they can conceive a self-existent creator. The mystery which they recognize in this great fact surrounding them on every side, they transfer to an alleged source of this great fact; and then suppose that they have solved the mystery. But they delude themselves. As was proved at the outset of the argument, self-existence is rigorously inconceivable; and this holds true whatever be the nature of the object of which it is predicated. Whoever agrees that the atheistic hypothesis is untenable because it involves the impossible idea of self-existence, must perforce admit that the theistic hypothesis is untenable if it contains the same impossible idea.

Thus these three different suppositions respecting the origin of things, verbally intelligible though they are, and severally seeming to their respective adherents quite rational, turn out, when critically examined, to be literally unthinkable. It is not a question of probability, or credibility, but of conceivability. Experiment proves that the elements of these hypotheses cannot even be put together in consciousness; and we can entertain them only as we entertain such pseud-ideas as a square fluid and a moral substance—only by abstaining from the endeavor to render them into actual thoughts. Or, reverting to our original mode of statement, we may say that they severally involve symbolic conceptions of the illegitimate and illusive kind. Differing so widely as they seem to do, the atheistic, the pantheistic, and the theistic hypotheses contain the same ultimate element. It is impossible to avoid making the assumption of self-existence somewhere; and whether that assumption be made nakedly, or under complicated disguises, it is equally vicious, equally unthinkable. Be it a fragment of matter, or some fancied potential form of matter, or some more remote and still less imaginable cause, our conception of its self-existence can be formed only by joining with it the notion of unlimited duration through past time. And as unlimited duration is inconceivable, all those formal ideas into which it enters are inconceivable; and indeed, if such an expression is allowable, are the more inconceivable in proportion as the other elements of the ideas are indefinite. So that in fact, impossible as it is to think of the actual universe as self-existing, we do but multiply impossibilities of thought by every attempt we make to explain its existence.

§ 12. If from the origin of the Universe we turn to its nature, the like insurmountable difficulties rise up before us on all sides—or, rather, the same difficulties under new aspects. We find ourselves on the one hand obliged to make certain assumptions; and yet on the other hand we find these assumptions cannot be represented in thought.

When we inquire what is the meaning of the various effects produced upon our senses—when we ask how there come to be in our consciousness impressions of sounds, of colors, of tastes, and of those various attributes which we ascribe to bodies—we are compelled to regard them as the effects of some cause. We may stop short in the belief that this cause is what we call matter. Or we may conclude, as some do, that matter is only a certain mode of manifestation of spirit; which is therefore the true cause. Or, regarding matter and spirit as proximate agencies, we may attribute all the changes wrought in our consciousness to immediate divine power. But be the cause we assign what it may, we are obliged to suppose *some* cause. And we are not only obliged to suppose some cause, but also a first cause. The matter, or spirit, or whatever we assume to be the agent producing on us these various impressions, must either be the first cause of them or not. If it is the first cause, the conclusion is reached. If it is not the first cause, then by implication there must be a cause behind it; which thus becomes the real cause of the effect. Manifestly, however complicated the assumptions, the same conclusion must inevitably be reached. We cannot think at all about the impressions which the external world produces on us, without thinking of them as caused; and we cannot carry out an inquiry concerning their causation, without inevitably committing ourselves to the hypothesis of a First Cause.

But now if we go a step further, and ask what is the nature of this First Cause, we are driven by an inexorable logic to certain further conclusions. Is the First Cause finite or infinite? If we say finite we involve ourselves in a dilemma. To think of the First Cause as finite, is to think of it as limited. To think of it as limited, necessarily implies a conception of something beyond its limits; it is absolutely impossible to conceive a thing as bounded without conceiving a region surrounding its boundaries. What now must we say of this region? If the First Cause is limited, and there consequently lies something outside of it, this something must have no First Cause—must be uncaused. But if we admit that there can be something uncaused, there is no reason to assume a cause for anything. If beyond that finite region over which the First Cause extends, there lies a region, which we are compelled to regard as infinite, over which it does not extend—if we admit that there is an infinite uncaused surrounding the finite caused—we tacitly abandon the hypothesis of causation altogether. Thus it is impossible to consider the First Cause as finite. And if it cannot be finite it must be infinite.

Another inference concerning the First Cause is equally unavoidable. It must be independent. If it is dependent it cannot be the First Cause; for that must be the First Cause on which it depends. It is not enough to say that it is partially independent; since this implies some necessity which determines its partial dependence, and this necessity, be it what it may, must be a higher cause, or the true First Cause, which is a contradiction. But to think of the First Cause as totally independent, is to think of it as that which exists in the absence of all other existence; seeing that if the presence of any other existence is necessary, it must be partially

dependent on that other existence, and so cannot be the First
Cause. Not only, however, must the First Cause be a form
of being which has no necessary relation to any other form
of being, but it can have no necessary relation within itself.
There can be nothing in it which determines change, and
yet nothing which prevents change. For if it contains
something which imposes such necessities or restraints, this
something must be a cause higher than the First Cause,
which is absurd. Thus the First Cause must be in every
sense perfect, complete, total; including within itself all
power, and transcending all law. Or, to use the established
word, it must be absolute.

Here then respecting the nature of the Universe, we seem
committed to certain unavoidable conclusions. The objects
and actions surrounding us, not less than the phenomena of
our own consciousness, compel us to ask a cause; in our
search for a cause, we discover no resting-place until we arrive at the hypothesis of a First Cause; and we have no alternative but to regard this First Cause as Infinite and Absolute. These are inferences forced upon us by arguments
from which there appears no escape. It is hardly needful,
however, to show those who have followed thus far how
illusive are these reasonings and their results. But that it
would tax the reader's patience to no purpose, it might
easily be proved that the materials of which the argument
is built, equally with the conclusions based on them, are
merely symbolic conceptions of the illegitimate order.
Instead, however, of repeating the disproof used above,
it will be desirable to pursue another method; showing
the fallacy of these conclusions, by disclosing their mutual
contradictions.

Here I cannot do better than avail myself of the demonstration which Mr. Mansel, carrying out in detail the doctrine of Sir William Hamilton, has given in his "Limits of
Religious Thought." And I gladly do this, not only because his mode of presentation cannot be improved, but also
because, writing as he does in defence of the current Theol-

ogy, his reasonings will be the more acceptable to the majority of readers.

§ 13. Having given preliminary definitions of the First Cause, of the Infinite, and of the Absolute, Mr. Mansel says:

"But these three conceptions, the Cause, the Absolute, the Infinite, all equally indispensable, do they not imply contradiction to each other, when viewed in conjunction, as attributes of one and the same Being? A Cause cannot, as such, be absolute; the Absolute cannot, as such, be a cause. The cause, as such, exists only in relation to its effect: the cause is a cause of the effect; the effect is an effect of the cause. On the other hand, the conception of the Absolute implies a possible existence out of all relation. We attempt to escape from this apparent contradiction, by introducing the idea of succession in time. The Absolute exists first by itself, and afterward becomes a Cause. But here we are checked by the third conception, that of the Infinite. How can the Infinite become that which it was not from the first? If Causation is a possible mode of existence, that which exists without causing is not infinite; that which becomes a cause has passed beyond its former limits. . . .

"Supposing the Absolute to become a cause, it will follow that it operates by means of freewill and consciousness. For a necessary cause cannot be conceived as absolute and infinite. If necessitated by something beyond itself, it is thereby limited by a superior power; and if necessitated by itself, it has in its own nature a necessary relation to its effect. The act of causation must therefore be voluntary; and volition is only possible in a conscious being. But consciousness again is only conceivable as a relation. There must be a conscious subject, and an object of which he is conscious. The subject is a subject to the object; the object is an object to the subject; and neither can exist by itself as the Absolute. This difficulty, again, may be for the moment evaded, by distinguishing between the Absolute as related to another and the Absolute as related to itself. The

Absolute, it may be said, may possibly be conscious, provided it is only conscious of itself. But this alternative is, in ultimate analysis, no less self-destructive than the other. For the object of consciousness, whether a mode of the subject's existence or not, is either created in and by the act of consciousness, or has an existence independent of it. In the former case, the object depends upon the subject, and the subject alone is the true Absolute. In the latter case, the subject depends upon the object, and the object alone is the true Absolute. Or if we attempt a third hypothesis, and maintain that each exists independently of the other, we have no Absolute at all, but only a pair of relatives; for co-existence, whether in consciousness or not, is itself a relation.

"The corollary from this reasoning is obvious. Not only is the Absolute, as conceived, incapable of necessary relation to anything else; but it is also incapable of containing, by the constitution of its own nature, an essential relation within itself; as a whole, for instance, composed of parts, or as a substance consisting of attributes, or as a conscious subject in antithesis to an object. For if there is in the Absolute any principle of unity, distinct from the mere accumulation of parts or attributes, this principle alone is the true Absolute. If, on the other hand, there is no such principle, then there is no Absolute at all, but only a plurality of relatives. The almost unanimous voice of philosophy, in pronouncing that the Absolute is both one and simple, must be accepted as the voice of reason also, so far as reason has any voice in the matter. But this absolute unity, as indifferent and containing no attributes, can neither be distinguished from the multiplicity of finite beings by any characteristic feature, nor be identified with them in their multiplicity. Thus we are landed in an inextricable dilemma. The Absolute cannot be conceived as conscious, neither can it be conceived as unconscious: it cannot be conceived as complex, neither can it be conceived as simple: it cannot be conceived by difference, neither can it be conceived by the absence of difference; it cannot be identified with the universe, neither can it be distinguished from it. The One and the Many, regarded as the beginning of existence, are thus alike incomprehensible.

"The fundamental conceptions of Rational Theology being thus self-destructive, we may naturally expect to find the same antagonism manifested in their special applications. . . . How, for example, can Infinite Power be able to do all things, and yet Infinite Goodness be unable to do evil? How can Infinite Justice exact the utmost penalty for every sin, and yet Infinite Mercy pardon the sinner? How can Infinite Wisdom know all that is to come, and yet Infinite Freedom be at liberty to do or to forbear? How is the existence of Evil compatible with that of an infinitely perfect Being; for, if he wills it, he is not infinitely good; and if he wills it not, his will is thwarted and his sphere of action limited? . . .

"Let us, however, suppose for an instant that these difficulties are surmounted, and the existence of the Absolute securely established on the testimony of reason. Still we have not succeeded in reconciling this idea with that of a Cause: we have done nothing toward explaining how the Absolute can give rise to the relative, the Infinite to the finite. If the condition of casual activity is a higher state than that of quiescence, the Absolute, whether acting voluntarily or involuntarily, has passed from a condition of comparative imperfection to one of comparative perfection; and therefore was not originally perfect. If the state of activity is an inferior state to that of quiescence, the Absolute, in becoming a cause, has lost its original perfection. There remains only the supposition that the two states are equal, and the act of creation one of complete indifference. But this supposition annihilates the unity of the absolute, or it annihilates itself. If the act of creation is real, and yet indifferent, we must admit the possibility of two conceptions of the Absolute, the one as productive, the other as nonproductive. If the act is not real, the supposition itself vanishes. . . .

"Again, how can the relative be conceived as coming into being? If it is a distinct reality from the Absolute, it must be conceived as passing from non-existence into existence. But to conceive an object as non-existent, is again a self-contradiction; for that which is conceived exists, as an object of thought, in and by that conception. We may abstain from thinking of an object at all; but, if we think of it, we cannot but think of it as existing. It is possible at one time not to think of an object at all, and at another to think of it as already in being; but to think of it in the act of becoming, in the progress from not being into being, is to think that which, in the very thought, annihilates itself. . . .

"To sum up briefly this portion of my argument. The conception of the Absolute and Infinite, from whatever side we view it, appears encompassed with contradictions. There is a contradiction in supposing such an object to exist, whether alone or in conjunction with others; and there is a contradiction in supposing it not to exist. There is a contradiction in conceiving it as one; and there is a contradiction in conceiving it as many. There is a contradiction in conceiving it as personal; and there is a contradiction in conceiving it as impersonal. It cannot, without contradiction, be represented as active; nor, without equal contradiction, be represented as inactive. It cannot be conceived as the sum of all existence; nor yet can it be conceived as a part only of that sum."

§ 14. And now what is the bearing of these results on the question before us? Our examination of Ultimate Religious Ideas has been carried on with the view of making manifest some fundamental verity contained in them. Thus far, however, we have arrived at negative conclusions only. Criticising the essential conceptions involved in the different orders of beliefs, we find no one of them to be logically defensible. Passing over the consideration of credibility, and confining ourselves to that of conceivability, we see that Atheism, Pantheism, and Theism, when rigorously analyzed, severally prove to be absolutely unthinkable. Instead of disclosing a fundamental verity existing in each, our investigation seems rather to have shown that there is no fundamental verity contained in any. To carry away this conclusion, however, would be a fatal error; as we shall shortly see.

Leaving out the accompanying moral code, which is in all cases a supplementary growth, a religious creed is definable as a theory of original causation. By the lowest savages the genesis of things is not inquired about: anomalous appearances alone raise the question of agency. But be it in the primitive Ghost-theory which assumes a human personality behind each unusual phenomenon; be it in Polytheism, in which these personalities are partially generalized; be it in Monotheism, in which they are wholly generalized; or be it in Pantheism, in which the generalized personality becomes one with the phenomena—we equally find a hypothesis which is supposed to render the Universe comprehensible. Nay, even that which is commonly regarded as the negation of all Religion—even positive Atheism, comes within the definition; for it, too, in asserting the self-existence of Space, Matter, and Motion, which it regards as adequate causes of every appearance, propounds an *à priori* theory from which it holds the facts to be deducible. Now every theory tacitly asserts two things: first, that there is something to be explained; secondly, that such and such is the explanation. Hence, however widely different speculators may disagree in the solutions they give of the same problem, yet by implication they agree that there is a problem to be solved. Here then is an element which all creeds have in common. Religions diametrically opposed in their overt dogmas are yet perfectly at one in the tacit conviction that the existence of the world, with all it contains and all which surrounds it, is a mystery ever pressing for interpretation. On this point, if on no other, there is entire unanimity.

Thus we come within sight of that which we seek. In the

last chapter, reasons were given for inferring that human beliefs in general, and especially the perennial ones, contain, under whatever disguises of error, some soul of truth; and here we have arrived at a truth underlying even the grossest superstitions. We saw further that this soul of truth was most likely to be some constituent common to conflicting opinions of the same order; and here we have a constituent which may be claimed alike by all religions. It was pointed out that this soul of truth would almost certainly be more abstract than any of the beliefs involving it; and the truth we have arrived at is one exceeding in abstractness the most abstract religious doctrines. In every respect, therefore, our conclusion answers to the requirements. It has all the characteristics which we inferred must belong to that fundamental verity expressed by religions in general.

That this is the vital element in all religions is further proved by the fact that it is the element which not only survives every change, but grows more distinct the more highly the religion is developed. Aboriginal creeds, though pervaded by the idea of personal agencies which are usually unseen, yet conceive these agencies under perfectly concrete and ordinary forms—class them with the visible agencies of men and animals; and so hide a vague perception of mystery in disguises as unmysterious as possible. The Polytheistic conceptions in their advanced phases represent the presiding personalities in greatly idealized shapes, existing in a remote region, working in subtle ways, and communicating with men by omens or through inspired persons; that is, the ultimate causes of things are regarded as less familiar and comprehensible. The growth of a Monotheistic faith, accompanied as it is by a denial of those beliefs in which the divine nature is assimilated to the human in all its lower propensities, shows us a further step in the same direction; and however imperfectly this higher faith is at first realized, we yet see in altars "to the unknown and unknowable God," and in the worship of a God that cannot by any searching be found out, that there is a clearer recognition of the inscrutableness of creation. Further developments of theology, ending in such assertions as that "a God understood would be no God at all," and "to think that God is, as we can think him to be, is blasphemy," exhibit this recognition still more distinctly; and it pervades all the cultivated theology of the present day. Thus, while other constituents of religious creeds one by one drop away, this remains and grows ever more manifest; and so is shown to be the essential constituent.

Nor does the evidence end here. Not only is the omnipresence of something which passes comprehension, that most abstract belief which is common to all religions, which becomes the more distinct in proportion as they develop, and which remains after their discordant elements have been mutually cancelled; but it is that belief which the most unsparing criticism of each leaves unquestionable—or rather makes ever clearer. It has nothing to fear from the most inexorable logic; but on the contrary is a belief which the most inexorable logic shows to be more profoundly true than any religion supposes. For every religion, setting out though it does with the tacit assertion of a mystery, forthwith proceeds to give some solution of this mystery; and so asserts that it is not a mystery passing human comprehension. But an examination of the solutions they severally propound shows them to be uniformly invalid. The analysis of every possible hypothesis proves, not simply that no hypothesis is sufficient, but that no hypothesis is even thinkable. And thus the mystery which all religions recognize turns out to be a far more transcendent mystery than any of them suspect—not a relative, but an absolute mystery.

Here, then, is an ultimate religious truth of the highest possible certainty—a truth in which religions in general are at one with each other, and with a philosophy antagonistic to their special dogmas. And this truth, respecting which there is a latent agreement among all mankind from the fetish-worshipper to the most stoical critic of human creeds, must be the one we seek. If Religion and Science are to be reconciled, the basis of reconciliation must be this deepest, widest, and most certain of all facts—that the Power which the Universe manifests to us is utterly inscrutable.

CHAPTER III

ULTIMATE SCIENTIFIC IDEAS

§ 15. WHAT are Space and Time? Two hypotheses are current respecting them; the one that they are objective, and the other that they are subjective—the one that they are external to, and independent of, ourselves, the other that they are internal, and appertain to our own consciousness. Let us see what becomes of these hypotheses under analysis.

To say that Space and Time exist objectively, is to say that they are entities. The assertion that they are non-entities is self-destructive: non-entities are non-existences; and to allege that non-existences exist objectively is a contradiction in terms. Moreover, to deny that Space and Time are things, and so by implication to call them nothings, involves the absurdity that there are two kinds of nothing. Neither can they be regarded as attributes of some entity; seeing not only that it is impossible really to conceive any entity of which they are attributes, but seeing further that we cannot think of them as disappearing, even if everything else disappeared; whereas attributes necessarily disappear along with the entities they belong to. Thus as Space and Time cannot be either non-entities, nor the attributes of entities, we have no choice but consider them as entities. But while, on the hypothesis of their objectivity, Space and Time must be classed as things, we find, on experiment, that to represent them in thought as things is impossible. To be conceived at all, a thing must be conceived as having attributes. We can distinguish something from nothing, only by the power which the something has to act on our consciousness; the several affections it produces on our consciousness (or else the hypothetical causes of them) we attribute to it, and call its attributes; and the absence of these attributes is the absence of the terms in which the something is conceived, and involves the absence of a conception. What now are the attributes of Space? The only one which it is possible for a moment to think of as belonging to it, is that of extension; and to credit it with this implies a confusion of thought. For extension and Space are convertible terms: by extension, as we ascribe it to surrounding objects, we mean occupancy of Space; and thus to say that Space is extended, is to say that Space occupies Space. How we are similarly unable to assign any attribute to Time, scarcely needs pointing out. Nor are Time and Space unthinkable as entities only from the absence of attributes; there is another peculiarity, familiar to readers of metaphysics, which ing it positively separate it from the class of limited entities. which we actually know as such, are limited; and even if we suppose ourselves either to know or to be able to conceive some unlimited entity, we of necessity in so classing it positively separate it from the class of limited entities. But of Space and Time we cannot assert either limitation or the absence of limitation. We find ourselves totally unable to form any mental image of unbounded Space; and yet totally unable to imagine bounds beyond which there is no Space. Similarly at the other extreme: it is impossible to think of a limit to the divisibility of Space, yet equally impossible to think of its infinite divisibility. And, without stating them, it will be seen that we labor under like impotencies in respect to Time. Thus we cannot conceive Space and Time as entities, and are equally disabled from conceiving them as either the attributes of entities or as non-entities. We are compelled to think of them as existing; and yet cannot bring them within those conditions under which existences are represented in thought.

Shall we then take refuge in the Kantian doctrine? shall we say that Space and Time are forms of the intellect —"*à priori* laws or conditions of the conscious mind"? To do this is to escape from great difficulties by rushing into greater. The proposition with which Kant's philosophy sets out, verbally intelligible though it is, cannot by any effort be rendered into thought—cannot be interpreted into an idea properly so called, but stands merely for a pseud-idea. In the first place, to assert that Space and Time, as we are conscious of them, are subjective conditions, is by implication to assert that they are not objective realities: if the Space and Time present to our minds belong to the *ego,* then of necessity they do not belong to the *non-ego.* Now it is absolutely impossible to think this. The very fact on which Kant bases his hypothesis—namely, that our consciousness of Space and Time cannot be suppressed—testifies as much; for that consciousness of Space and Time which we cannot rid ourselves of, is the consciousness of them as existing objectively. It is useless to reply that such an inability must inevitably result if they are subjective forms. The question here is—What does consciousness directly testify? And the direct testimony of consciousness is, that Time and Space are not within but without the mind; and so absolutely independent of it that they cannot be conceived to become non-existent even were the mind to become non-existent. Besides being positively unthinkable in what it tacitly denies, the theory of Kant is equally unthinkable in what it openly affirms. It is not simply that we cannot combine the thought of Space with the thought of our own personality, and contemplate the one as a property of the other—though our inability to do this would prove the inconceivableness of the hypothesis—but it is that the hypothesis carries in itself the proof of its own inconceivableness. For if Space and Time are forms of thought, they can never be thought of; since it is impossible for anything to be at once the *form* of thought and the *matter* of thought. That Space and Time are objects of consciousness, Kant emphatically asserts by saying that it is impossible to suppress the consciousness of them. How then, if they are *objects* of consciousness, can they at the same time be *conditions* of consciousness? If

Space and Time are the *conditions* under which we think, then when we think of Space and Time themselves, our thoughts must be unconditioned; and if there can thus be unconditioned thoughts, what becomes of the theory?

It results therefore that Space and Time are wholly incomprehensible. The immediate knowledge which we seem to have of them proves, when examined, to be total ignorance. While our belief in their objective reality is insurmountable, we are unable to give any rational account of it. And to posit the alternative belief (possible to state but impossible to realize) is merely to multiply irrationalities.

§ 16. Were it not for the necessities of the argument, it would be inexcusable to occupy the reader's attention with the threadbare, and yet unended, controversy respecting the divisibility of matter. Matter is either infinitely divisible or it is not: no third possibility can be named. Which of the alternatives shall we accept? If we say that Matter is infinitely divisible, we commit ourselves to a supposition not realizable in thought. We can bisect and rebisect a body, and continually repeating the act until we reduce its parts to a size no longer physically divisible, may then mentally continue the process without limit. To do this, however, is not really to conceive the infinite divisibility of matter, but to form a symbolic conception incapable of expansion into a real one, and not admitting of other verification. Really to conceive the infinite divisibility of matter is mentally to follow out the divisions to infinity; and to do this would require infinite time. On the other hand, to assert that matter is not infinitely divisible is to assert that it is reducible to parts which no conceivable power can divide; and this verbal supposition can no more be represented in thought than the other. For each of such ultimate parts, did they exist, must have an under and an upper surface, a right and a left side, like any larger fragment. Now it is impossible to imagine its sides so near that no plane of section can be conceived between them; and, however great be the assumed force of cohesion, it is impossible to shut out the idea of a greater force capable of overcoming it. So that to human intelligence the one hypothesis is no more acceptable than the other; and yet the conclusion that one or other must agree with the fact seems to human intelligence unavoidable.

Again, leaving this insoluble question, let us ask whether substance has, in reality, anything like that extended solidity which it presents to our consciousness. The portion of space occupied by a piece of metal seems to eyes and fingers perfectly filled: we perceive a homogeneous, resisting mass, without any breach of continuity. Shall we then say that Matter is as actually solid as it appears? Shall we say that whether it consists of an infinitely divisible element or of ultimate units incapable of further division, its parts are everywhere in actual contact? To assert as much entangles us in insuperable difficulties. Were Matter thus absolutely solid, it would be, what it is not—absolutely incompressible; since compressibility, implying the nearer approach of constituent parts, is not thinkable unless there is unoccupied space between the parts. Nor is this all. It is an established mechanical truth, that if a body, moving at a given velocity, strikes an equal body at rest in such wise that the two move on together, their joint velocity will be but half that of the striking body. Now it is a law of which the negation is inconceivable, that in passing from any one degree of magnitude to any other, all intermediate degrees must be passed through. Or, in the case before us, a body moving at velocity 4 cannot, by collision, be reduced to velocity 2, without passing through all velocities between 4 and 2. But were Matter truly solid—were its units absolutely incompressible and in absolute contact—this "law of continuity," as it is called, would be broken in every case of collision. For when, of two such units, one moving at velocity 4 strikes another at rest, the striking unit must have its velocity 4 instantaneously reduced to velocity 2; must pass from velocity 4 to velocity 2 without any lapse of time, and without passing through intermediate velocities; must be moving with velocities 4 and 2 at the same instant, which is impossible.

The supposition that Matter is absolutely solid being untenable, there presents itself the Newtonian supposition, that it consists of solid atoms not in contact but acting on each other by attractive and repulsive forces, varying with the distances. To assume this, however, merely shifts the difficulty: the problem is simply transferred from the aggregated masses of matter to these hypothetical atoms. For granting that Matter, as we perceive it, is made up of such dense extended units surrounded by atmospheres of force, the question still arises—What is the constitution of these units? We have no alternative but to regard each of them as a small piece of matter. Looked at through a mental microscope, each becomes a mass of substance such as we have just been contemplating. Exactly the same inquiries may be made respecting the parts of which each atom consists; while exactly the same difficulties stand in the way of every answer. And manifestly, even were the hypothetical atom assumed to consist of still minuter ones, the difficulty would reappear at the next step; nor could it be got rid of even by an infinite series of such assumptions.

Boscovich's conception yet remains to us. Seeing that Matter could not, as Leibnitz suggested, be composed of unextended monads (since the juxtaposition of an infinity of points having no extension could not produce that extension which matter possesses), and perceiving objections to the view entertained by Newton, Boscovich proposed an intermediate theory, uniting, as he considered, the advantages of both and avoiding their difficulties. His theory is, that the constituents of Matter are centres of force—points without dimensions, which attract and repel each other in such wise as to be kept at specific distances apart. And he argues, mathematically, that the forces possessed by such centres might so vary with the distances that under given conditions the centres would remain in stable equilibrium with definite interspaces; and yet, under other conditions,

would maintain larger or smaller interspaces. This speculation, however, ingeniously as it is elaborated, and eluding
though it does various difficulties, posits a proposition which
cannot by any effort be represented in thought: it escapes
all the inconceivabilities above indicated, by merging them
in the one inconceivability with which it sets out. A centre of force absolutely without extension is unthinkable:
answering to these words we can form nothing more than
a symbolic conception of the illegitimate order. The idea
of resistance cannot be separated in thought from the idea
of an extended body which offers resistance. To suppose
that central forces can reside in points not infinitesimally
small but occupying no space whatever—points having position only, with nothing to mark their position—points in no
respect distinguishable from the surrounding points that
are not centres of force: to suppose this, is utterly beyond
human power.

Here it may possibly be said, that though all hypotheses
respecting the constitution of Matter commit us to inconceivable conclusions when logically developed, yet we have
reason to think that one of them corresponds with the fact.
Though the conception of Matter as consisting of dense indivisible units is symbolic and incapable of being completely
thought out, it may yet be supposed to find indirect verification in the truths of chemistry. These, it is argued, necessitate the belief that Matter consists of particles of specific
weights, and therefore of specific sizes. The general law of
definite proportions seems impossible on any other condition
than the existence of ultimate atoms; and though the combining weights of the respective elements are termed by
chemists their "equivalents," for the purpose of avoiding
a questionable assumption, we are unable to think of the
combination of such definite weights, without supposing it
to take place between definite numbers of definite particles.
And thus it would appear that the Newtonian view is at
any rate preferable to that of Boscovich. A disciple of
Boscovich, however, may reply that his master's theory

is involved in that of Newton, and cannot indeed be escaped. "What," he may ask, "is it that holds together the parts of these ultimate atoms?" "A cohesive force," his opponent must answer. "And what," he may continue, "is it that holds together the parts of any fragments into which, by sufficient force, an ultimate atom might be broken?" Again the answer must be—a cohesive force. "And what," he may still ask, "if the ultimate atom were, as we can imagine it to be, reduced to parts as small in proportion to it as it is in proportion to a tangible mass of matter—what must give each part the ability to sustain itself, and to occupy space?" Still there is no answer but—a cohesive force. Carry the process in thought as far as we may, until the extension of the parts is less than can be imagined, we still cannot escape the admission of forces by which the extension is upheld; and we can find no limit until we arrive at the conception of centres of force without any extension.

Matter then, in its ultimate nature, is as absolutely incomprehensible as Space and Time. Frame whas suppositions we may, we find on tracing out their implications that they leave us nothing but a choice between opposite absurdities.

§ 17. A body impelled by the hand is clearly perceived to move, and to move in a definite direction: there seems at first sight no possibility of doubting that its motion is real, or that it is toward a given point. Yet it is easy to show that we not only may be, but usually are, quite wrong in both these judgments. Here, for instance, is a ship which, for simplicity's sake, we will suppose to be anchored at the equator with her head to the West. When the captain walks from stem to stern, in what direction does he move? East is the obvious answer—an answer which for the moment may pass without criticism. But now the anchor is heaved, and the vessel sails to the West with a velocity equal to that at which the captain walks. In what direction does he now move when he goes from stem to stern? You cannot say East, for the vessel is carrying him as fast toward the West as he walks to the East; and you cannot say West for the converse reason. In respect to surrounding space he is stationary; though to all on board the ship he seems to be moving. But now are we quite sure of this conclusion?— Is he really stationary? When we take into account the Earth's motion round its axis, we find that instead of being stationary he is travelling at the rate of 1,000 miles per hour to the East; so that neither the perception of one who looks at him, nor the inference of one who allows for the ship's motion, is anything like the truth. Nor indeed, on further consideration, shall we find this revised conclusion to be much better. For we have forgotten to allow for the Earth's motion in its orbit. This being some 68,000 miles per hour, it follows that, assuming the time to be mid-day, he is moving, not at the rate of 1,000 miles per hour to the East, but at the rate of 67,000 miles per hour to the West. Nay, not even now have we discovered the true rate and the true direction of his movement. With the Earth's progress in its orbit, we have to join that of the whole Solar System toward the constellation Hercules; and when we do this, we perceive that he is moving neither East nor West, but in a line inclined to the plane of the Ecliptic, and at a velocity greater or less (according to the time of the year) than that above named. To which let us add, that were the dynamic arrangements of our sidereal system fully known to us, we should probably discover the direction and rate of his actual movement to differ considerably even from these. How illusive are our ideas of Motion, is thus made sufficiently manifest. That which seems moving proves to be stationary; that which seems stationary proves to be moving; while that which we conclude to be going rapidly in one direction turns out to be going much more rapidly in the opposite direction. And so we are taught that what we are conscious of is not the real motion of any object, either in its rate or direction; but merely its motion as measured from an assigned position—either the position we ourselves occupy or some other. Yet in this very process of concluding that the motions we perceive are not the real motions, we tacitly assume that there are real motions. In revising our successive judgments concerning a body's course or velocity, we take for granted that there is an actual course and an actual velocity—we take for granted that there are fixed points in space with respect to which all motions are absolute; and we find it impossible to rid ourselves of this idea. Nevertheless, absolute motion cannot even be imagined, much less known. Motion as taking place apart from those limitations of space which we habitually associate with it, is totally unthinkable. For motion is change of place; but in unlimited space change of place is inconceivable, because place itself is inconceivable. Place can be conceived only by reference to other places; and in the absence of objects dispersed through space, a place could be conceived only in relation to the limits of space; whence it follows that in unlimited space place cannot be conceived —all places must be equidistant from boundaries that do not exist. Thus while we are obliged to think that there is an absolute motion, we find absolute motion incomprehensible.

Another insuperable difficulty presents itself when we contemplate the transfer of Motion. Habit blinds us to the marvellousness of this phenomenon. Familiar with the fact from childhood, we see nothing remarkable in the ability of a moving thing to generate movement in a thing that is stationary. It is, however, impossible to understand it. In what respect does a body after impact differ from itself before impact? What is this added to it which does not sensibly affect any of its properties and yet enables it to traverse space? Here is an object at rest and here is the same object moving. In the one state it has no tendency to change its place; but in the other it is obliged at each instant to assume a new position. What is it which will forever go on producing this effect without being exhausted?

and how does it dwell in the object?   The motion you say has been communicated.   But how?—What has been communicated?   The striking body has not transferred a *thing* to the body struck; and it is equally out of the question to say that it has transferred an *attribute*.   What then has it transferred?

Once more there is the old puzzle concerning the connection between Motion and Rest.   We daily witness the gradual retardation and final stoppage of things projected from the hand or otherwise impelled; and we equally often witness the change from Rest to Motion produced by the application of force.   But truly to represent these transitions in thought, we find impossible.   For a breach of the law of continuity seems necessarily involved; and yet no breach of it is conceivable.   A body travelling at a given velocity cannot be brought to a state of rest, or no velocity, without passing through all intermediate velocities.   At first sight nothing seems easier than to imagine it doing this.   It is quite possible to think of its motion as diminishing insensibly until it becomes infinitesimal; and many will think equally possible to pass in thought from infinitesimal motion to no motion.   But this is an error.   Mentally follow out the decreasing velocity as long as you please, and there still remains *some* velocity.   Halve and again halve the rate of movement forever, yet movement still exists; and the smallest movement is separated by an impassable gap from no movement.   As something, however minute, is infinitely great in comparison with nothing; so is even the least conceivable motion infinite as compared with rest.   The converse perplexities attendant on the transition from Rest to Motion need not be specified.   These, equally with the foregoing, show us that though we are obliged to think of such changes as actually occurring, their occurrence cannot be realized.

Thus neither when considered in connection with Space, nor when considered in connection with Matter, nor when considered in connection with Rest, do we find that Motion is truly cognizable. All efforts to understand its essential nature do but bring us to alternative impossibilities of thought.

§ 18. On lifting a chair, the force exerted we regard as equal to that antagonistic force called the weight of the chair, and we cannot think of these as equal without thinking of them as like in kind; since equality is conceivable only between things that are connatural. The axiom that action and reaction are equal and in opposite directions, commonly exemplified by this very instance of muscular effort *versus* weight, cannot be mentally realized on any other condition. Yet, contrariwise, it is incredible that the force as existing in the chair really resembles the force as present to our minds. It scarcely needs to point out that the weight of the chair produces in us various feelings according as we support it by a single finger, or the whole hand, or the leg; and hence to argue that as it cannot be like all these sensations there is no reason to believe it like any. It suffices to remark that since the force as known to us is an affection of consciousness we cannot conceive the force existing in the chair under the same form without endowing the chair with consciousness. So that it is absurd to think of Force as in itself like our sensation of it, and yet necessary so to think of it if we realize it in consciousness at all.

How, again, can we understand the connection between Force and Matter? Matter is known to us only through its manifestations of Force. Our ultimate test of Matter is the ability to resist. Abstract its resistance and there remains nothing but empty extension. Yet, on the other hand, resistance is equally unthinkable apart from Matter—apart from something extended. Not only, as pointed out some pages back, are centres of force devoid of extension unimaginable; but, as an inevitable corollary, we cannot imagine either extended or unextended centres of force to attract and repel other such centres at a distance, without the intermediation of some kind of matter. We have here to remark what could not without anticipation be remarked when treating of Matter, that the hypothesis of Newton, equally with that of Boscovich, is open to the charge that it supposes one thing to act upon another through a space which is absolutely empty—a supposition which cannot be represented in thought. This charge is indeed met by the introduction of a hypothetical fluid existing between the atoms or centres. But the problem is not thus solved; it is simply shifted, and reappears when the constitution of this fluid is inquired into. How impossible it is to elude the difficulty presented by the transfer of Force through space, is best seen in the case of astronomical forces. The Sun acts upon us in such way as to produce the sensations of light and heat; and we have ascertained that between the cause as existing in the Sun and the effect as experienced on the Earth a lapse of about eight minutes occurs; whence unavoidably result in us the conceptions of both a force and a motion. So that for the assumption of a luminiferous ether there is the defence not only that the exercise of force through 95,000,000 of miles of absolute vacuum is inconceivable, but also that it is impossible to conceive motion in the absence of something moved. Similarly in the case of gravitation, Newton described himself as unable to think that the attraction of one body for another at a distance could be exerted in the absence of an intervening medium. But now let us ask how much the forwarder we are if an intervening medium be assumed. This ether, whose undulations according to the received hypothesis constitute heat and light, and which is the vehicle of gravitation—how is it constituted? We must regard it in the way that physicists do regard it, as composed of atoms which attract and repel each other—infinitesimal it may be in comparison with those of ordinary matter, but still atoms. And remembering that this ether is imponderable, we are obliged to conclude that the ratio between the interspaces of these atoms and the atoms themselves is incommensurably greater than the like ratio in ponderable matter, else the densities could not be incommensurable. Instead then of a direct action by the Sun upon the Earth, without anything intervening, we have to conceive the Sun's action propagated through a medium whose molecules are probably as small relatively to their interspaces as are the Sun and Earth compared with the space between them. We have to conceive these infinitesimal molecules acting on each other through absolutely vacant spaces, which are immense in comparison with their own dimensions. How is this conception easier than the other? We still have mentally to represent a body as acting where it is not, and in the absence of anything by which its action may be transferred; and what matters it whether this takes place on a large or a small scale? We see, therefore, that the exercise of Force is altogether unintelligible. We cannot imagine it except through the instrumentality of something having extension; and yet when we have assumed this something we find the perplexity is not got rid of but only postponed. We are obliged to conclude that matter, whether ponderable or imponderable, and whether aggregated or in its hypothetical units, acts upon matter through absolutely vacant space; and yet this conclusion is positively unthinkable.

Yet another difficulty of conception, converse in nature, but equally insurmountable, must be added. If, on the one hand, we cannot in thought see matter acting upon matter through a vast interval of space which is absolutely void; on the other hand, that the gravitation of one particle of matter toward another, and toward all others, should be absolutely the same whether the intervening space is filled with matter or not, is incomprehensible. I lift from the ground, and continue to hold, a pound weight. Now, into the vacancy between it and the ground is introduced a mass of matter of any kind whatever, in any state whatever—hot or cold, liquid or solid, transparent or opaque, light or dense; and the gravitation of the weight is entirely unaffected. The whole Earth, as well as each individual of the infinity of particles composing the Earth, acts on the pound in abso-

lutely the same way, whatever intervenes, or if nothing intervenes. Through eight thousand miles of the Earth's
substance each molecule at the antipodes affects each molecule of the weight I hold, in utter indifference to the fulness
or emptiness of the space between them. So that each portion of matter in its dealings with remote portions treats
all intervening portions as though they did not exist; and
yet at the same time it recognizes their existence with
scrupulous exactness in its direct dealings with them. We
have to regard gravitation as a force to which everything in
the Universe is at once perfectly opaque in respect of itself
and perfectly transparent in respect of other things.

While, then, it is impossible to form any idea of Force
in itself, it is equally impossible to comprehend its mode
of exercise.

§ 19. Turning now from the outer to the inner world,
let us contemplate not the agencies to which we ascribe our
subjective modifications, but the subjective modifications
themselves. These constitute a series. Difficult as we find
it distinctly to separate and individualize them, it is nevertheless beyond question that our states of consciousness
occur in succession.

Is this chain of states of consciousness infinite or finite?
We cannot say infinite; not only because we have indirectly
reached the conclusion that there was a period when it commenced, but also because all infinity is inconceivable—an
infinite series included. We cannnot say finite; for we have
no knowledge of either of its ends. Go back in memory as
far as we may, we are wholly unable to identify our first
states of consciousness. The perspective of our thoughts
vanishes in a dim obscurity where we can make out nothing. Similarly at the other extreme. We have no immediate knowledge of a termination to the series at a future
time, and we cannot really lay hold of that temporary termination of the series reached at the present moment. For the
state of consciousness recognized by us as our last is not

truly our last. That any mental affection may be contemplated as one of the series it must be remembered—*represented* in thought, not *presented*. The truly last state of consciousness is that which is passing in the very act of contemplating a state just past—that in which we are thinking of the one before as the last. So that the proximate end of the chain eludes us, as well as the remote end.

"But," it may be said, "though we cannot directly *know* consciousness to be finite in duration, because neither of its limits can be actually reached, yet we can very well *conceive* it to be so." No; not even this is true. In the first place, we cannot *con*ceive the terminations of that consciousness which alone we really know—our own—any more than we can *per*ceive its terminations. For in truth the two acts are here one. In either case such terminations must be, as above said, not presented in thought, but represented; and they must be represented as in the act of occurring. Now, to represent the termination of consciousness as occurring in ourselves is to think of ourselves as contemplating the cessation of the last state of consciousness; and this implies a supposed continuance of consciousness after its last state, which is absurd. In the second place, if we regard the matter objectively—if we study the phenomena as occurring in others, or in the abstract, we are equally foiled. Consciousness implies perpetual change and the perpetual establishment of relations between its successive phases. To be known at all, any mental affection must be known as such or such—as like these foregoing ones or unlike those. If it is not thought of in connection with others—not distinguished or identified by comparison with others, it is not recognized—is not a state of consciousness at all. A last state of consciousness, then, like any other, can exist only through a perception of its relations to previous states. But such perception of its relations must constitute a state later than the last, which is a contradiction. Or, to put the difficulty in another form; if ceaseless change of state is the condition on which alone consciousness exists, then

when the supposed last state has been reached by the completion of the preceding change, change has ceased; therefore consciousness has ceased; therefore the supposed last
state is not a state of consciousness at all; therefore there
can be no last state of consciousness. In short, the perplexity is like that presented by the relations of Motion and
Rest. As we found it was impossible really to conceive
Rest becoming Motion or Motion becoming Rest; so here
we find it is impossible really to conceive either the beginning or the ending of those changes which constitute consciousness.

Hence, while we are unable either to believe or to conceive that the duration of consciousness is infinite, we are
equally unable either to know it as finite or to conceive it
as finite.

§ 20. Nor do we meet with any greater success when, instead of the extent of consciousness, we consider its substance. The question, What is this that thinks? admits of
no better solution than the question to which we have just
found none but inconceivable answers.

The existence of each individual as known to himself has
been always held by mankind at large the most incontro-
vertible of truths. To say "I am as sure of it as I am sure
that I exist" is, in common speech, the most emphatic expression of certainty. And this fact of personal existence, testified to by the universal consciousness of men,
has been made the basis of sundry philosophies; whence
may be drawn the inference that it is held by thinkers,
as well as by the vulgar, to be beyond all facts unquestionable.

Belief in the reality of self is indeed a belief which no
hypothesis enables us to escape. What shall we say of
these successive impressions and ideas which constitute
consciousness? Shall we say that they are the affections
of something called mind, which, as being the subject of
them, is the real *ego*? If we say this we manifestly imply

that the *ego* is an entity. Shall we assert that these impressions and ideas are not the mere superficial changes wrought on some thinking substance, but are themselves the very body of this substance—are severally the modified forms which it from moment to moment assumes? This hypothesis, equally with the foregoing, implies that the individual exists as a permanent and distinct being; since modifications necessarily involve something modified. Shall we then betake ourselves to the sceptic's position, and argue that we know nothing more than our impressions and ideas themselves—that these are to us the only existences; and that the personality said to underlie them is a mere fiction? We do not even thus escape; since this proposition, verbally intelligible but really unthinkable, itself makes the assumption which it professes to repudiate. For how can consciousness be wholly resolved into impressions and ideas when an impression of necessity implies something impressed? Or, again, how can the sceptic who has decomposed his consciousness into impressions and ideas explain the fact that he considers them as *his* impressions and ideas? Or, once more, if, as he must, he admits that he has an impression of his personal existence, what warrant can he show for rejecting this impression as unreal while he accepts all his other impressions as real? Unless he can give satisfactory answers to these queries, which he cannot, he must abandon his conclusions, and must admit the reality of the individual mind.

But now, unavoidable as is this belief—established though it is not only by the assent of mankind at large, indorsed by divers philosophers, but by the suicide of the sceptical argument—it is yet a belief admitting of no justification by reason; nay, indeed, it is a belief which reason when pressed for a distinct answer rejects. One of the most recent writers who has touched upon this question, Mr. Mansel, does indeed contend that in the consciousness of self we have a piece of real knowledge. The validity of immediate intuition he holds in this case unquestionable, remarking that

"Let system-makers say what they will, the unsophisticated sense of mankind refuses to acknowledge that mind is but a bundle of states of consciousness, as matter is (possibly) a bundle of sensible qualities." On which position the obvious comment is that it does not seem altogether a consistent one for a Kantist, who pays but small respect to "the unsophisticated sense of mankind" when it testifies to the objectivity of space. Passing over this, however, it may readily be shown that a cognition of self, properly so called, is absolutely negatived by the laws of thought. The fundamental condition to all consciousness emphatically insisted upon by Mr. Mansel, in common with Sir William Hamilton and others, is the antithesis of subject and object. And on this "primitive dualism of consciousness," "from which the explanations of philosophy must take their start," Mr. Mansel founds his refutation of the German absolutists. But now, what is the corollary from this doctrine, as bearing on the consciousness of self? The mental act in which self is known implies, like every other mental act, a perceiving subject and a perceived object. If, then, the object perceived is self, what is the subject that perceives? or, if it is the true self which thinks, what other self can it be that is thought of? Clearly, a true cognition of self implies a state in which the knowing and the known are one—in which subject and object are identified; and this Mr. Mansel rightly holds to be the annihiliation of both.

So that the personality of which each is conscious, and of which the existence is to each a fact beyond all others the most certain, is yet a thing which cannot truly be known at all. Knowledge of it is forbidden by the very nature of thought.

§ 21. Ultimate Scientific Ideas, then, are all representative of realities that cannot be comprehended. After no matter how great a progress in the colligation of facts and the establishment of generalizations ever wider and wider; after the merging of limited and derivative truths in truths that are larger and deeper has been carried no matter how far, the fundamental truth remains as much beyond reach as ever. The explanation of that which is explicable does but bring out into greater clearness the inexplicableness of that which remains behind. Alike in the external and the internal worlds, the man of science sees himself in the midst of perpetual changes, of which he can discover neither the beginning nor the end. If, tracing back the evolution of things, he allows himself to entertain the hypothesis that the Universe once existed in a diffused form, he finds it utterly impossible to conceive how this came to be so; and equally, if he speculates on the future he can assign no limit to the grand succession of phenomena ever unfolding themselves before him. In like manner, if he looks inward, he perceives that both ends of the thread of consciousness are beyond his grasp; nay, even beyond his power to think of as having existed or as existing in time to come. When, again, he turns from the succession of phenomena, external or internal, to their intrinsic nature, he is just as much at fault. Supposing him in every case able to resolve the appearances, properties, and movements of things into manifestations of Force in Space and Time, he still finds that Force, Space, and Time pass all understanding. Similarly, though the analysis of mental actions may finally bring him down to sensations, as the original materials out of which all thought is woven, yet he is little forwarder; for he can give no account either of sensations themselves or of that something which is conscious of sensations. Objective and subjective things he thus ascertains to be alike inscrutable in their substance and genesis. In all directions his investigations eventually bring him face to face with an insoluble enigma; and he ever more clearly perceives it to be an insoluble enigma. He learns at once the greatness and the littleness of the human intellect—its power in dealing with all that comes within the range of experience, its impotence in dealing with all that transcends experience. He realizes with a special vividness the utter incomprehensibleness of the simplest fact, considered in itself. He, more than any other, truly *knows* that in its ultimate essence nothing can be known.

———

CHAPTER IV

THE RELATIVITY OF ALL KNOWLEDGE

§ 22. THE same conclusion is thus arrived at, from whichever point we set out. If, respecting the origin and nature of things, we make some assumption, we find that through an inexorable logic it inevitably commits us to alternative impossibilities of thought; and this holds true of every assumption that can be imagined. If, contrariwise, we make no assumption, but set out from the sensible properties of surrounding objects, and, ascertaining their special laws of dependence, go on to merge these in laws more and more general, until we bring them all under some most general laws; we still find ourselves as far as ever from knowing what it is which manifests these properties to us: clearly as we seem to know it, our apparent knowledge proves on examination to be utterly irreconcilable with itself. Ultimate religious ideas and ultimate scientific ideas alike turn out to be merely symbols of the actual, not cognitions of it.

The conviction so reached, that human intelligence is incapable of absolute knowledge, is one that has been slowly gaining ground as civilization has advanced. Each new ontological theory, from time to time propounded in lieu of previous ones shown to be untenable, has been followed by a new criticism leading to a new scepticism. All possible conceptions have been one by one tried and found wanting; and so the entire field of speculation has been gradually exhausted without positive result; the only result arrived at being the negative one above stated—that the reality existing behind all appearances is, and must ever be, unknown. To this conclusion almost every thinker of note has subscribed. "With the exception," says Sir William Hamil-

ton, "of a few late Absolutist theorizers in Germany, this is
perhaps the truth of all others most harmoniously re-echoed
by every philosopher of every school." And among these
he names Protagoras, Aristotle, St. Augustine, Boethius,
Averroes, Albertus Magnus, Gerson, Leo Hebræus, Me-
lanchthon, Scaliger, Francis Piccolomini, Giordano Bruno,
Campanella, Bacon, Spinoza, Newton, Kant.

It yet remains to point out how this belief may be established rationally, as well as empirically. Not only is it that,
as in the earlier thinkers above named, a vague perception
of the inscrutableness of things in themselves results from
discovering the illusiveness of sense-impressions, and not
only is it that, as shown in the foregoing chapters, definite
experiments evolve alternative impossibilities of thought out
of every ultimate conception we can frame, but it is that the
relativity of our knowledge is demonstrable analytically.
The induction drawn from general and special experiences
may be confirmed by a deduction from the nature of our intelligence. Two ways of reaching such a deduction exist.
Proof that our cognitions are not, and never can be, absolute
is obtainable by analyzing either the *product* of thought or
the *process* of thought. Let us analyze each.

§ 23. If, when walking through the fields some day in
September you hear a rustle a few yards in advance, and, on
observing the ditch-side where it occurs, see the herbage agitated, you will probably turn toward the spot to learn by
what this sound and motion are produced. As you approach
there flutters into the ditch a partridge; on seeing which
your curiosity is satisfied—you have what you call an *explanation* of the appearances. The explanation, mark, amounts
to this; that whereas throughout life you have had countless
experiences of disturbance among small stationary bodies,
accompanying the movement of other bodies among them,
and have generalized the relation between such disturbances
and such movements, you consider this particular disturbance explained on finding it to present an instance of the

like relation. Suppose you catch the partridge, and, wishing to ascertain why it did not escape, examine it and find at one spot a slight trace of blood upon its feathers. You now *understand*, as you say, what has disabled the partridge. It has been wounded by a sportsman—adds another case to the many cases already seen by you, of birds being killed or injured by the shot discharged at them from fowling-pieces. And in assimilating this case to other such cases consists your understanding of it. But now, on consideration, a difficulty suggests itself. Only a single shot has struck the partridge, and that not in a vital place. The wings are uninjured, as are also those muscles which move them; and the creature proves by its struggles that it has abundant strength. Why, then, you inquire of yourself, does it not fly? Occasion favoring, you put the question to an anatomist, who furnishes you with *a solution*. He points out that this solitary shot has passed close to the place at which the nerve supplying the wing-muscles of one side diverges from the spine, and that a slight injury to this nerve, extending even to the rupture of a few fibres, may, by preventing a perfect co-ordination in the actions of the two wings, destroy the power of flight. You are no longer puzzled. But what has happened? What has changed your state from one of perplexity to one of *comprehension?* Simply the disclosure of a class of previously known cases, along with which you can include this case. The connection between lesions of the nervous system and paralysis of limbs has been already many times brought under your notice, and you here find a relation of cause and effect that is essentially similar.

Let us suppose you are led on to make further inquiries concerning organic actions, which, conspicuous and remarkable as they are, you had not before cared to understand. How is respiration effected? you ask—why does air periodically rush into the lungs? The answer is, that in the higher vertebrata, as in ourselves, influx of air is caused by an enlargement of the thoracic cavity, due partly to depression of the diaphragm, partly to elevation of the ribs. But how

does elevation of the ribs enlarge the cavity? In reply the
anatomist shows you that the plane of each pair of ribs
makes an acute angle with the spine, that this angle widens
when the movable ends of the ribs are raised; and he makes
you realize the consequent dilatation of the cavity, by pointing out how the area of the parallelogram increases as its
angles approach to right angles. You understand this special fact when you see it to be an instance of a general geometrical fact. There still arises, however, the question,
Why does the air rush into this enlarged cavity? To which
comes the answer, that when the thoracic cavity is enlarged
the contained air, partially relieved from pressure, expands,
and so loses some of its resisting power—that hence it opposes to the pressure of the external air a less pressure, and
that as air, like every other fluid, presses equally in all
directions, motion must result along any line in which the
resistance is less than elsewhere; whence follows an inward
current. And this *interpretation* you recognize as one, when
a few facts of like kind, exhibited more plainly in a visible
fluid such as water, are cited in illustration. Again, when
it was pointed out that the limbs are compound levers acting
in essentially the same way as levers of iron or wood, you
might consider yourself as having obtained a partial *rationale*
of animal movements. The contraction of a muscle, seeming before utterly unaccountable, would seem less unaccountable were you shown how, by a galvanic current, a series of
soft iron magnets could be made to shorten itself through
the attraction of each magnet for its neighbors—an alleged
analogy which especially answers the purpose of our argument; since, whether real or fancied, it equally illustrates
the mental illumination that results on finding a class of
cases within which a particular case may possibly be included. And it may be further noted how, in the instance
here named, an additional feeling of comprehension arises
on remembering that the influence conveyed through the
nerves to the muscles is, though not positively electric, yet
a form of force nearly allied to the electric. Similarly, when

you learn that animal heat arises from chemical combination, and so is evolved as heat is evolved in other chemical combinations—when you learn that the absorption of nutrient fluids through the coats of the intestines is an instance of osmotic action—when you learn that the changes undergone by food during digestion are like changes artificially producible in the laboratory, you regard yourself as *knowing* something about the natures of these phenomena.

Observe now what we have been doing. Turning to the general question, let us note where these successive interpretations have carried us. We began with quite special and concrete facts. In explaining each, and afterward explaining the more general facts of which they are instances, we have got down to certain highly general facts; to a geometrical principle or property of space, to a simple law of mechanical action, to a law of fluid equilibrium—to truths in physics, in chemistry, in thermology, in electricity. The particular phenomena with which we set out have been merged in larger and larger groups of phenomena, and as they have been so merged we have arrived at solutions that we consider profound in proportion as this process has been carried far. Still deeper explanations are simply further steps in the same direction. When, for instance, it is asked why the law of action of the lever is what it is, or why fluid equilibrium and fluid motion exhibit the relations which they do, the answer furnished by mathematicians consists in the disclosure of the principle of virtual velocities—a principle holding true alike in fluids and solids, a principle under which the others are comprehended. And similarly, the insight obtained into the phenomena of chemical combination, heat, electricity, etc., implies that a rationale of them, when found, will be the exposition of some highly general fact respecting the constitution of matter, of which chemical, electrical, and thermal facts are merely different manifestations.

Is this process limited or unlimited? Can we go on forever explaining classes of facts by including them in larger classes, or must we eventually come to a largest class? The supposition that the process is unlimited, were any one absurd enough to espouse it, would still imply that an ultimate explanation could not be reached; since infinite time would be required to reach it. While the unavoidable conclusion that it is limited (proved not only by the finite sphere of observation open to us, but also by the diminution in the number of generalizations that necessarily accompanies increase of their breadth) equally implies that the ultimate fact cannot be understood. For if the successively deeper interpretations of nature which constitute advancing knowledge are merely successive inclusions of special truths in general truths, and of general truths in truths still more general; it obviously follows that the most general truth, not admitting of inclusion in any other, does not admit of interpretation. Manifestly, as the *most* general cognition at which we arrive cannot be reduced to a *more* general one, it cannot be understood. Of necessity, therefore, explanation must eventually bring us down to the inexplicable. The deepest truth which we can get at must be unaccountable. Comprehension must become something other than comprehension before the ultimate fact can be comprehended.

§ 24. The inference which we thus find forced upon us when we analyze the product of thought as exhibited objectively in scientific generalizations is equally forced upon us by an analysis of the process of thought as exhibited subjectively in consciousness. The demonstration of the necessarily relative character of our knowledge, as deduced from the nature of intelligence, has been brought to its most definite shape by Sir William Hamilton. I cannot here do better than extract from his essay on the "Philosophy of the Unconditioned" the passage containing the substance of his doctrine.

"The mind can conceive," he argues, "and consequently can know, only the *limited, and the conditionally limited.* The unconditionally unlimited, or the *Infinite,* the unconditionally limited, or the *Absolute,* cannot positively be con-

strued to the mind; they can be conceived only by a thinking away from, or abstraction of, those very conditions under
which thought itself is realized; consequently, the notion of
the Unconditioned is only negative—negative of the conceivable itself. For example, on the one hand we can positively
conceive neither an absolute whole—that is, a whole so great
that we cannot also conceive it as a relative part of a still
greater whole; nor an absolute part—that is, a part so small
that we cannot also conceive it as a relative whole divisible
into smaller parts. On the other hand we cannot positively
represent, or realize, or construe to the mind (as here understanding and imagination coincide), an infinite whole; for
this could only be done by the infinite synthesis in thought
of finite wholes, which would itself require an infinite time
for its accomplishment. Nor, for the same reason, can we
follow out in thought an infinite divisibility of parts. The
result is the same, whether we apply the process to limitation in *space,* in *time,* or in *degree.* The unconditional
negation, and the unconditional affirmation of limitation;
in other words, the *infinite and absolute, properly so called,*
are thus equally inconceivable to us.

"As the conditionally limited (which we may briefly call
the *conditioned*) is thus the only possible object of knowledge
and of positive thought—thought necessarily supposes conditions. To *think* is *to condition;* and conditional limitation
is the fundamental law of the possibility of thought. For,
as the greyhound cannot outstrip his shadow, nor (by a more
appropriate simile) the eagle outsoar the atmosphere in which
he floats, and by which alone he may be supported; so the
mind cannot transcend that sphere of limitation within and
through which exclusively the possibility of thought is realized. Thought is only of the conditioned; because, as we
have said, to think is simply to condition. The *absolute* is
conceived merely by a negation of conceivability, and all
that we know is only known as

　　　　—'won from the void and formless *infinite.*'
How, indeed, it could ever be doubted that thought is only

of the conditioned may well be deemed a matter of the profoundest admiration. Thought cannot transcend consciousness; consciousness is only possible under the antithesis of a subject and object of thought, known only in correlation, and mutually limiting each other; while independently of this all that we know either of subject or object, either of mind or matter, is only a knowledge in each of the particular, of the plural, of the different, of the modified, of the phenomenal. We admit that the consequence of this doctrine is—that philosophy, if viewed as more than a science of the conditioned, is impossible. Departing from the particular, we admit that we can never, in our highest generalizations, rise above the finite—that our knowledge, whether of mind or matter, can be nothing more than a knowledge of the relative manifestations of an existence, which in itself it is our highest wisdom to recognize as beyond the reach of philosophy—in the language of St. Augustine, '*cognoscendo ignorari, et ignorando cognosci.*'

"The conditioned is the mean between two extremes—two inconditionates, exclusive of each other, neither of which *can be conceived as possible,* but of which, on the principles of contradiction and excluded middle, one *must be admitted as necessary.* On this opinion, therefore, reason is shown to be weak, but not deceitful. The mind is not represented as conceiving two propositions subversive of each other, as equally possible; but only as unable to understand as possible either of two extremes—one of which, however, on the ground of their mutual repugnance, it is compelled to recognize as true. We are thus taught the salutary lesson that the capacity of thought is not to be constituted into the measure of existence, and are warned from recognizing the domain of our knowledge as necessarily co-extensive with the horizon of our faith. And by a wonderful revelation, we are thus, in the very consciousness of our inability to conceive aught above the relative and finite, inspired with a belief in the existence of something unconditioned beyond the sphere of all comprehensible reality."

88   *FIRST PRINCIPLES*

Clear and conclusive as this statement of the case appears when carefully studied, it is expressed in so abstract a manner as to be not very intelligible to the general reader. A more popular presentation of it, with illustrative applications, as given by Mr. Mansel in his "Limits of Religious Thought," will make it more fully understood. The following extracts, which I take the liberty of making from his pages, will suffice:

"The very conception of consciousness, in whatever mode it may be manifested, necessarily implies *distinction between one object and another*. To be conscious, we must be conscious of something, and that something can only be known as that which it is by being distinguished from that which it is not. But distinction is necessarily limitation; for if one object is to be distinguished from another it must possess some form of existence which the other has not, or it must not possess some form which the other has. But it is obvious that the Infinite cannot be distinguished, as such, from the Finite by the absence of any quality which the Finite possesses; for such absence would be a limitation. Nor yet can it be distinguished by the presence of an attribute which the Finite has not; for, as no finite part can be a constituent of an infinite whole, this differential characteristic must itself be infinite, and must at the same time have nothing in common with the finite. We are thus thrown back upon our former impossibility, for this second infinite will be distinguished from the finite by the absence of qualities which the latter possesses. A consciousness of the Infinite, as such, thus necessarily involves a self-contradiction; for it implies the recognition, by limitation and difference, of that which can only be given as unlimited and indifferent. . . .

"This contradiction, which is utterly inexplicable on the supposition that the infinite is a positive object of human thought, is at once accounted for when it is regarded as the mere negation of thought. If all thought is limitation—if whatever we conceive is, by the very act of conception, regarded as finite—*the infinite,* from a human point of view, is merely a name for the absence of those conditions under which thought is possible. To speak of a *Conception of the Infinite* is, therefore, at once to affirm those conditions and to deny them. The contradiction which we discover in such a conception is only that which we have ourselves placed there by tacitly assuming the conceivability of the inconceivable. The condition of consciousness is distinction, and condition of distinction is limitation. We can have no consciousness of Being in general which is not some Being in particular. A *thing,* in consciousness, is one thing out of many. In assuming the possibility of an infinite object of consciousness I assume, therefore, that it is at the same time limited and unlimited—actually something, without which it could not be an object of consciousness, and actually nothing, without which it could not be infinite. . . .

"A second characteristic of Consciousness is that it is only possible in the form of a *relation.* There must be a Subject, or person conscious, and an Object, or thing of which he is conscious. There can be no consciousness without the union of these two factors, and in that union each exists only as it is related to the other. The subject is a subject only in so far as it is conscious of an object; the object is an object only in so far as it is apprehended by a subject; and the destruction of either is the destruction of consciousness itself. It is thus manifest that a consciousness of the Absolute is equally self-contradictory with that of the Infinite. To be conscious of the Absolute, as such, we must know that an object which is given in relation to our consciousness is identical with one which exists in its own nature, out of all relation to consciousness. But to know this identity we must be able to compare the two together; and such a comparison is itself a contradiction. We are in fact required to compare that of which we are conscious with that of which we are not conscious; the comparison itself being an act of consciousness, and only possible through the consciousness of both its objects. It is thus manifest that, even if we could be conscious of the absolute, we could not possibly know that it *is* the absolute; and, as we can be conscious of an object, as such, only by knowing it to be what it is, this is equivalent to an admission that we cannot be conscious of the absolute at all. As an object of consciousness everything is necessarily relative, and what a thing may be out of consciousness no mode of consciousness can tell us.

"This contradiction, again, admits of the same explanation as the former. Our whole notion of existence is necessarily relative, for it is existence as conceived by us. But *Existence*, as we conceive it, is but a name for the several ways in which objects are presented to our consciousness— a general term, embracing a variety of relations. *The Absolute*, on the other hand, is a term expressing no object of thought, but only a denial of the relation by which thought is constituted. To assume absolute existence as an object of thought is thus to suppose a relation existing when the related terms exist no longer. An object of thought exists, as such, in and through its relation to a thinker; while the Absolute, as such, is independent of all relation. *The Conception of the Absolute* thus implies at the same time the presence and absence of the relation by which thought is constituted, and our various endeavors to represent it are only so many modified forms of the contradiction involved in our original assumption. Here, too, the contradiction is one which we ourselves have made. It does not imply that the Absolute cannot exist, but it implies most certainly that we cannot conceive it as existing."

Here let me point out how the same general inference may be evolved from another fundamental condition of thought, omitted by Sir W. Hamilton, and not supplied by Mr. Mansel—a condition which, under its obverse aspect, we have already contemplated in the last section. Every complete act of consciousness, besides distinction and relation, also implies likeness. Before it can become an idea, or constitute a piece of knowledge, a mental state must not only be known as separate in kind from certain foregoing states to which it is known as related by succession; but it must further be known as of the same kind with certain other foregoing states. That organization of changes which constitutes thinking involves continuous integration as well as continuous differentiation. Were each new affection of the mind perceived simply as an affection in some way contrasted with the preceding ones—were there but a chain of impressions, each of which as it arose was merely distinguished from its predecessors, consciousness would be an utter chaos. To produce that orderly consciousness which we call intelligence there requires the assimilation of each impression to others, that occurred earlier in the series. Both the successive mental states and the successive relations which they bear to each other, must be classified, and classification involves not only a parting of the unlike, but also a binding together of the like. In brief, a true cognition is possible only through an accompanying recognition. Should it be objected that if so there cannot be a first cognition, and hence there can be no cognition; the reply is that cognition proper arises gradually—that during the first stage of incipient intelligence, before the feelings produced by intercourse with the outer world have been put into order, there *are* no cognitions, strictly so-called; and that, as every infant shows us, these slowly emerge out of the confusion of unfolding consciousness as fast as the experiences are arranged into groups—as fast as the most frequently repeated sensations and their relations to each other become familiar enough to admit of their recognition as such or such whenever they recur. Should it be further objected that if cognition pre-supposes recognition there can be no cognition, even by an adult, of an object never before seen, there is still the sufficient answer that in so far as it is not assimilated to previously seen objects it is *not* known, and that it *is* known in so far as it is assimilated to them. Of this paradox the interpretation is, that an object is classifiable in various ways, with various degrees of completeness. An animal hitherto *unknown* (mark the word), though not referable to any established species or genus, is yet *recognized* as belonging to one of the larger divisions—mammals, birds, reptiles, or fishes; or should it be so anomalous that its alliance with any of these is not determinable, it may yet be classed as vertebrate or invertebrate; or, if it be one of those organisms of which it is doubtful whether the animal or vegetable characteristics predominate, it is still known as a living body; even should it be questioned whether it is organic, it remains beyond question that it is a material object, and it is cognized by being recognized as such. Whence it is manifest that a thing is perfectly known only when it is in all respects like certain things previously observed—that in proportion to the number of respects in which it is unlike them is the extent to which it is unknown; and that hence, when it has absolutely no attribute in common with anything else, it must be absolutely beyond the bounds of knowledge.

Observe the corollary which here concerns us. A cognition of the Real as distinguished from the Phenomenal must, if it exists, conform to this law of cognition in general. The First Cause, the Infinite, the Absolute, to be known at all, must be classed. To be positively thought of, it must be thought of as such or such—as of this or that kind. Can it be like in kind to anything of which we have sensible experience? Obviously not. Between the creating and the created there must be a distinction transcending any of the distinctions existing between different divisions of the created. That which is uncaused cannot be assimilated to that which is caused; the two being in the very naming antithetically opposed. The Infinite cannot be grouped along with something that is finite; since in being so grouped it must be regarded as not-infinite. It is impossible to put the Absolute in the same category with anything relative, so long as the Absolute is defined as that of which no necessary relation can be predicated. Is it then that the Actual, though unthinkable by classification with the Apparent, is thinkable by classification with itself? This supposition

is equally absurd with the other. It implies the plurality
of the First Cause, the Infinite, the Absolute; and this implication is self-contradictory. There cannot be more than
one First Cause; seeing that the existence of more than one
would involve the existence of something necessitating more
than one, which something would be the true First Cause.
How self-destructive is the assumption of two or more
Infinites is manifest on remembering that such Infinites,
by limiting each other, would become finite. And similarly, an Absolute which existed not alone, but along with
other Absolutes, would no longer be an absolute but a relative. The Unconditioned, therefore, as classable neither
with any form of the conditioned nor with any other Unconditioned, cannot be classed at all. And to admit that
it cannot be known as of such or such kind is to admit
that it is unknowable.

Thus, from the very nature of thought, the relativity of
our knowledge is inferable in three several ways. As we
find by analyzing it, and as we see it objectively displayed
in every proposition, a thought involves *relation, difference,
likeness*. Whatever does not present each of these does not
admit of cognition. And hence we may say that the Unconditioned, as presenting none of them, is trebly unthinkable.

§ 25. From yet another point of view we may discern the
same great truth. If, instead of examining our intellectual
powers directly as exhibited in the act of thought, or indirectly as exhibited in thought when expressed by words, we
look at the connection between the mind and the world,
a like conclusion is forced upon us. In the very definition
of Life, when reduced to its most abstract shape, this ultimate implication becomes visible.

All vital actions, considered not separately but in their
ensemble, have for their final purpose the balancing of
certain outer processes by certain inner processes. There
are unceasing external forces tending to bring the matter
of which organic bodies consist into that state of stable

equilibrium displayed by inorganic bodies; there are internal forces by which this tendency is constantly antagonized; and the perpetual changes which constitute Life may be regarded as incidental to the maintenance of the antagonism. To preserve the erect posture, for instance, we see that certain weights have to be neutralized by certain strains; each limb or other organ gravitating to the Earth and pulling down the parts to which it is attached has to be preserved in position by the tension of sundry muscles; or, in other words, the group of forces which would, if allowed, bring the body to the ground, has to be counterbalanced by another group of forces. Again, to keep up the temperature at a particular point the external process of radiation and absorption of heat by the surrounding medium must be met by a corresponding internal process of chemical combination, whereby more heat may be evolved; to which add, that if from atmospheric changes the loss becomes greater or less the production must become greater or less. And similarly throughout the organic actions in general.

When we contemplate the lower kinds of life we see that the correspondences thus maintained are direct and simple; as in a plant, the vitality of which mainly consists in osmotic and chemical actions responding to the co-existence of light, heat, water, and carbonic acid around it. But in animals, and especially in the higher orders of them, the correspondences become extremely complex. Materials for growth and repair not being, like those which plants require, everywhere present, but being widely dispersed and under special forms, have to be found, to be secured, and to be reduced to a fit state for assimilation. Hence the need for locomotion; hence the need for the senses; hence the need for prehensile and destructive appliances; hence the need for an elaborate digestive apparatus. Observe, however, that these successive complications are essentially nothing but aids to the maintenance of the organic balance in its integrity, in opposition to those physical, chemical, and other agencies which tend to overturn it. And observe, moreover, that while these successive complications subserve this fundamental adaptation of inner to outer actions, they are themselves nothing else but further adaptations of inner to outer actions. For what are those movements by which a predatory creature pursues its prey, or by which its prey seeks to escape, but certain changes in the organism fitted to meet certain changes in its environment? What is that compound operation which constitutes the perception of a piece of food, but a particular correlation of nervous modifications answering to a particular correlation of physical properties? What is that process by which food when swallowed is reduced to a fit form for assimilation but a set of mechanical and chemical actions responding to the mechanical and chemical actions which distinguish the food? Whence it becomes manifest that while Life in its simplest form is the correspondence of certain inner physico-chemical actions with certain outer physico-chemical actions, each advance to a higher form of Life consists in a better preservation of this primary correspondence by the establishment of other correspondences.

Divesting this conception of all superfluities and reducing it to its most abstract shape, we see that Life is definable as the continuous adjustment of internal relations to external relations. And when we so define it we discover that the physical and the psychical life are equally comprehended by the definition. We perceive that this which we call Intelligence shows itself when the external relations to which the internal ones are adjusted begin to be numerous, complex, and remote in time or space; that every advance in Intelligence essentially consists in the establishment of more varied, more complete, and more involved adjustments; and that even the highest achievements of science are resolvable into mental relations of co-existence and sequence, so co-ordinated as exactly to tally with certain relations of co-existence and sequence that occur externally. A caterpillar wandering at random and at length finding its way on to a plant having a certain odor, begins to eat—has inside of it an organic relation between a particular impression and a particular set of actions, answering to the relation outside of it, between scent and nutriment. The sparrow, guided by the more complex correlation of impressions which the color, form, and movements of the caterpillar gave it; and guided also by other correlations, which measure the position and distance of the caterpillar; adjusts certain correlated muscular movements in such way as to seize the caterpillar. Through a much greater distance in space is the hawk, hovering above, affected by the relations of shape and motion which the sparrow presents; and the much more complicated and prolonged series of related nervous and muscular changes, gone through in correspondence with the sparrow's changing relations of position, finally succeed when they are precisely adjusted to these changing relations. In the fowler experience has established a relation between the appearance and flight of a hawk and the destruction of other birds, including game. There is also in him an established relation between those visual impressions answering to a certain distance in space and the range of his gun; and he has learned, too, by frequent observation, what relations of position the sights must bear to a point somewhat in advance of the flying bird, before he can fire with success. Similarly, if we go back to the manufacture of the gun. By relations of co-existence between color, density, and place in the earth, a particular mineral is known as one which yields iron; and the obtainment of iron from it results when certain correlated acts of ours are adjusted to certain correlated affinities displayed by ironstone, coal, and lime, at a high temperature. If we descend yet a step further, and ask a chemist to explain the explosion of gunpowder, or apply to a mathematician for a theory of projectiles, we still find that special or general relations of co-existence and sequence between properties, motions, spaces, etc., are all they can teach us. And lastly, let it be noted that what we call *truth,* guiding us to successful action and the consequent maintenance of life, is simply

the accurate correspondence of subjective to objective relations; while *error,* leading to failure and therefore toward
death, is the absence of such accurate correspondence.

If, then, Life in all its manifestations, inclusive of Intelligence in its highest forms, consists in the continuous
adjustment of internal relations to external relations, the
necessarily relative character of our knowledge becomes
obvious. The simplest cognition being the establishment
of some connection between subjective states, answering to
some connection between objective agencies; and each successively more complex cognition being the establishment
of some more involved connection of such states, answering
to some more involved connection of such agencies; it is
clear that the process, no matter how far it be carried, can
never bring within the reach of Intelligence either the states
themselves or the agencies themselves. Ascertaining which
things occur along with which, and what things follow what,
supposing it to be pursued exhaustively, must still leave us
with co-existences and sequences only. If every act of
knowing is the formation of a relation in consciousness
parallel to a relation in the environment, then the relativity
of knowledge is self-evident—becomes, indeed, a truism.
Thinking being relationing, no thought can ever express
more than relations.

And here let us not omit to mark how that to which our
intelligence is confined is that with which alone our intelligence is concerned. The knowledge within our reach is the
only knowledge that can be of service to us. This maintenance of a correspondence between internal actions and
external actions, which both constitutes our life at each moment and is the means whereby life is continued through
subsequent moments, merely requires that the agencies acting upon us shall be known in their co-existences and sequences, and not that they shall be known in themselves.
If x and y are two uniformly connected properties in some
outer object, while a and b are the effects they produce in
our consciousness; and if while the property x produces in

us the indifferent mental state a, the property y produces
in us the painful mental state b (answering to a physical
injury); then, all that is requisite for our guidance is, that
x being the uniform accompaniment of y externally, a shall
be the uniform accompaniment of b internally; so that when,
by the presence of x, a is produced in consciousness, b, or
rather the idea of b, shall follow it, and excite the motions
by which the effect of y may be escaped. The sole need is
that a and b and the relation between them, shall always
answer to x and y and the relation between them. It matters nothing to us if a and b are like x and y or not. Could
they be exactly identical with them we should not be one
whit the better off, and their total dissimilarity is no dis-
advantage to us.

Deep down, then, in the very nature of Life the relativity
of our knowledge is discernible. The analysis of vital actions in general leads not only to the conclusion that things
in themselves cannot be known to us, but also to the conclusion that knowledge of them, were it possible, would
be useless.

§ 26. There still remains the final question, What must
we say concerning that which transcends knowledge? Are
we to rest wholly in the consciousness of phenomena? Is
the result of inquiry to exclude utterly from our minds
everything but the relative? or must we also believe in
something beyond the relative?

The answer of pure logic is held to be, that by the limits
of our intelligence we are rigorously confined within the
relative, and that anything transcending the relative can be
thought of only as a pure negation or as a non-existence.
"The *absolute* is conceived merely by a negation of conceivability," writes Sir William Hamilton. "The *Absolute*
and the *Infinite*," says Mr. Mansel, "are thus, like the *Inconceivable* and the *Imperceptible*, names indicating, not an
object of thought or of consciousness at all, but the mere
absence of the conditions under which consciousness is pos-

sible." From each of which extracts may be deduced the conclusion, that since reason cannot warrant us in affirming the positive existence of what is cognizable only as a negation, we cannot rationally affirm the positive existence of anything beyond phenomena.

Unavoidable as this conclusion seems, it involves, I think, a grave error. If the premise be granted, the inference must doubtless be admitted; but the premise, in the form presented by Sir William Hamilton and Mr. Mansel, is not strictly true. Though, in the foregoing pages, the arguments used by these writers to show that the Absolute is unknowable have been approvingly quoted, and though these arguments have been enforced by others equally thoroughgoing, yet there remains to be stated a qualification which saves us from that scepticism otherwise necessitated. It is not to be denied that so long as we confine ourselves to the purely logical aspect of the question the propositions quoted above must be accepted in their entirety; but when we contemplate its more general, or psychological, aspect we find that these propositions are imperfect statements of the truth—omitting, or rather excluding, as they do, an all-important fact. To speak specifically: Besides that *definite* consciousness of which Logic formulates the laws, there is also an *indefinite* consciousness, which cannot be formulated. Besides complete thoughts, and besides the thoughts which though incomplete admit of completion, there are thoughts which it is impossible to complete, and yet which are still real, in the sense that they are normal affections of the intellect.

Observe in the first place that every one of the arguments by which the relativity of our knowledge is demonstrated distinctly postulates the positive existence of something beyond the relative. To say that we cannot know the Absolute is, by implication, to affirm that there *is* an Absolute. In the very denial of our power to learn *what* the Absolute is, there lies hidden the assumption *that* it is; and the making of this assumption proves that the Absolute has been present to the mind, not as a nothing, but as a something. Similarly with every step in the reasoning by which this doctrine is upheld. The Noumenon, everywhere named as the antithesis of the Phenomenon, is throughout necessarily thought of as an actuality. It is rigorously impossible to conceive that our knowledge is a knowledge of Appearances only, without at the same time conceiving a Reality of which they are appearances; for appearance without reality is unthinkable. Strike out from the argument the terms Unconditioned, Infinite, Absolute, with their equivalents, and in place of them write "negation of conceivability," or "absence of the conditions under which consciousness is possible," and you find that the argument becomes nonsense. Truly to realize in thought any one of the propositions of which the argument consists, the Unconditioned must be represented as positive and not negative. How, then, can it be a legitimate conclusion from the argument that our consciousness of it is negative? An argument, the very construction of which assigns to a certain term a certain meaning, but which ends in showing that this term has no such meaning, is simply an elaborate suicide. Clearly, then, the very demonstration that a *definite* consciousness of the Absolute is impossible to us, unavoidably presupposes an *indefinite* consciousness of it.

Perhaps the best way of showing that by the necessary conditions of thought we are obliged to form a positive though vague consciousness of this which transcends distinct consciousness, is to analyze our conception of the antithesis between relative and absolute. It is a doctrine called in question by none, that such antinomies of thought as Whole and Part, Equal and Unequal, Singular and Plural are necessarily conceived as correlatives. The conception of a part is impossible without the conception of a whole. There can be no idea of equality without one of inequality. And it is admitted that in the same manner the Relative is itself conceivable as such only by opposition to the Irrelative or Absolute. Sir William Hamilton, however, in his trenchant (and in most parts unanswerable) criticism on Cousin, contends, in conformity with his position above stated, that one of these correlatives is nothing whatever beyond the negation of the other. "Correlatives," he says, "certainly suggest each other, but correlatives may or may not be equally real and positive. In thought contradictories necessarily imply each other, for the knowledge of contradictories is one. But the reality of one contradictory, so far from guaranteeing the reality of the other, is nothing else than its negation. Thus every positive notion (the concept of a thing by what it is) suggests a negative notion (the concept of a thing by what it is not); and the highest positive notion, the notion of the conceivable, is not without its corresponding negative in the notion of the inconceivable. But though these mutually suggest each other, the positive alone is real; the negative is only an abstraction of the other, and in the highest generality even an abstraction of thought itself." Now the assertion that of such contradictories "the negative is *only* an abstraction of the other"—"is *nothing else* than its negation"—is not true. In such correlatives as Equal and Unequal it is obvious enough that the negative concept contains something besides the negation of the positive one; for the things of which equality is denied are not abolished from consciousness by the denial. And the fact overlooked by Sir William Hamilton is, that the like holds even with those correlatives of which the negative is inconceivable, in the strict sense of the word. Take, for example, the Limited and the Unlimited. Our notion of the Limited is composed first of a consciousness of some kind of being, and secondly of a consciousness of the limits under which it is known. In the antithetical notion of the Unlimited the consciousness of limits is abolished, but not the consciousness of some kind of being. It is quite true that in the absence of conceived limits this consciousness ceases to be a concept, properly so called; but it is none the less true that it remains as a mode of consciousness. If in such cases the negative contradictory were, as alleged, "*nothing else*" than the negation of the other, and therefore a mere nonentity, then it would clearly follow that negative contradictories could be used interchangeably. The Unlimited might be thought of as antithetical to the Divisible, and the Indivisible as antithetical to the Limited; while the fact that they cannot be so used proves that in consciousness the Unlimited and the indivisible are qualitatively distinct and therefore positive or real; since distinction cannot exist between nothings. The error (very naturally fallen into by philosophers intent on demonstrating the limits and conditions of consciousness) consists in assuming that consciousness contains *nothing but* limits and conditions, to the entire neglect of that which is limited and conditioned. It is forgotten that there is something which alike forms the raw material of definite thought and remains after the definiteness which thinking gave to it has been destroyed. Now all this applies by change of terms to the last and highest of these antinomies—that between the Relative and the Non-relative. We are conscious of the Relative as existence under conditions and limits; it is impossible that these conditions and limits can be thought of apart from something to which they give the form; the abstraction of these conditions and limits is, by the hypothesis, the abstraction of them *only;* consequently there must be a residuary consciousness of something which filled up their outlines, and this indefinite something constitutes our consciousness of the Non-relative or Absolute. Impossible though it is to give to this consciousness any qualitative or quantitative expression whatever, it is not the less certain that it remains with us as a positive and indestructible element of thought.

Still more manifest will this truth become when it is observed that our conception of the Relative itself disappears if our conception of the Absolute is a pure negation. It is admitted, or rather it is contended, by the writers I have quoted above, that contradictories can be known only in relation to each other; that Equality, for instance, is unthinkable apart from its correlative Inequality; and that thus the

Relative can itself be conceived only by opposition to the Non-relative. It is also admitted, or rather contended, that the consciousness of a relation implies a consciousness of both the related members. If we are required to conceive the relation between the Relative and Non-relative without being conscious of both, "we are in fact" (to quote the words of Mr. Mansel differently applied) "required to compare that of which we are conscious with that of which we are not conscious; the comparison itself being an act of consciousness, and only possible through the consciousness of both its objects." What then becomes of the assertion that "the Absolute is conceived merely by a negation of conceivability," or as "the mere absence of the conditions under which consciousness is possible"? If the Non-relative or Absolute is present in thought only as a mere negation, then the relation between it and the Relative becomes unthinkable, because one of the terms of the relation is absent from consciousness. And if this relation is unthinkable, then is the Relative itself unthinkable for want of its antithesis; whence results the disappearance of all thought whatever.

Let me here point out that both Sir William Hamilton and Mr. Mansel do, in other places, distinctly imply that our consciousness of the Absolute, indefinite though it is, is positive and not negative. The very passage already quoted from Sir William Hamilton, in which he asserts that "the *absolute* is conceived merely by a negation of conceivability," itself ends with the remark that "by a wonderful revelation, we are thus, in the very consciousness of our inability to conceive aught above the relative and finite, inspired with a belief in the existence of something unconditioned beyond the sphere of all comprehensible reality." The last of these assertions practically admits that which the other denied. By the laws of thought, as Sir William Hamilton has interpreted them, he finds himself forced to the conclusion that our consciousness of the Absolute is a pure negation. He nevertheless finds that there does exist in consciousness an irresistible conviction of the real "existence of something unconditioned." And he gets over the inconsistency by speaking of this conviction as "a wonderful revelation"—"a belief" with which we are "inspired": thus apparently hinting that it is supernaturally at variance with the laws of thought. Mr. Mansel is betrayed into a like inconsistency. When he says that "we are compelled by the constitution of our minds to believe in the existence of an Absolute and Infinite Being—a belief which appears forced upon us as the complement of our consciousness of the relative and the finite," he clearly says by implication that this consciousness is positive and not negative. He tacitly admits that we are obliged to regard the Absolute as something more than a negation—that our consciousness of it is *not* "the mere absence of the conditions under which consciousness is possible."

The supreme importance of this question must be my apology for taxing the reader's attention a little further, in the hope of clearing up the remaining difficulties. The necessarily positive character of our consciousness of the Unconditioned, which, as we have seen, follows from an ultimate law of thought, will be better understood on contemplating the process of thought.

One of the arguments used to prove the relativity of our knowledge is that we cannot conceive Space or Time as either limited or unlimited. It is pointed out that when we imagine a limit there simultaneously arises the consciousness of a space or time existing beyond the limit. This remoter space or time, though not contemplated as definite, is yet contemplated as real. Though we do not form of it a conception proper, since we do not bring it within bounds, there is yet in our minds the unshaped material of a conception. Similarly with our consciousness of Cause. We are no more able to form a circumscribed idea of Cause than of Space or Time; and we are consequently obliged to think of the Cause which transcends the limits of our thought as positive though indefinite. Just in the same manner that on conceiving any bounded space there arises a nascent consciousness of space outside the bounds, so when we think of any definite cause there arises a nascent consciousness of a cause behind it; and in the one case as in the other, this nascent consciousness is in substance like that which suggests it, though without form. The momentum of thought inevitably carries us beyond conditioned existence to unconditioned existence; and this ever persists in us as the body of a thought to which we can give no shape. Hence our firm belief in objective reality—a belief which metaphysical criticisms cannot for a moment shake. When we are taught that a piece of matter regarded by us as existing externally cannot be really known, but that we can know only certain impressions produced on us, we are yet, by the relativity of our thought, compelled to think of these in relation to a positive cause—the notion of a real existence which generated these impressions becomes nascent. If it be proved to us that every notion of a real existence which we can frame is utterly inconsistent with itself—that matter, however conceived by us, cannot be matter as it actually is, our conception, though transfigured, is not destroyed. There remains the sense of reality, dissociated as far as possible from those special forms under which it was before represented in thought. Though Philosophy condemns successively each attempted conception of the Absolute—though it proves to us that the Absolute is not this, nor that, nor that—though in obedience to it we negative, one after another, each idea as it arises; yet, as we cannot expel the entire contents of consciousness, there ever remains behind an element which passes into new shapes. The continual negation of each particular form and limit simply results in the more or less complete abstraction of all forms and limits, and so ends in an indefinite consciousness of the unformed and unlimited.

And here we come face to face with the ultimate difficulty: How can there possibly be constituted a consciousness of the unformed and unlimited, when, by its very nature, consciousness is possible only under forms and limits? If every consciousness of existence is a consciousness of ex-

istence as conditioned, then how, after the negation of conditions, can there be any residuum?   Though not directly
withdrawn by the withdrawal of its conditions, must not the
raw material of consciousness be withdrawn by implication?
Must it not vanish when the conditions of its existence vanish?   That there must be a solution of this difficulty is
manifest; since even those who would put it, do, as already
shown, admit that we have some such consciousness; and
the solution appears to be that above shadowed forth.   Such
consciousness is not, and cannot be, constituted by any single mental act, but is the product of many mental acts.   In
each concept there is an element which persists.   It is alike
impossible for this element to be absent from consciousness
and for it to be present in consciousness alone.   Either alternative involves unconsciousness—the one from the want
of the substance, the other from the want of the form.   But
the persistence of this element under successive conditions
necessitates a sense of it as distinguished from the conditions
and independent of them.   The sense of a something that is
conditioned in every thought cannot be got rid of, because
the something cannot be got rid of.   How then must the
sense of this something be constituted?   Evidently by combining successive concepts deprived of their limits and conditions.   We form this indefinite thought as we form many
of our definite thoughts, by the coalescence of a series of
thoughts.   Let me illustrate this.   A large complex object,
having attributes too numerous to be represented at once, is
yet tolerably well conceived by the union of several representations, each standing for part of its attributes.   On
thinking of a piano there first rises in imagination its visual
appearance, to which are instantly added (though by separate mental acts) the ideas of its remote side and of its solid
substance.   A complete conception, however, involves the
strings, the hammers, the dampers, the pedals; and while successively adding these to the conception, the attributes first
thought of lapse more or less completely out of consciousness.   Nevertheless, the whole group constitutes a represen-

tation of the piano. Now as in this case we form a definite concept of a special existence, by imposing limits and conditions in successive acts; so, in the converse case, by taking away the limits and conditions in successive acts, we form an indefinite notion of general existence. By fusing a series of states of consciousness, in each of which, as it arises, the limitations and conditions are abolished, there is produced a consciousness of something unconditioned. To speak more rigorously: this consciousness is not the abstract of any one group of thoughts, ideas, or conceptions; but it is the abstract of *all* thoughts, ideas, or conceptions. That which is common to them all, and cannot be got rid of, is what we predicate by the word existence. Dissociated as this becomes from each of its modes by the perpetual change of those modes, it remains as an indefinite consciousness of something constant under all modes—of being apart from its appearances. The distinction we feel between special and general existence, is the distinction between that which is changeable in us, and that which is unchangeable. The contrast between the Absolute and the Relative in our minds, is really the contrast between that mental element which exists absolutely, and those which exist relatively.

By its very nature, therefore, this ultimate mental element is at once necessarily indefinite and necessarily indestructible. Our consciousness of the unconditioned being literally the unconditioned consciousness, or raw material of thought to which in thinking we give definite forms, it follows that an ever-present sense of real existence is the very basis of our intelligence. As we can in successive mental acts get rid of all particular conditions and replace them by others, but cannot get rid of that undifferentiated substance of consciousness which is conditioned anew in every thought; there ever remains with us a sense of that which exists persistently and independently of conditions. At the same time that by the laws of thought we are rigorously prevented from forming a conception of absolute existence, we are by the laws of thought equally prevented from ridding ourselves of the consciousness of absolute existence; this consciousness being, as we here see, the obverse of our self-consciousness. And since the only possible measure of relative validity among our beliefs, is the degree of their persistence in opposition to the efforts made to change them, it follows that this which persists at all times, under all circumstances, and cannot cease until consciousness ceases, has the highest validity of any.

To sum up this somewhat too elaborate argument: We have seen how in the very assertion that all our knowledge, properly so called, is Relative, there is involved the assertion that there exists a Non-relative. We have seen how, in each step of the argument by which this doctrine is established, the same assumption is made. We have seen how, from the very necessity of thinking in relations, it follows that the Relative is itself inconceivable, except as related to a real Non-relative. We have seen that unless a real Non-relative or Absolute be postulated, the Relative itself becomes absolute; and so brings the argument to a contradiction. And on contemplating the process of thought, we have equally seen how impossible it is to get rid of the consciousness of an actuality lying behind appearances; and how, from this impossibility, results our indestructible belief in that actuality.

CHAPTER V

THE RECONCILIATION

§ 27. THUS do all lines of argument converge to the same conclusion. The inference reached *à priori*, in the last chapter, confirms the inferences which, in the two preceding chapters, were reached *à posteriori*. Those imbecilities of the understanding that disclose themselves when we try to answer the highest questions of objective science, subjective science proves to be necessitated by the laws of that understanding. We not only learn by the frustration of all our efforts, that the reality underlying appearances is totally and forever inconceivable by us, but we also learn why, from the very nature of our intelligence, it must be so. Finally we discover that this conclusion, which, in its unqualified form, seems opposed to the instinctive convictions of mankind, falls into harmony with them when the missing qualification is supplied. Though the Absolute cannot in any manner or degree be known, in the strict sense of knowing, yet we find that its positive existence is a necessary datum of consciousness; that, so long as consciousness continues, we cannot for an instant rid it of this datum; and that thus the belief which this datum constitutes has a higher warrant than any other whatever.

Here then is that basis of agreement we set out to seek. This conclusion which objective science illustrates, and subjective science shows to be unavoidable—this conclusion which, while it in the main expresses the doctrine of the English school of philosophy, recognizes also a soul of truth in the doctrine of the antagonist German school—this conclusion which brings the results of speculation into harmony with those of common sense, is also the conclusion which reconciles Religion with Science. Common Sense asserts the existence of a reality; Objective Science proves that this reality cannot be what we think it; Subjective Science shows why we cannot think of it as it is, and yet are compelled to think of it as existing; and in this assertion of a Reality utterly inscrutable in nature, Religion finds an assertion essentially coinciding with her own. We are obliged to regard every phenomenon as a manifestation of some Power by which we are acted upon; though Omnipresence is unthinkable, yet, as experience discloses no bounds to the diffusion of phenomena, we are unable to think of limits to the presence of this Power; while the criticisms of Science teach us that this Power is incomprehensible. And this consciousness of an Incomprehensible Power, called Omnipresent from inability to assign its limits, is just that consciousness on which Religion dwells.

To understand fully how real is the reconciliation thus reached, it will be needful to look at the respective attitudes that Religion and Science have all along maintained toward this conclusion. We must observe how, all along, the imperfections of each have been undergoing correction by the other; and how the final outcome of their mutual criticisms can be nothing else than an entire agreement on this deepest and widest of all truths.

§ 28. In Religion let us recognize the high merit that from the beginning it has dimly discerned the ultimate verity, and has never ceased to insist upon it. In its earliest and crudest forms it manifested, however vaguely and inconsistently, an intuition forming the germ of this highest belief in which all philosophies finally unite. The consciousness of a mystery is traceable in the rudest fetichism. Each higher religious creed, rejecting those definite and simple interpretations of Nature previously given, has become more religious by doing this. As the quite concrete and conceivable agencies alleged as the causes of things have been replaced by agencies less concrete and conceivable, the element of mystery has of necessity become more predominant. Through all its successive phases the disappearance of those positive dogmas by which the mystery was made unmysterious, has formed the essential change delineated in religious history. And so Religion has ever been approximating toward that complete recognition of this mystery which is its goal.

For its essentially valid belief, Religion has constantly done battle. Gross as were the disguises under which it first espoused this belief, and cherishing this belief though it still is, under disfiguring vestments, it has never ceased to maintain and defend it. It has everywhere established and propagated one or other modification of the doctrine that all things are manifestations of a Power that transcends our knowledge. Though from age to age, Science has continually defeated it wherever they have come in collision, and has obliged it to relinquish one or more of its positions, it has still held the remaining ones with undiminished tenacity. No exposure of the logical inconsistency of its conclusions—no proof that each of its particular dogmas was absurd, has been able to weaken its allegiance to that ultimate verity for which it stands. After criticism has abolished all its arguments and reduced it to silence, there has still remained with it the indestructible consciousness of a truth which, however faulty the mode in which it had been expressed, was yet a truth beyond cavil. To this conviction its adherence has been substantially sincere. And for the guardianship and diffusion of it, Humanity has ever been, and must ever be, its debtor.

But while, from the beginning, Religion has had the all-essential office of preventing men from being wholly absorbed in the relative or immediate, and of awakening them to a consciousness of something beyond it, this office has been but very imperfectly discharged. Religion has ever been more or less irreligious; and it continues to be partially irreligious even now. In the first place, as implied above, it has all along professed to have some knowledge of that which transcends knowledge; and has so contradicted its own teachings. While with one breath it has asserted that the Cause of all things passes understanding, it has, with the next breath, asserted that the Cause of all things possesses such or such attributes—can be in so far understood. In the second place, while in great part sincere in its fealty to the great truth it has had to uphold, it has often been insincere, and consequently irreligious, in maintaining the untenable doctrines by which it has obscured this great truth. Each assertion respecting the nature, acts, or motives of that Power which the Universe manifests to us, has been repeatedly called in question, and proved to be inconsistent with itself, or with accompanying assertions. Yet each of them has been age after age insisted on, in spite of a secret consciousness that it would not bear examination. Just as though unaware that its central position was impregnable,

Religion has obstinately held every outpost long after it was obviously indefensible. And this naturally introduces us to the third and most serious form of irreligion which Religion has displayed; namely, an imperfect belief in that which it especially professes to believe. How truly its central position *is* impregnable, Religion has never adequately realized. In the devoutest faith, as we habitually see it, there lies hidden an innermost core of scepticism; and it is this scepticism which causes that dread of inquiry displayed by Religion when face to face with Science. Obliged to abandon one by one the superstitions it once tenaciously held, and daily finding its cherished beliefs more and more shaken, Religion shows a secret fear that all things may some day be explained; and thus itself betrays a lurking doubt whether that Incomprehensible Cause of which it is conscious is really incomprehensible.

Of Religion, then, we must always remember, that amid its many errors and corruptions it has asserted and diffused a supreme verity. From the first, the recognition of this supreme verity, in however imperfect a manner, has been its vital element; and its various defects, once extreme but gradually diminishing, have been so many failures to recognize in full that which it recognized in part. The truly religious element of Religion has always been good; that which has proved untenable in doctrine and vicious in practice has been its irreligious element; and from this it has been ever undergoing purification.

§ 29. And now observe that, all along, the agent which has affected the purification has been Science. We habitually overlook the fact that this has been one of its functions. Religion ignores its immense debt to Science; and Science is scarcely at all conscious how much Religion owes it. Yet it is demonstrable that every step by which Religion has progressed from its first low conception to the comparatively high one it has now reached, Science has helped it, or rather forced it, to take; and that even now, Science is urging further steps in the same direction.

Using the word Science in its true sense, as comprehending all positive and definite knowledge of the order existing among surrounding phenomena, it becomes manifest that, from the outset, the discovery of an established order has modified that conception of disorder, or undetermined order, which underlies every superstition. As fast as experience proves that certain familiar changes always happen in the same sequence, there begins to fade from the mind the conception of a special personality to whose variable will they were before ascribed. And when, step by step, accumulating observations do the like with the less familiar changes, a similar modification of belief takes place with respect to them.

While this process seems to those who effect, and those who undergo it, an anti-religious one, it is really the reverse. Instead of the specific comprehensible agency before assigned, there is substituted a less specific and less comprehensible agency; and though this, standing in opposition to the previous one, cannot at first call forth the same feeling, yet, as being less comprehensible, it must eventually call forth this feeling more fully. Take an instance. Of old the Sun was regarded as the chariot of a god, drawn by horses. How far the idea thus grossly expressed was idealized we need not inquire. It suffices to remark that this accounting for the apparent motion of the Sun by an agency like certain visible terrestrial agencies, reduced a daily wonder to the level of the commonest intellect. When, many centuries after, Kepler discovered that the planets moved round the Sun in ellipses and described equal areas in equal times, he concluded that in each planet there must exist a spirit to guide its movements. Here we see that, with the progress of Science, there had disappeared the idea of a gross mechanical traction, such as was first assigned in the case of the Sun; but that while for this there was substituted an indefinite and less-easily conceivable force, it was still thought needful to assume a special personal agent as a cause of the regular irregularity of motion. When, finally, it was proved that these planetary revolutions, with all their

variations and disturbances, conformed to one universal law
—when the presiding spirits which Kepler conceived were
set aside, and the force of gravitation put in their place—
the change was really the abolition of an imaginable agency,
and the substitution of an unimaginable one. For though
the *law* of gravitation is within our mental grasp, it is impossible to realize in thought the *force* of gravitation. Newton himself confessed the force of gravitation to be incomprehensible without the intermediation of an ether; and, as
we have already seen (§ 18), the assumption of an ether does
not in the least help us. Thus it is with Science in general.
Its progress in grouping particular relations of phenomena
under laws, and these special laws under laws more and more
general, is of necessity a progress to causes that are more
and more abstract. And causes more and more abstract are
of necessity causes less and less conceivable; since the formation of an abstract conception involves the dropping of
certain concrete elements of thought. Hence the most abstract conception, to which Science is ever slowly approaching, is one that merges into the inconceivable or unthinkable, by the dropping of all concrete elements of thought.
And so is justified the assertion, that the beliefs which
Science has forced upon Religion have been intrinsically
more religious than those which they supplanted.

Science, however, like Religion, has but very incompletely fulfilled its office. As Religion has fallen short of
its function in so far as it has been irreligious, so has Science
fallen short of its function in so far as it has been unscientific. Let us note the several parallelisms. In its earlier
stages, Science, while it began to teach the constant relations of phenomena, and so discredited the belief in separate personalities as the causes of them, itself substituted the
belief in causal agencies which, if not personal, were yet
concrete. When certain facts were said to show "Nature's
abhorrence of a vacuum," when the properties of gold were
explained as due to some entity called "aureity," and when
the phenomena of life were attributed to "a vital principle,"

there was set up a mode of interpreting the facts, which, while antagonistic to the religious mode, because assigning other agencies, was also unscientific, because it professed to know that about which nothing was known. Having abandoned these metaphysical agencies—having seen that they were not independent existences, but merely special combinations of general causes, Science has more recently ascribed extensive groups of phenomena to electricity, chemical affinity, and other like general powers. But in speaking of these as ultimate and independent entities, Science has preserved substantially the same attitude as before. Accounting thus for all phenomena, those of Life and Thought included, it has not only maintained its seeming antagonism to Religion by alleging agencies of a radically unlike kind; but, in so far as it has tacitly assumed a knowledge of these agencies, it has continued unscientific. At the present time, however, the most advanced men of science are abandoning these later conceptions, as their predecessors abandoned the earlier ones. Magnetism, heat, light, etc., which were a while since spoken of as so many distinct imponderables, physicists are now beginning to regard as different modes of manifestation of some one universal force; and in so doing are ceasing to think of this force as comprehensible. In each phase of its progress, Science has thus stopped short with superficial solutions— has unscientifically neglected to ask what was the nature of the agents it so familiarly invoked. Though in each succeeding phase it has gone a little deeper, and merged its supposed agents in more general and abstract ones, it has still, as before, rested content with these as if they were ascertained realities. And this, which has all along been the unscientific characteristic of Science, has all along been a part cause of its conflict with Religion.

§ 30. We see then that, from the first, the faults of both Religion and Science have been the faults of imperfect development. Originally a mere rudiment, each has been growing into a more complete form; the vice of each has in all times been its incompleteness; the disagreements between them have throughout been nothing more than the consequences of their incompleteness; and as they reach their final forms, they come into entire harmony.

The progress of intelligence has throughout been dual. Though it has not seemed so to those who made it, every step in advance has been a step toward both the natural and the supernatural. The better interpretation of each phenomenon has been, on the one hand, the rejection of a cause that was relatively conceivable in its nature but unknown in the order of its actions, and, on the other hand, the adoption of a cause that was known in the order of its actions but relatively inconceivable in its nature. The first advance out of universal fetichism manifestly involved the conception of agencies less assimilable to the familiar agencies of men and animals, and therefore less understood; while, at the same time, such newly-conceived agencies, in so far as they were distinguished by their uniform effects, were better understood than those they replaced. All subsequent advances display the same double result. Every deeper and more general power arrived at as a cause of phenomena has been at once less comprehensible than the special ones it superseded, in the sense of being less definitely representable in thought; while it has been more comprehensible in the sense that its actions have been more completely predicable. The progress has thus been as much toward the establishment of a positively unknown as toward the establishment of a positively known. Though as knowledge approaches its culmination, every unaccountable and seemingly supernatural fact is brought into the category of facts that are accountable or natural; yet, at the same time, all accountable or natural facts are proved to be in their ultimate genesis unaccountable and supernatural. And so there arise two antithetical states of mind, answering to the opposite sides of that existence about which we think. While our consciousness of Nature under the one aspect constitutes Science, our consciousness of it under the other aspect constitutes Religion.

Otherwise contemplating the facts, we may say that Religion and Science have been undergoing a slow differentiation; and that their ceaseless conflicts have been due to the imperfect separation of their spheres and functions. Religion has, from the first, struggled to unite more or less science with its nescience; Science has, from the first, kept hold of more or less nescience as though it were a part of science. Each has been obliged gradually to relinquish that territory which it wrongly claimed, while it has gained from the other that to which it had a right; and the antagonism between them has been an inevitable accompaniment of this process. A more specific statement will make this clear. Religion, though at the outset it asserted a mystery, also made numerous definite assertions respecting this mystery—professed to know its nature in the minutest detail, and in so far as it claimed positive knowledge, it trespassed upon the province of Science. From the times of early mythologies, when such intimate acquaintance with the mystery was alleged, down to our own days, when but a few abstract and vague propositions are maintained, Religion has been compelled by Science to give up one after another of its dogmas—of those assumed cognitions which it could not substantiate. In the meantime, Science substituted for the personalities to which Religion ascribed phenomena, certain metaphysical entities; and in doing this it trespassed on the province of Religion; since it classed among the things which it comprehended certain forms of the incomprehensible. Partly by the criticisms of Religion, which has occasionally called in question its assumptions, and partly as a consequence of spontaneous growth, Science has been obliged to abandon these attempts to include within the boundaries of knowledge that which cannot be known; and has so yielded up to Religion that which of right belonged to it. So long as this process of differentiation is incomplete, more or less of antagonism must continue. Gradually as the limits of possible cognition are established, the causes of conflict will diminish. And a permanent peace will be reached when Science becomes fully convinced that its explanations are proximate and relative; while Religion becomes fully convinced that the mystery it contemplates is ultimate and absolute.

Religion and Science are therefore necessary correlatives. As already hinted, they stand respectively for those two antithetical modes of consciousness which cannot exist asunder. A known cannot be thought of apart from an unknown; nor can an unknown be thought of apart from a known. And by consequence, neither can become more distinct without giving greater distinctness to the other. To carry further a metaphor before used—they are the positive and negative poles of thought; of which neither can gain in intensity without increasing the intensity of the other.

§ 31. Thus the consciousness of an Inscrutable Power manifested to us through all phenomena has been growing ever clearer; and must eventually be freed from its imperfections. The certainty that on the one hand such a Power exists, while on the other hand its nature transcends intuition and is beyond imagination, is the certainty toward which intelligence has from the first been progressing. To this conclusion Science inevitably arrives as it reaches its confines; while to this conclusion Religion is irresistibly driven by criticism. And satisfying as it does the demands of the most rigorous logic at the same time that it gives the religious sentiment the widest possible sphere of action, it is the conclusion we are bound to accept without reserve or qualification.

Some do indeed allege that though the Ultimate Cause of things cannot really be thought of by us as having specified attributes, it is yet incumbent upon us to assert these attributes. Though the forms of our consciousness are such that the Absolute cannot in any manner or degree be brought within them, we are nevertheless told that we must represent the Absolute to ourselves under these forms. As writes Mr. Mansel, in the work from which I have already quoted largely: "It is our duty, then, to think of God as personal; and it is our duty to believe that He is infinite."

That this is not the conclusion here adopted, needs hardly be said. If there be any meaning in the foregoing arguments, duty requires us neither to affirm nor deny personality. Our duty is to submit ourselves with all humility to the established limits of our intelligence; and not perversely to rebel against them. Let those who can, believe that there is eternal war set between our intellectual faculties and our moral obligations. I, for one, admit no such radical vice in the constitution of things.

This which to most will seem an essentially irreligious position, is an essentially religious one—nay is *the* religious one, to which, as already shown, all others are but approximations. In the estimate it implies of the Ultimate Cause, it does not fall short of the alternative position but exceeds it. Those who espouse this alternative position make the erroneous assumption that the choice is between personality and something lower than personality; whereas the choice is rather between personality and something higher. Is it not just possible that there is a mode of being as much transcending Intelligence and Will, as these transcend mechanical motion? It is true that we are totally unable to conceive any such higher mode of being. But this is not a reason for questioning its existence; it is rather the reverse. Have we not seen how utterly incompetent our minds are to form even an approach to a conception of that which underlies all phenomena? Is it not proved that this incompetency is the incompetency of the Conditioned to grasp the Unconditioned? Does it not follow that the Ultimate Cause cannot in any respect be conceived by us because it is in every respect greater than can be conceived? And may we not therefore rightly refrain from assigning to it any attributes whatever, on the ground that such attributes, derived as they must be from our own natures, are not elevations but degradations? Indeed it seems somewhat strange that men should suppose the highest worship to lie in assimilating the object of their worship to themselves. Not in asserting a transcendent difference, but in asserting a certain likeness, consists the element of their creed which they think essential. It is true that from the time when the rudest savages imagined the causes of all things to be creatures of flesh and blood like themselves, down to our own time, the degree of assumed likeness has been diminishing. But though a bodily form and substance similar to that of man has long since ceased, among cultivated races, to be a literally-conceived attribute of the Ultimate Cause—though the grosser human desires have been also rejected as unfit elements of the conception—though there is some hesitation in ascribing even the higher human feelings, save in greatly idealized shapes; yet it is still thought not only proper, but imperative, to ascribe the most abstract qualities of our nature. To think of the Creative Power as in all respects anthropomorphous, is now considered impious by men who yet hold themselves bound to think of the Creative Power as in some respects anthropomorphous; and who do not see that the one proceeding is but an evanescent form of the other. And then, most marvellous of all, this course is persisted in even by those who contend that we are wholly unable to frame any conception whatever of the Creative Power. After it has been shown that every supposition respecting the genesis of the Universe commits us to alternative impossibilities of thought—after it has been shown that each attempt to conceive real existence ends in an intellectual suicide—after it has been shown why, by the very constitution of our minds, we are eternally debarred from thinking of the Absolute; it is still asserted that we ought to think of the Absolute thus and thus. In all imaginable ways we find thrust upon us the truth, that we are not permitted to know—nay, are not even permitted to conceive—that Reality which is behind the veil of Appearance; and yet it is said to be our duty to believe (and in so far to conceive) that this Reality exists in a certain defined manner. Shall we call this reverence? or shall we call it the reverse?

Volumes might be written upon the impiety of the pious. Through the printed and spoken thoughts of religious teachers may almost everywhere be traced a professed familiarity with the ultimate mystery of things, which, to say the least of it, seems anything but congruous with the accompanying expressions of humility. And, surprisingly enough, those tenets which most clearly display this familiarity are those insisted upon as forming the vital elements of religious belief. The attitude thus assumed can be fitly represented only by further developing a simile long current in theological controversies—the simile of the watch. If for a moment we made the grotesque supposition that the tickings and other movements of a watch constituted a kind of consciousness; and that a watch possessed of such a consciousness insisted on regarding the watchmaker's actions as determined like its own by springs and escapements; we should simply complete a parallel of which religious teachers think much. And were we to suppose that a watch not only formulated the cause of its existence in these mechanical terms but held that watches were bound out of reverence so to formulate this cause, and even vituperated, as atheistic watches, any that did not venture so to formulate it; we should merely illustrate the presumption of theologians by carrying their own argument a step further. A few extracts will bring home to the reader the justice of this comparison. We are told, for example, by one of high repute among religious thinkers, that the Universe is "the manifestation and abode of a Free Mind, like our own; embodying His personal thought in its adjustments, realizing His own ideal in its phenomena, just as we express our inner faculty and character through the natural language of an external life. In this view, we interpret Nature by Humanity; we find the key to her aspects in such purposes and affections as our own consciousness enables us to conceive; we look everywhere for physical signals of an ever-living Will; and decipher the universe as the autobiography of an Infinite Spirit, repeating itself in miniature within our Finite Spirit." The same writer goes still further. He not only thus parallels the assimilation of the watchmaker to the watch—he not only thinks the created can "decipher" "the autobiography" of the Creating; but he asserts that the necessary limits of the one are necessary limits of the other. The primary qualities of bodies, he says, "belong eternally to the material datum objective to God" and control his acts; while the secondary ones are "products of pure Inventive Reason and Determining Will"—constitute "the realm of Divine originality." . . . "While on this Secondary field His Mind and ours are thus contrasted, they meet in resemblance again upon the Primary; for the evolutions of deductive Reason there is but one track possible to all intelligences; no *merum arbitrium* can interchange the false and true, or make more than one geometry, one scheme of pure Physics, for all worlds; and the Omnipotent Architect Himself, in realizing the Cosmical conception, in shaping the orbits out of immensity and determining seasons out of eternity, could but follow the laws of curvature, measure and proportion. That is to say, the Ultimate Cause is like a human mechanic, not only as 'shaping' the 'material datum objective to' Him, but also as being obliged to conform to the necessary properties of that datum." Nor is this all. There follows some account of "the Divine psychology," to the extent of saying that "we learn" "the character of God—the order of affections in Him" from "the distribution of authority in the hierarchy of our impulses." In other words, it is alleged that the Ultimate Cause has desires that are to be classed as higher and lower like our own.[1] Every one has heard of the king who wished he had been present at the creation of the world, that he might have given good advice. He was humble, however, compared with those who profess to understand not only the relation of the Creating to the created, but also how the Creating is constituted. And yet this transcendent audacity, which claims to penetrate the secrets of the Power manifested to us through all existence—nay even to stand

---

[1] These extracts are from an article entitled "Nature and God," published in the "National Review" for October, 1860.

behind that Power and note the conditions to its action—this it is which passes current as piety! May we not without hesitation affirm that a sincere recognition of the truth that our own and all other existence is a mystery absolutely and forever beyond our comprehension, contains more of true religion than all the dogmatic theology ever written?

Meanwhile let us recognize whatever of permanent good there is in these persistent attempts to frame conceptions of that which cannot be conceived. From the beginning it has been only through the successive failures of such conceptions to satisfy the mind, that higher and higher ones have been gradually reached; and doubtless, the conceptions now current are indispensable as transitional modes of thought. Even more than this may be willingly conceded. It is possible, nay probable, that under their most abstract forms, ideas of this order will always continue to occupy the background of our consciousness. Very likely there will ever remain a need to give shape to that indefinite sense of an Ultimate Existence, which forms the basis of our intelligence. We shall always be under the necessity of contemplating it as *some* mode of being; that is, of representing it to ourselves in *some* form of thought, however vague. And we shall not err in doing this so long as we treat every notion we thus frame as merely a symbol, utterly without resemblance to that for which it stands. Perhaps the constant formation of such symbols and constant rejection of them as inadequate may be hereafter, as it has hitherto been, a means of discipline. Perpetually to construct ideas requiring the utmost stretch of our faculties, and perpetually to find that such ideas must be abandoned as futile imaginations, may realize to us, more fully than any other course, the greatness of that which we vainly strive to grasp. Such efforts and failures may serve to maintain in our minds a due sense of the incommensurable difference between the Conditioned and the Unconditioned. By continually seeking to know and being continually thrown back with a deepened conviction of the impossibility of knowing, we may keep alive the consciousness that it is alike our highest wisdom and our highest duty to regard that through which all things exist as The Unknowable.

§32. An immense majority will refuse, with more or less of indignation, a belief seeming to them so shadowy and indefinite. Having always embodied the Ultimate Cause so far as was needful to its mental realization, they must necessarily resent the substitution of an Ultimate Cause which cannot be mentally realized at all. "You offer us," they say, "an unthinkable abstraction in place of a Being toward whom we may entertain definite feelings. Though we are told that the Absolute is real, yet since we are not allowed to conceive it, it might as well be a pure negation. Instead of a Power which we can regard as having some sympathy with us, you would have us contemplate a Power to which no emotion whatever can be ascribed. And so we are to be deprived of the very substance of our faith."

This kind of protest of necessity accompanies every change from a lower creed to a higher. The belief in a community of nature between himself and the object of his worship has always been to man a satisfactory one; and he has always accepted with reluctance those successively less concrete conceptions which have been forced upon him. Doubtless, in all times and places, it has consoled the barbarian to think of his deities as so exactly like himself in nature that they could be bribed by offerings of food; and the assurance that deities could not be so propitiated must have been repugnant, because it deprived him of an easy method of gaining supernatural protection. To the Greeks it was manifestly a source of comfort that on occasions of difficulty they could obtain, through oracles, the advice of their gods—nay, might even get the personal aid of their gods in battle; and it was probably a very genuine anger which they visited upon philosophers who called in question these gross ideas of their mythology. A religion which teaches the Hindu that it is impossible to purchase eternal happiness by placing himself under the wheel of Juggernaut, can scarcely fail to seem a cruel one to him; since it deprives him of the pleasurable consciousness that he can at will exchange miseries for joys. Nor is it less clear that to our Catholic ancestors the beliefs that crimes could be compounded for by the building of churches, that their own punishments and those of their relatives could be abridged by the saying of masses, and that divine aid or forgiveness might be gained through the intercession of saints, were highly solacing ones; and that Protestantism, in substituting the conception of a God so comparatively unlike ourselves as not to be influenced by such methods, must have appeared to them hard and cold. Naturally, therefore, we must expect a further step in the same direction to meet with a similar resistance from outraged sentiments. No mental revolution can be accomplished without more or less of laceration. Be it a change of habit or a change of conviction, it must, if the habit or conviction be strong, do violence to some of the feelings; and these must of course oppose it. For long-experienced, and therefore definite, sources of satisfaction, have to be substituted sources of satisfaction that have not been experienced, and are therefore indefinite. That which is relatively well known and real has to be given up for that which is relatively unknown and ideal. And of course such an exchange cannot be made without a conflict involving pain. Especially then must there arise a strong antagonism to any alteration in so deep and vital a conception as that with which we are here dealing. Underlying as this conception does all others, a modification of it threatens to reduce the superstructure to ruins. Or, to change the metaphor—being the root with which are connected our ideas of goodness, rectitude, or duty, it appears impossible that it should be transformed without causing these to wither away and die. The whole higher part of the nature almost of necessity takes up arms against a change which, by destroying the established associations of thought, seems to eradicate morality.

This is by no means all that has to be said for such pro-
tests. There is a much deeper meaning in them. They do
not simply express the natural repugnance to a revolution of
belief, here made specially intense by the vital importance
of the belief to be revolutionized; but they also express an
instinctive adhesion to a belief that is in one sense the best
—the best for those who thus cling to it, though not ab-
stractedly the best. For here let me remark that what were
above spoken of as the imperfections of Religion, at first
great, but gradually diminishing, have been imperfections
only as measured by an absolute standard, and not as measured by a relative one. Speaking generally, the religion
current in each age and among each people has been as near
an approximation to the truth as it was then and there possible for men to receive: the more or less concrete forms
in which it has embodied the truth have simply been the
means of making thinkable what would otherwise have been
unthinkable; and so have, for the time being, served to increase its impressiveness. If we consider the conditions of
the case we shall find this to be an unavoidable conclusion.
During each stage of evolution men must think in such terms
of thought as they possess. While all the conspicuous
changes of which they can observe the origins have men and
animals as antecedents, they are unable to think of antecedents in general under any other shapes; and hence creative
agencies are of necessity conceived by them in these shapes.
If during this phase these concrete conceptions were taken
from them, and the attempt made to give them comparatively abstract conceptions, the result would be to leave
their minds with none at all; since the substituted ones
could not be mentally represented. Similarly with every
successive stage of religious belief down to the last. Though,
as accumulating experiences slowly modify the earliest ideas
of causal personalities, there grow up more general and
vague ideas of them, yet these cannot be at once replaced
by others still more general and vague. Further experiences
must supply the needful further abstractions before the men-

tal void left by the destruction of such inferior ideas can be filled by ideas of a superior order. And at the present time the refusal to abandon a relatively concrete notion for a relatively abstract one, implies the inability to frame the relatively abstract one, and so proves that the change would be premature and injurious. Still more clearly shall we see the injuriousness of any such premature change on observing that the effects of a belief upon conduct must be diminished in proportion as the vividness with which it is realized becomes less. Evils and benefits akin to those which the savage has personally felt or learned from those who have felt them, are the only evils and benefits he can understand, and these must be looked for as coming in ways like those of which he has had experience. His deities must be imagined to have like motives and passions and methods with the beings around him; for motives and passions and methods of a higher character being unknown to him, and in great measure unthinkable by him, cannot be so realized in thought as to influence his deeds. During every phase of civilization the actions of the Unseen Reality, as well as the resulting rewards and punishments, being conceivable only in such forms as experience furnishes, to supplant them by higher ones before wider experiences have made higher ones conceivable is to set up vague and uninfluential motives for definite and influential ones. Even now, for the great mass of men, unable through lack of culture to trace out with due clearness those good and bad consequences which conduct brings round through the established order of the Unknowable, it is needful that there should be vividly depicted future torments and future joys—pains and pleasures of a definite kind, produced in a manner direct and simple enough to be clearly imagined. Nay, still more must be conceded. Few, if any, are as yet fitted wholly to dispense with such conceptions as are current. The highest abstractions take so great a mental power to realize with any vividness, and are so inoperative upon conduct unless they are vividly realized, that their regulative effects must for a long period to come be appreciable on but a small minority. To see clearly how a right or wrong act generates consequences, internal and external, that go on branching out more widely as years progress, requires a rare power of analysis. To mentally represent even a single series of these consequences, as it stretches out into the remote future, requires an equally rare power of imagination. And to estimate these consequences in their totality, ever multiplying in number while diminishing in intensity, requires a grasp of thought possessed by none. Yet it is only by such analysis, such imagination, and such grasp that conduct can be rightly guided in the absence of all other control: only so can ultimate rewards and penalties be made to outweigh proximate pains and pleasures. Indeed, were it not that throughout the progress of the race men's experiences of the effects of conduct have been slowly generalized into principles—were it not that these principles have been from generation to generation insisted on by parents, upheld by public opinion, sanctified by religion, and enforced by threats of eternal damnation for disobedience— were it not that under these potent influences habits have been modified and the feelings proper to them made innate —were it not, in short, that we have been rendered in a considerable degree organically moral; it is certain that disastrous results would ensue from the removal of those strong and distinct motives which the current belief supplies. Even as it is, those who relinquish the faith in which they have been brought up for this most abstract faith in which Science and Religion unite, may not uncommonly fail to act up to their convictions. Left to their organic morality, enforced only by general reasonings imperfectly wrought out and difficult to keep before the mind, their defects of nature will often come out more strongly than they would have done under their previous creed. The substituted creed can become adequately operative only when it becomes, like the present one, an element in early education, and has the support of a strong social sanction. Nor will men be quite ready for it until, through the continuance of a discipline which has already partially molded them to the conditions of social existence, they are completely molded to those conditions.

We must therefore recognize the resistance to a change of theological opinion as in great measure salutary. It is not simply that strong and deep-rooted feelings are necessarily excited to antagonism—it is not simply that the highest moral sentiments join in the condemnation of a change which seems to undermine their authority; but it is that a real adaptation exists between an established belief and the natures of those who defend it, and that the tenacity of the defence measures the completeness of the adaptation. Forms of religion, like forms of government, must be fit for those who live under them; and in the one case as in the other, that form which is fittest is that for which there is an instinctive preference. As certainly as a barbarous race needs a harsh terrestrial rule and habitually shows attachment to a despotism capable of the necessary rigor, so certainly does such a race need a belief in a celestial rule that is similarly harsh, and habitually shows attachment to such a belief. And just in the same way that the sudden substitution of free institutions for tyrannical ones is sure to be followed by a reaction; so, if a creed full of dreadful ideal penalties is all at once replaced by one presenting ideal penalties that are comparatively gentle, there will inevitably be a return to some modification of the old belief. The parallelism holds yet further. During those early stages in which there is an extreme incongruity between the relatively best and the absolutely best, both political and religious changes, when at rare intervals they occur, are necessarily violent, and necessarily entail violent retrogressions. But as the incongruity between that which is and that which should be, diminishes, the changes become more moderate, and are succeeded by more moderate retrogressions; until, as these movements and counter-movements decrease in amount and increase in frequency, they merge into an almost continuous growth. That adhesion to old institutions and beliefs which, in primitive societies, opposes an iron barrier to any advance, and which, after the barrier has been at length burst through, brings back the institutions and beliefs from that too-forward position to which the momentum of change had carried them, and so helps to readapt social conditions to the popular character—this adhesion to old institutions and beliefs eventually becomes the constant check by which the constant advance is prevented from being too rapid. This holds true of religious creeds and forms, as of civil ones. And so we learn that theological conservatism, like political conservatism, has an all-important function.

§ 33. That spirit of toleration which is so marked a characteristic of modern times, and is daily growing more conspicuous, has thus a far deeper meaning than is supposed. What we commonly regard simply as a due respect for the right of private judgment is really a necessary condition to the balancing of the progressive and conservative tendencies —is a means of maintaining the adaptation between men's beliefs and their natures. It is therefore a spirit to be fostered; and it is a spirit which the catholic thinker, who perceives the functions of these various conflicting creeds, should above all other men display. Doubtless whoever feels the greatness of the error to which his fellows cling and the greatness of the truth which they reject, will find it hard to show a due patience. It is hard for him to listen calmly to the futile arguments used in support of irrational doctrines and to the misrepresentation of antagonist doctrines. It is hard for him to bear the manifestation of that pride of ignorance which so far exceeds the pride of science. Naturally enough, such a one will be indignant when charged with irreligion because he declines to accept the carpenter-theory of creation as the most worthy one. He may think it needless as it is difficult to conceal his repugnance to a creed which tacitly ascribes to The Unknowable a love of adulation such as would be despised in a human being. Convinced as he is that all punishment, as we see it wrought out in the order of nature, is but a disguised beneficence, there will perhaps escape from him an angry condemnation of the belief that punishment is a divine vengeance, and that divine vengeance is eternal. He may be tempted to show his contempt when he is told that actions instigated by an unselfish sympathy or by a pure love of rectitude are intrinsically sinful, and that conduct is truly good only when it is due to a faith whose openly-professed motive is other-wordliness; but he must restrain such feelings. Though he may be unable to do this during the excitement of controversy, or when otherwise brought face to face with current superstitions, he must yet qualify his antagonism in calmer moments; so that his mature judgment and resulting conduct may be without bias.

To this end let him ever bear in mind three cardinal facts —two of them already dwelt upon, and one still to be pointed out. The first is that with which we set out; namely, the existence of a fundamental verity under all forms of religion, however degraded. In each of them there is a soul of truth. Through the gross body of dogmas, traditions and rites which contain it, it is always visible—dimly or clearly, as the case may be. This it is which gives vitality even to the rudest creed; this it is which survives every modification; and this it is which we must not forget when condemning the forms under which it is presented. The second of these cardinal facts, set forth at length in the foregoing section, is, that while those concrete elements in which each creed embodies this soul of truth are bad as measured by an absolute standard, they are good as measured by a relative standard. Though from higher perceptions they hide the abstract verity within them, yet to lower perceptions they render this verity more appreciable than it would otherwise be. They serve to make real and influential over men that which would else be unreal and uninfluential. Or we may call them the protective envelopes, without which the contained truth would die. The remaining cardinal fact is that these various beliefs are parts of the constituted order of things, and not accidental but necessary parts. Seeing how one or other of them is everywhere present, is of perennial growth, and when cut down redevelops in a form but slightly modified, we cannot avoid the inference that they are needful accompaniments of human life, severally fitted to the societies in which they are indigenous. From the highest point of view we must recognize them as elements in that great evolution of which the beginning and end are beyond our knowledge or conception—as modes of manifestation of The Unknowable, and as having this for their warrant.

Our toleration therefore should be the widest possible. Or, rather, we should aim at something beyond toleration, as commonly understood. In dealing with alien beliefs our endeavor must be, not simply to refrain from injustice of word or deed, but also to do justice by an open recognition of positive worth. We must qualify our disagreement with as much as may be of sympathy.

§ 34. These admissions will perhaps be held to imply that the current theology should be passively accepted; or, at any rate, should not be actively opposed. "Why," it may be asked, "if all creeds have an average fitness to their times and places, should we not rest content with that to which we are born? If the established belief contains an essential truth—if the forms under which it presents this truth, though intrinsically bad, are extrinsically good—if the abolition of these forms would be at present detrimental to the great majority—nay, if there are scarcely any to whom the ultimate and most abstract belief can furnish an adequate rule of life, surely it is wrong, for the present at least, to propagate this ultimate and most abstract belief."

The reply is, that though existing religious ideas and institutions have an average adaptation to the characters of the people who live under them; yet, as these characters are ever changing, the adaptation is ever becoming imperfect; and the ideas and institutions need remodelling with a frequency proportionate to the rapidity of the change. Hence, while it is requisite that free play should be given to conservative thought and action, progressive thought and action must also have free play. Without the agency of both, there cannot be those continual readaptations which orderly progress demands.

Whoever hesitates to utter that which he thinks the highest truth, lest it should be too much in advance of the time, may reassure himself by looking at his acts from an impersonal point of view. Let him duly realize the fact that opinion is the agency through which character adapts external arrangements to itself—that his opinion rightly forms part of this agency—is a unit of force, constituting, with other such units, the general power which works out social changes; and he will perceive that he may properly give full utterance to his innermost conviction, leaving it to produce what effect it may. It is not for nothing that he has in him these sympathies with some principles and repugnance to others. He, with all his capacities and aspirations and beliefs, is not an accident, but a product of the time. He must remember that while he is a descendant of the past he is a parent of the future, and that his thoughts are as children born to him, which he may not carelessly let die. He, like every other man, may properly consider himself as one of the myriad agencies through whom works the Unknown Cause; and when the Unknown Cause produces in him a certain belief, he is thereby authorized to profess and act out that belief. For, to render in their highest sense the words of the poet:

> ——— Nature is made better by no mean,
> But nature makes that mean: over that art
> Which you say adds to nature, is an art
> That nature makes.

Not as adventitious, therefore, will the wise man regard the faith which is in him. The highest truth he sees he will fearlessly utter; knowing that, let what may come of it, he is thus playing his right part in the world—knowing that if he can effect the change he aims at—well; if not—well also; though not *so* well.

PART TWO

THE KNOWABLE

CHAPTER I

PHILOSOPHY DEFINED

§ 35. AFTER concluding that we cannot know the ultimate nature of that which is manifested to us, there arise the questions—What is it that we know? In what sense do we know it? And in what consists our highest knowledge of it? Having repudiated as impossible the Philosophy which professes to formulate Being as distinguished from Appearance, it becomes needful to say what Philosophy truly is— not simply to specify its limits, but to specify its character within those limits. Given a certain sphere as the sphere to which human intelligence is restricted, and there remains to define the peculiar product of human intelligence which may still be called Philosophy.

In doing this we may advantageously avail ourselves of the method followed at the outset, of separating from conceptions that are partially or mainly erroneous the element of truth they contain. As in the chapter on "Religion and Science" it was inferred that religious beliefs, wrong as they might individually be in their particular forms, nevertheless probably each contained an essential verity, and that this was most likely common to them all—so in this place it is to be inferred that past and present beliefs respecting the nature of Philosophy are none of them wholly false, and that that in which they are true is that in which they agree. We have here, then, to do what was done there—"to compare all opinions of the same genus; to set aside as more or less discrediting one another those various special and concrete elements in which such opinions disagree; to observe what remains after the discordant constituents have been eliminated; and to find for this remaining constituent that abstract expression which holds true throughout its divergent modifications."

§ 36. Earlier speculations being passed over, we see that among the Greeks, before there had arisen any notion of Philosophy in general, apart from particular forms of Philosophy, the particular forms of it from which the general notion was to arise were hypotheses respecting some universal principle that constituted the essence of all concrete kinds of being. To the question—"What is that *invariable existence* of which these are *variable states?*" there were sundry answers—Water, Air, Fire. A class of hypotheses of this all-embracing character having been propounded, it became possible for Pythagoras to conceive of Philosophy in the abstract as knowledge the most remote from practical ends; and to define it as "knowledge of immaterial and eternal things" —"the cause of the material existence of things" being, in his view, Number. Thereafter we find continued a pursuit of Philosophy as some ultimate interpretation of the Universe, assumed to be possible whether actually reached in any case or not. And in the course of this pursuit various such ultimate interpretations were given, as that "One is the beginning of all things," that "the One is God," that "the One is Finite," that "the One is Infinite," that "Intelligence is the governing principle of things," and so on. From all which it is plain that the knowledge supposed to constitute Philosophy differed from other knowledge in its transcendent, exhaustive character. In the subsequent course of speculation, after the Sceptics had shaken men's faith in their powers of reaching such transcendent knowledge, there grew up a much-restricted conception of Philosophy. Under Socrates, and still more under the Stoics, Philosophy became little else than the doctrine of right living. Its subject-matter was practically cut down to the proper ruling of conduct, public and private. Not, indeed, that the proper ruling of conduct, as conceived by sundry of the later Greek thinkers to constitute subject-matter of Philosophy, answered to what was popularly understood by the proper ruling of conduct. The injunctions of Zeno were not of the same class as those which guided men from early times downward, in their daily observances, sacrifices, customs— all having more or less of religious sanction; but they were principles of action enunciated without reference to times, or persons, or special cases. What, then, was the constant element in these unlike ideas of Philosophy held by the ancients? Clearly, the character in which this last idea agrees with the first is, that within its sphere of inquiry Philosophy seeks for wide and deep truths as distinguished from the multitudinous detailed truths which the surfaces of things and actions present.

By comparing the conceptions of Philosophy that have been current in modern times, we get a like result. The disciples of Schelling, Fichte, and their kindred, join the Hegelian in ridiculing the so-called Philosophy which has usurped the title in England. Not without reason, they laugh on reading of "Philosophical instruments," and would deny that any one of the papers in the *Philosophical Transactions* has the least claim to come under such a title. Retaliating on their critics, the English may, and most of them do, reject as absurd the imagined Philosophy of the German schools. As consciousness cannot be transcended, they hold that whether consciousness does or does not vouch for the existence of something beyond itself, it at any rate cannot comprehend that something; and that hence, in so far as any Philosophy professes to be an Ontology, it is false. These two views cancel one another over large parts of their areas. The English criticism on the Germans cuts off from Philosophy all that is regarded as absolute knowledge. The German criticism on the English tacitly implies that if Philosophy is limited to the relative, it is at any rate not concerned with those aspects of the relative which are embodied in mathematical formulæ, in accounts of physical researches, in chemical analyses, or in descriptions of species and reports of physiological experiments. Now what has the too-wide German conception in common with the conception general among English men of science; which, narrow and crude as it is, is not so narrow and crude as their misuse of the word philosophical indicates? The two have this in common, that neither Germans nor English apply the word to unsystematized knowledge—to knowledge quite uncoördinated with other knowledge. Even the most limited specialist would not describe as philosophical an essay which, dealing wholly with details, manifested no perception of the bearings of those details on wider truths.

The vague idea thus raised of that in which the various conceptions of Philosophy agree may be rendered more definite by comparing what has been known in England as Natural Philosophy with that development of it called Positive Philosophy. Though, as M. Comte admits, the two consist of knowledge essentially the same in kind; yet, by having put this kind of knowledge into a more coherent form, he has given it more of that character to which the term philosophical is applied. Without expressing any opinion respecting the truth of his co-ordination, it must be conceded that by the fact of its co-ordination the body of knowledge organized by him has a better claim to the title Philosophy than has the comparatively unorganized body of knowledge named Natural Philosophy.

If subdivisions of Philosophy, or more special forms of it, be contrasted with one another, or with the whole, the same implication comes out. Moral Philosophy and Political Philosophy agree with Philosophy at large in the comprehensiveness of their reasonings and conclusions. Though under the head of Moral Philosophy we treat of human actions as right or wrong, we do not include special directions for behavior in the nursery, at table, or on the exchange; and though Political Philosophy has for its topic the conduct of men in their public relations, it does not concern itself with modes of voting or details of administration. Both of these sections of Philosophy contemplate particular instances, only as illustrating truths of wide application.

§ 37. Thus every one of these conceptions implies the belief in a possible way of knowing things more completely than they are known through simple experiences mechanically accumulated in memory or heaped up in cyclopedias. Though in the extent of the sphere which they have supposed Philosophy to fill, men have differed and still differ very widely, yet there is a real if unavowed agreement among them in signifying by this title a knowledge which transcends ordinary knowledge. That which remains as the common element in these conceptions of philosophy, after the elimination of their discordant elements, is—*knowledge of the highest degree of generality.* We see this tacitly asserted by the simultaneous inclusion of God, Nature, and Man within its scope; or still more distantly by the division of Philosophy as a whole into Theological, Physical, Ethical, etc. For that which characterizes the genus of which these are species must be something more general than that which distinguishes any one species.

What must be the specific shape here given to this conception? The range of intelligence we find to be limited to the relative. Though persistently conscious of a Power manifested to us, we have abandoned as futile the attempt to learn anything respecting the nature of that Power; and so have shut out Philosophy from much of the domain supposed to belong to it. The domain left is that occupied by Science. Science concerns itself with the co-existences and sequences among phenomena, grouping these at first into generalizations of a simple or low order, and rising gradually to higher and more extended generalizations. But if so, where remains any subject-matter for Philosophy?

The reply is, Philosophy may still properly be the title retained for knowledge of the highest generality. Science means merely the family of the Sciences—stands for nothing more than the sum of knowledge formed of their contributions, and ignores the knowledge constituted by the *fusion* of all these contributions into a whole. As usage has defined it, Science consists of truths existing more or less separated, and does not recognize these truths as entirely integrated. An illustration will make the difference clear.

If we ascribe the flow of a river to the same force which causes the fall of a stone, we make a statement, true as far as it goes, that belongs to a certain division of Science. If, in further explanation of a movement produced by gravitation in a direction almost horizontal, we cite the law that fluids subject to mechanical forces exert reactive forces which are equal in all directions, we formulate a wider fact, containing the scientific interpretation of many other phenomena, as those presented by the fountain, the hydraulic press, the steam-engine, the air-pump. And when this proposition, extending only to the dynamics of fluids, is merged in a proposition of general dynamics, comprehending the laws of movement of solids as well as of fluids, there is reached a yet higher truth, but still a truth that comes wholly within the realm of Science. Again, looking around at Birds and Mammals, suppose we say that air-breathing animals are hot-blooded; and that then, remembering how Reptiles, which also breathe air, are not much warmer than their media, we say, more truly, that animals (bulks being equal) have temperatures proportionate to the quantities of air they breathe; and that then, calling to mind certain large fish which maintain a heat considerably above that of the water they swim in, we further correct the generalization by saying that the temperature varies as the rate of oxygenation of the blood; and that then, modifying the statement to meet other criticisms, we finally assert the relation to be between the amount of heat and the amount of molecular change—supposing we do all this, we state scientific truths that are successively wider and more complete, but truths which to the last remain purely scientific. Once more, if, guided by mercantile experiences, we reach the conclusion that prices rise when the demand exceeds the supply; and that commodities flow from places where they are abundant to places where they are scarce; and that the industries of different localities are determined in their kinds mainly by the facilities which the localities afford for them; and if, studying these generalizations of political economy, we trace them all to the truth that each man seeks satisfaction for his desires in ways costing the smallest efforts— such social phenomena being *resultants* of individual actions so guided—we are still dealing with the propositions of Science only.

And now how is Philosophy constituted? It is constituted by carrying a stage further the process indicated. So long as these truths are known only apart and regarded as independent, even the most general of them cannot without laxity of speech be called philosophical. But when, having been severally reduced to a simple mechanical axiom, a principle of molecular physics, and a law of social action, they are contemplated together as corollaries of some ultimate truth, then we rise to the kind of knowledge that constitutes Philosophy proper.

The truths of Philosophy thus bear the same relation to the highest scientific truths that each of these bears to lower scientific truths. As each widest generalization of Science comprehends and consolidates the narrower generalizations of its own division, so the generalizations of Philosophy comprehend and consolidate the widest generalizations of Science. It is therefore a knowledge the extreme opposite in kind to that which experience first accumulates. It is the final product of that process which begins with a mere colligation of crude observations, goes on establishing propositions that are broader and more separated from particular cases, and ends in universal propositions. Or to bring the definition to its simplest and clearest form—knowledge of the lowest kind is *un-unified* knowledge; Science is *partially-unified* knowledge; Philosophy is *completely-unified* knowledge.

§ 38. Such, at least, is the meaning we must here give to the word Philosophy, if we employ it at all. In so defining it, we accept that which is common to the various conceptions of it current among both ancients and moderns—rejecting those elements in which these conceptions disagree or exceed the possible range of intelligence. In short, we are simply giving precision to that application of the word which is gradually establishing itself.

Two forms of Philosophy, as thus understood, may be distinguished and dealt with separately. On the one hand the things contemplated may be the universal truths: all particular truths referred to being used simply for proof or elucidation of these universal truths. On the other hand, setting out with the universal truths as granted, the things contemplated may be the particular truths as interpreted by them. In both cases we deal with the universal truths; but in the one case they are passive and in the other case active —in the one case they form the products of exploration and in the other case the instruments of exploration. These divisions we may appropriately call General Philosophy and Special Philosophy respectively.

The remainder of this volume will be devoted to General Philosophy. Special Philosophy, divided into parts determined by the natures of the phenomena treated, will be the subject-matter of subsequent volumes.

CHAPTER II

THE DATA OF PHILOSOPHY

§ 39. EVERY thought involves a whole system of thoughts; and ceases to exist if severed from its various correlatives. As we cannot isolate a single organ of a living body, and deal with it as though it had a life independent of the rest; so, from the organized structure of our cognitions, we cannot cut out one and proceed as though it had survived the separation. The development of formless protoplasm into an embryo is a specialization of parts, the distinctness of which increases only as fast as their combination increases—each becomes a distinguishable organ only on condition that it is bound up with others, which have simultaneously become distinguishable organs; and, similarly, from the unformed material of consciousness, a developed intelligence can arise only by a process which, in making thoughts defined, also makes them mutually dependent—establishes among them certain vital connections the destruction of which causes instant death of the thoughts. Overlooking this all-important truth, however, speculators have habitually set out with some professedly simple datum or data; have supposed themselves to assume nothing beyond this datum or these data; and have thereupon proceeded to prove or disprove propositions which were, by implication, already unconsciously asserted along with that which was consciously asserted.

This reasoning in a circle has resulted from the misuse of words: not that misuse commonly enlarged upon—not the misapplication or change of meaning whence so much error arises; but a more radical and less obvious misuse. Only that thought which is directly indicated by each word has been contemplated; while numerous thoughts indirectly indicated have been left out of consideration. Because a spoken or written word can be detached from all others, it has been inadvertently assumed that the thing signified by a word can be detached from the things signified by all other words. Though more deeply hidden, the mistake is of the same order as that made by the Greeks, who were continually led astray by the belief in some community of nature between the symbol and that which it symbolized. For though here community of nature is not assumed to the same extent as of old, it is assumed to this extent, that because the symbol is separable from all other symbols, and can be contemplated as having an independent existence, so the thought symbolized may be thus separated and thus contemplated. How profoundly this error vitiates the conclusions of one who makes it, we shall quickly see on taking a case. The sceptical metaphysician, wishing his reasonings to be as rigorous as possible, says to himself, "I will take for granted only this one thing." What now are the tacit assumptions inseparable from his avowed assumption? The resolve itself indirectly asserts that there is some other thing, or are some other things, which he might assume; for it is impossible to think of unity without thinking of a correlative duality or multiplicity. In the very act, therefore, of restricting himself, he takes in much that is professedly left out. Again, before proceeding he must give a definition of that which he assumes. Is nothing unexpressed involved in the thought of a thing as defined? There is the thought of something excluded by the definition—there is, as before, the thought of other existence. But there is much more. Defining a thing, or setting a limit to it, implies the thought of a limit; and limit cannot be thought of apart from some notion of quantity—extensive, protensive, or intensive. Further, definition is impossible unless there enters into it the thought of difference; and difference, besides being unthinkable without having two things that differ, implies the existence of other differences than the one recognized; since otherwise there can be no general conception of difference. Nor is this all. As before pointed out (§ 24) all thought involves the consciousness of likeness: the one thing avowedly postulated cannot be known absolutely as one thing, but can be known only as of such or such kind—only as classed with other things in virtue of some common attribute. Thus along with the single avowed datum, we have surreptitiously brought in a number of unavowed data—*existence other than that alleged, quantity, number, limit, difference, likeness, class, attribute.* Saying nothing of the many more which an exhaustive analysis would disclose, we have in these unacknowledged postulates the outlines of a general theory; and that theory can be neither proved nor disproved by the metaphysician's argument. Insist that his symbol shall be interpreted at every step into its full meaning, with all the complementary thoughts implied by that meaning, and you find already taken for granted in the premises that which in the conclusion is asserted or denied.

In what way, then, must Philosophy set out? The developed intelligence is framed upon certain organized and consolidated conceptions of which it cannot divest itself; and which it can no more stir without using than the body can stir without help of its limbs. In what way, then, is it possible for intelligence, striving after Philosophy, to give any account of these conceptions, and to show either their validity or their invalidity? There is but one way. Those of them which are vital, or cannot be severed from the rest without mental dissolution, must be assumed as true *provisionally*. The fundamental intuitions that are essential to the process of thinking must be temporarily accepted as unquestionable, leaving the assumption of their unquestionableness to be justified by the results.

§ 40. How is it to be justified by the results? As any other assumption is justified—by ascertaining that all the conclusions deducible from it correspond with the facts as directly observed—by showing the agreement between the experiences it leads us to anticipate, and the actual experiences. There is no mode of establishing the validity of any belief, except that of showing its entire congruity with all other beliefs. If we suppose that a mass which has a certain color and lustre is the substance called gold, how do we proceed to prove the hypothesis that it is gold? We represent to ourselves certain other impressions which gold produces on us, and then observe whether, under the appropriate conditions, this particular mass produces on us such impressions. We remember, as we say, that gold has a high specific gravity; and if, on poising this substance on the finger, we find that its weight is great considering its bulk, we take the correspondence between the represented impression and the presented impression as further evidence that the sub-

stance is gold. In response to a demand for more proof, we
compare certain other ideal and real effects. Knowing that
gold, unlike most metals, is insoluble in nitric acid, we imagine to ourselves a drop of nitric acid placed on the surface
of this yellow, glittering, heavy substance, without causing
corrosion; and when, after so placing a drop of nitric acid,
no effervescence or other change follows, we hold this agreement between the anticipation and the experience to be an
additional reason for thinking that the substance is gold.
And if, similarly, the great malleability possessed by gold
we find to be paralleled by the great malleability of this substance; if, like gold, it fuses at about 2,000 degrees; crys-
tallizes in octahedrons; is dissolved by selenic acid; and,
under all conditions, does what gold does under such conditions; the conviction that it is gold reaches what we regard
as the highest certainty—we know it to be gold in the fullest
sense of knowing. For, as we here see, our whole knowledge of gold consists in nothing more than the consciousness
of a definite set of impressions, standing in definite relations,
disclosed under definite conditions; and if, in a present experience, the impressions, relations, and conditions perfectly
correspond with those in past experiences, the cognition has
all the validity of which it is capable. So that, generalizing
the statement, hypotheses, down even to those simple ones
which we make from moment to moment in our acts of recognition, are verified when entire congruity is found to exist
between the states of consciousness constituting them, and
certain other states of consciousness given in perception, or
reflection, or both; and no other knowledge is possible for
us than that which consists of the consciousness of such congruities and their correlative incongruities.

Hence Philosophy, compelled to make those fundamental assumptions without which thought is impossible, has to
justify them by showing their congruity with all other dicta
of consciousness. Debarred as we are from everything beyond the relative, truth, raised to its highest form, can be
for us nothing more than perfect agreement, throughout the

whole range of our experience, between those representations of things which we distinguish as ideal and those presentations of things which we distinguish as real. If, by discovering a proposition to be untrue, we mean nothing more than discovering a difference between a thing expected and a thing perceived; then a body of conclusions in which no such difference anywhere occurs, must be what we mean by an entirely true body of conclusions.

And here, indeed, it becomes also obvious that, setting out with these fundamental intuitions provisionally assumed to be true—that is, provisionally assumed to be congruous with all other dicta of consciousness—the process of proving or disproving the congruity becomes the business of Philosophy; and the complete establishment of the congruity becomes the same thing as the complete unification of knowledge in which Philosophy reaches its goal.

§ 41. What is this datum, or rather what are these data, which Philosophy cannot do without? Clearly one primordial datum is involved in the foregoing statement. Already by implication we have assumed, and must forever continue to assume, that congruities and incongruities exist, and are cognizable by us. We cannot avoid accepting as true the verdict of consciousness that some manifestations are like one another and some are unlike one another. Unless consciousness be a competent judge of the likeness and unlikeness of its states, there can never be established that congruity throughout the whole of our cognitions which constitutes Philosophy; nor can there ever be established that incongruity by which only any hypothesis, philosophical or other, can be shown erroneous.

The impossibility of moving toward either conviction or scepticism without postulating thus much, we shall see even more vividly on observing how every step in reasoning postulates thus much, over and over again. To say that all things of a certain class are characterized by a certain attribute, is to say that all things known as *like* in those various attributes connoted by their common name, are also *like* in having the particular attribute specified. To say that some object of immediate attention belongs to this class, is to say that it is *like* all the others in the various attributes connoted by their common name. To say that this object possesses the particular attribute specified, is to say that it is *like* the others in this respect also. While, contrariwise, the assertion that the attribute thus inferred to be possessed by it is not possessed, implies the assertion that in place of one of the alleged *likenesses* there exists an *unlikeness*. Neither affirmation nor denial, therefore, of any deliverance of reason, or any element of such deliverance, is possible without accepting the dictum of consciousness that certain of its states are like or unlike. Whence, besides seeing that the unified knowledge constituting a completed Philosophy, is a knowledge composed of parts that are universally congruous; and besides seeing that it is the business of Philosophy to establish their universal congruity; we also see that every act of the process by which this universal congruity is to be established, down even to the components of every inference and every observation, consists in the establishment of congruity.

Consequently, the assumption that a congruity or an incongruity exists when consciousness testifies to it, is an inevitable assumption. It is useless to say, as Sir W. Hamilton does, that "consciousness is to be presumed trustworthy until proved mendacious." It cannot be proved mendacious in this, its primordial act; since, as we see, proof involves a repeated acceptance of this primordial act. Nay more, the very thing supposed to be proved cannot be expressed without recognizing this primordial act as valid; since, unless we accept the verdict of consciousness that they differ, mendacity and trustworthiness become identical. Process and product of reasoning both disappear in the absence of this assumption.

It may, indeed, be often shown that what, after careless comparison, were supposed to be like states of consciousness,

are really unlike; or that what were carelessly supposed to
be unlike, are really like. But how is this shown? Simply
by a more careful comparison, mediately or immediately
made. And what does acceptance of the revised conclusion
imply? Simply that a deliberate verdict of consciousness is
preferable to a rash one; or, to speak more definitely—that
a consciousness of likeness or difference which survives critical examination must be accepted in place of one that does
not survive—the very survival being itself the acceptance.

And here we get to the bottom of the matter. The permanence of a consciousness of likeness or difference is our
ultimate warrant for asserting the existence of likeness or
difference; and, in fact, we mean by the existence of likeness
or difference, nothing more than the permanent consciousness of it. To say that a given congruity or incongruity
exists, is simply our way of saying that we invariably have
a consciousness of it along with a consciousness of the compared things. We know nothing more of existence than a
continued manifestation.

§ 42. But Philosophy requires for its datum some sub-
stantive proposition. To recognize as unquestionable a certain fundamental *process* of thought, is not enough; we must
recognize as unquestionable some fundamental *product* of
thought, reached by this process. If Philosophy is completely-unified knowledge—if the unification of knowledge
is to be effected only by showing that some ultimate proposition includes and consolidates all the results of experience;
then, clearly, this ultimate proposition, which has to be
proved congruous with all others, must express a piece of
knowledge, and not the validity of an act of knowing. Having assumed the trustworthiness of consciousness, we have
also to assume as trustworthy some deliverance of consciousness.

What must this be? Must it not be one affirming the
widest and most profound distinction which things present?
Must it not be a statement of congruities and incongruities

more general than any other? An ultimate principle that is
to unify all experience must be co-extensive with all experience—cannot be concerned with experience of one order or
several orders, but must be concerned with universal experience. That which Philosophy takes as its datum, must be
an assertion of some likeness and difference to which all
other likenesses and differences are secondary. If knowing
is classifying, or grouping the like and separating the unlike; and if the unification of knowledge proceeds by arrang-
ing the smaller classes of like experiences within the larger,
and these within the still larger; then, the proposition by
which knowledge is unified must be one specifying the
antithesis between two ultimate classes of experiences, in
which all others merge.

Let us now consider what these classes are. In drawing
the distinction between them, we cannot avoid using words
that have indirect implications wider than their direct meanings—we cannot avoid arousing thoughts that imply the very
distinction which it is the object of the analysis to establish.
Keeping this fact in mind, we can do no more than ignore
the connotations of the words, and attend only to the things
they avowedly denote.

§ 43. Setting out out from the conclusion lately reached,
that all things known to us are manifestations of the Unknowable; and suppressing, so far as we may, every hypothesis respecting the something which underlies one or other
order of these manifestations; we find that the manifestations, considered simply as such, are divisible into two great
classes, called by some *impressions* and *ideas*. The implications of these words are apt to vitiate the reasonings of those
who use the words; and though it may be possible to use
them only with reference to the differential characteristics
they are meant to indicate, it is best to avoid the risk of
making unacknowledged assumptions. The term *sensation,*
too, commonly used as the equivalent of impression, implies
certain psychological theories—tacitly, if not openly, postu-

lates a sensitive organism and something acting upon it; and can scarcely be employed without bringing these postulates into the thoughts and embodying them in the inferences. Similarly, the phrase *state of consciousness,* as signifying either an impression or an idea, is objectionable. As we cannot think of a state without thinking of something of which it is a state, and which is capable of different states, there is involved a foregone conclusion—an undeveloped system of metaphysics. Here, accepting the inevitable implication that the manifestations imply something manifested, our aim must be to avoid any further implications. Though we cannot exclude further implications from our thoughts, and cannot carry on our argument without tacit recognitions of them, we can at any rate refuse to recognize them in the terms with which we set out. We may do this most effectually by classing the manifestations as *vivid* and *faint* respectively. Let us consider what are the several distinctions that exist between these.

And first a few words on this most conspicuous distinction which these antithetical names imply. Manifestations that occur under the conditions called those of perception (and the conditions so called we must here, as much as possible, separate from all hypotheses, and regard simply as themselves a certain group of manifestations) are ordinarily far more distinct than those which occur under the conditions known as those of reflection, or memory, or imagination, or ideation. These vivid manifestations do, indeed, sometimes differ but little from the faint ones. When nearly dark we may be unable to decide whether a certain manifestation belongs to the vivid order or the faint order—whether, as we say, we really see something or fancy we see it. In like manner, between a very feeble sound and the imagination of a sound, it is occasionally difficult to discriminate. But these exceptional cases are extremely rare in comparison with the enormous mass of cases in which, from instant to instant, the vivid manifestations distinguish themselves unmistakably from the faint. Conversely, it also now and then happens (though under conditions which we significantly distinguish as abnormal) that manifestations of the faint order become so strong as to be mistaken for those of the vivid order. Ideal sights and sounds are in the insane so much intensified as to be classed with real sights and sounds—ideal and real being here supposed to imply no other contrast than that which we are considering. These cases of illusion, as we call them, bear, however, so small a ratio to the great mass of cases, that we may safely neglect them, and say that the relative faintness of these manifestations of the second order is so marked, that we are never in doubt as to their distinctness from those of the first order. Or if we recognize the exceptional occurrence of doubt, the recognition serves but to introduce the significant fact that we have other means of determining to which order a particular manifestation belongs, when the test of comparative vividness fails us.

Manifestations of the vivid order precede, in our experience, those of the faint order; or, in the terms quoted above, the idea is an imperfect and feeble repetition of the original impression. To put the facts in historical sequence—there is first a presented manifestation of the vivid order, and then, afterward, there may come a represented manifestation that is like it except in being much less distinct. Besides the universal experience that after having those vivid manifestations which we call particular places and persons and things, we can have those faint manifestations which we call recollections of the places, persons, and things, but cannot have these previously; and besides the universal experience that before tasting certain substances and smelling certain perfumes we are without the faint manifestations known as ideas of their tastes and smells; we have also the fact that where certain orders of the vivid manifestations are shut out (as the visible from the blind and the audible from the deaf), the corresponding faint manifestations never come into existence. It is true that in some cases the faint manifestations precede the vivid. What we call a conception of a machine may presently be followed by a vivid manifestation matching it—a so-called actual machine. But in the first place this occurrence of the vivid manifestation after the faint has no analogy with the occurrence of the faint after the vivid—its sequence is not spontaneous like that of the idea after the impression. And in the second place, though a faint manifestation of this kind may occur before the vivid one answering to it, yet its component parts may not. Without the foregoing vivid manifestations of wheels and bars and cranks, the inventor could have no faint manifestation of his new machine. Thus, the occurrence of the faint manifestations is made possible by the previous occurrence of the vivid. They are distinguished from one another as independent and dependent.

These two orders of manifestations form concurrent series; or rather let us call them, not series, which implies linear arrangements, but heterogeneous streams or processions. These run side by side; each now broadening and now narrowing, each now threatening to obliterate its neighbor, and now in turn threatened with obliteration, but neither ever quite excluding the other from their common channel. Let us watch the mutual actions of the two currents. During what we call our states of activity, the vivid manifestations predominate. We simultaneously receive many and varied presentations—a crowd of visual impressions, sounds more or less numerous, resistances, tastes, odors, etc.; some groups of them changing, and others temporarily fixed, but altering as we move; and when we compare in its breadth and massiveness this heterogeneous combination of vivid manifestations with the concurrent combination of faint manifestations, these last sink into relative insignificance. They never wholly disappear however. Always along with the vivid manifestations, even in their greatest obtrusiveness, analysis discloses a thread of thoughts and interpretations constituted of the faint manifestations. Or if it be contended that the occurrence of a deafening explosion or an intense pain may for a moment exclude every idea, it must yet be admitted that such breach of continuity can never be immediately known as occurring; since the act of knowing is impossible in the absence of ideas. On the other hand, after certain vivid manifestations which we call the acts of closing the eyes and adjusting ourselves so as to enfeeble the vivid manifestations of pressure, sound, etc., the manifestations of the faint order become relatively predominant. The ever-varying heterogeneous current of them, no longer obscured by the vivid current, grows more distinct, and seems almost to exclude the vivid current. But while what we call consciousness continues, the current of vivid manifestations, however small the dimensions to which it is reduced, still continues: pressure and touch do not wholly disappear. It is only on lapsing into the unconsciousness termed sleep, that manifestations of the vivid order cease to be distinguishable as such, and those of the faint order come to be mistaken for them. And even of this we remain unaware till the recurrence of manifestations of the vivid order on awakening: we can never infer that manifestations of the vivid order have been absent, until they are again present; and can therefore never directly know them to be absent. Thus, of the two concurrent compound series of manifestations, each preserves its continuity. As they flow side by side, each trenches on the other, but there never comes a moment at which it can be said that the one has, then and there, broken through the other.

Besides this longitudinal cohesion there is a lateral cohesion, both of the vivid to the vivid and of the faint to the faint. The components of the vivid series are bound together by ties of co-existence as well as by ties of succession; and the components of the faint series are similarly bound together. Between the degrees of union in the two cases there are, however, marked and very significant differences. Let us observe them. Over an area occupying part of the so-called field of view, lights and shades and colors and outlines constitute a group to which, as the signs of an object, we give a certain name; and while they continue present, these united vivid manifestations remain inseparable. So,

too, is it with co-existing groups of manifestations: each persists as a special combination; and most of them preserve
unchanging relations with those around. Such of them as
do not—such of them as are capable of what we call independent movements, nevertheless show us a constant connection between certain of the manifestations they include,
along with a variable connection of others. And though,
after certain vivid manifestations known as a change in the
conditions of perception, there is a change in the proportions
among the vivid manifestations constituting any group, their
cohesion continues—we do not succeed in detaching one or
more of them from the rest. Turning to the faint manifestations, we see that while there are lateral cohesions among
them, these are much less extensive, and in most cases are
by no means so rigorous. After closing my eyes, I can represent an object now standing in a certain place, as standing
in some other place, or as absent. While I look at a blue
vase, I cannot separate the vivid manifestation of blueness
from the vivid manifestation of a particular shape; but, in
the absence of these vivid manifestations, I can separate the
faint manifestation of the shape from the faint manifestation
of blueness, and replace the last by a faint manifestation of
redness. It is so throughout: the faint manifestations cling
together to a certain extent, but nevertheless most of them
may be rearranged with facility. Indeed none of the *individual* faint manifestations cohere in the same indissoluble
way as do the individual vivid manifestations. Though
along with a faint manifestation of pressure there is always
some faint manifestation of extension, yet no particular faint
manifestation of extension is bound up with a particular
faint manifestation of pressure. So that whereas in the vivid
order the individual manifestations cohere indissolubly, usually in large groups, in the faint order the individual manifestations none of them cohere indissolubly, and are most
of them loosely aggregated: the only indissoluble cohesions
among them being between certain of their generic forms.

While the components of each current cohere with one

another, they do not cohere at all strongly with those of the other current. Or, more correctly, we may say that the vivid current habitually flows on quite undisturbed by the faint current; and that the faint current, though often largely determined by the vivid, and always to some extent carried with it, may yet maintain a substantial independence, letting the vivid current slide by. We will glance at the interactions of the two. The successive faint manifestations constituting thought, fail to modify in the slightest degree the vivid manifestations that present themselves. Omitting a quite peculiar class of exceptions, hereafter to be dealt with, the vivid manifestations, fixed and changing, are not directly affected by the faint. Those which I distinguish as components of a landscape, as surgings of the sea, as whistlings of the wind, as movements of vehicles and people, are absolutely uninfluenced by the accompanying faint manifestations which I distinguish as my ideas. On the other hand, the current of faint manifestations is always somewhat perturbed by the vivid. Frequently it consists mainly of faint manifestations which cling to the vivid ones, and are carried with them as they pass—memories and suggestions as we call them, which, joined with the vivid manifestations producing them, form almost the whole body of the manifestations. At other times, when, as we say, absorbed in thought, the disturbance of the faint current is but superficial. The vivid manifestations drag after them such few faint manifestations only as constitute recognitions of them; to each impression adhere certain ideas which make up the interpretation of it as such or such. But there meanwhile flows on a main stream of faint manifestations wholly unrelated to the vivid manifestations—what we call a reverie, perhaps, or it may be a process of reasoning. And occasionally, during the state known as absence of mind, this current of faint manifestations so far predominates that the vivid current scarcely affects it at all. Hence, these concurrent series of manifestations, each coherent with itself longitudinally and laterally, have but a partial coherence with one another. The vivid series is quite unmoved by its passing neighbor; and though the faint series is always to some extent moved by the adjacent vivid series, and is often carried bodily along with the vivid series, it may nevertheless become in great measure separate.

Yet another all-important differential characteristic has to be specified. The conditions under which these respective orders of manifestations occur, are different; and the conditions of occurrence of each order belong to itself. Whenever the immediate antecedents of vivid manifestations are traceable, they prove to be other vivid manifestations; and though we cannot say that the antecedents of the faint manifestations always lie wholly among themselves, yet the essential ones lie wholly among themselves. These statements will need a good deal of explanation. Obviously, changes among any of the vivid manifestations we are contemplating —the motions and sounds and alterations of appearance, in what we call surrounding objects—are either changes that follow certain vivid manifestations, or changes of which the antecedents are unapparent. Some of the vivid manifestations, however, occur only under certain conditions that seem to be of another order. Those which we know as colors and visible forms presuppose open eyes. But what is the opening of the eyes, translated into the terms we are here using? Literally it is an occurrence of certain vivid manifestations. The preliminary idea of opening the eyes does, indeed, consist of faint manifestations, but the act of opening them consists of vivid manifestations. And the like is still more conspicuously the case with those movements of the eyes and the head which are followed by new groups of vivid manifestations. Similarly with the antecedents to the vivid manifestations which we distinguish as those of touch and pressure. All the changeable ones have for their conditions of occurrence certain vivid manifestations which we know as sensations of muscular tension. It is true that the conditions to these conditions are manifestations of the faint order —those ideas of muscular actions which precede muscular actions. And we are here introduced to a complication aris-ing from the fact that what is called the body, is present to us as a set of vivid manifestations connected with the faint manifestations in a special way—a way such that in it alone certain vivid manifestations are capable of being produced by faint manifestations. There must be named, too, the kindred exception furnished by the emotions—an exception which, however, serves to enforce the general proposition. For while it is true that the emotions are to be considered as a certain kind of vivid manifestations, and are yet capable of being produced by the faint manifestations we call ideas; it is also true that because the conditions to their occurrence thus exist among the faint manifestations, we class them as belonging to the same general aggregate as the faint manifes-tations—do not class them with such other vivid manifesta-tions as colors, sounds, pressures, smells, etc. But omitting these pecular vivid manifestations which we know as mus-cular tensions and emotions, and which we habitually class apart, we may say of all the rest, that the conditions to their existence as vivid manifestations are manifestations belong-ing to their own class. In the parallel current we find a parallel truth. Though many manifestations of the faint order are partly caused by manifestations of the vivid order, which call up memories as we say, and suggest inferences; yet these results mainly depend on certain antecedents be-longing to the faint order. A cloud drifts across the sun, and may or may not produce an effect on the current of ideas: the inference that it is about to rain may arise, or there may be a persistence in the previous train of thought—a differ-ence obviously determined by conditions among the thoughts. Again, such power as a vivid manifestation has of causing certain faint manifestations to arise, depends on the pre-ex-istence of certain appropriate faint manifestations. If I have never heard a curlew, the cry which an unseen one makes, fails to produce an idea of the bird. And we have but to remember what various trains of reflection are aroused by the same sight, to see how essentially the occurrence of each faint manifestation depends on its relations to other faint manifestations that have gone before or that co-exist.

Here we are introduced, lastly, to one of the most striking, and perhaps the most important, of the differences between those two orders of manifestations—a difference continuous with that just pointed out, but one which may with advantage be separately insisted upon. The conditions of occurrence are not distinguished solely by the fact that each set, when identifiable, belongs to its own order of manifestations; but they are further distinguished in a very significant way. Manifestations of the faint order have traceable antecedents; can be made to occur by establishing their conditions of occurrence; and can be suppressed by establishing other conditions. But manifestations of the vivid order continually occur without previous presentation of their antecedents; and in many cases they persist or cease, under either known or unknown conditions, in such way as to show that their conditions are wholly beyond control. The impression distinguished as a flash of lightning, breaks across the current of our thoughts, absolutely without notice. The sounds from a band that strikes up in the street or from a crash of china in the next room, are not connected with any of the previously-present manifestations, either of the faint or of the vivid order. Often these vivid manifestations, arising unexpectedly, persist in thrusting themselves across the current of the faint ones; which not only cannot directly affect them, but cannot even indirectly affect them. A wound produced by a violent blow from behind, is a vivid manifestation the conditions of occurrence of which were neither among the faint nor among the vivid manifestations; and the conditions to the persistence of which are bound up with the vivid manifestations in some unmanifested way. So that whereas in the faint order, the conditions of occurrence are always among the pre-existing or co-existing manifestations; in the vivid order, the conditions of occurrence are often not present.

Thus we find many salient characters in which manifestations of the one order are like one another, and unlike those of the other order. Let us briefly re-enumerate these salient characters. Manifestations of the one order are vivid and those of the other are faint. Those of the one order are originals, while those of the other order are copies. The first form with one another a series, or heterogeneous current, that is never broken; and the second also form with one another a parallel series or current that is never broken; or, to speak strictly, no breakage of either is ever directly known. Those of the first order cohere with one another, not only longitudinally but also transversely; as do also those of the second order with one another. Between manifestations of the first order the cohesions, both longitudinal and transverse, are indissoluble; but between manifestations of the second order, these cohesions are most of them dissoluble with ease. While the members of each series or current are so coherent with one another that the current cannot be broken, the two currents, running side by side as they do, have but little coherence—the great body of the vivid current is absolutely unmodifiable by the faint, and the faint may become almost separate from the vivid. The conditions under which manifestations of either order occur, themselves belong to that order; but whereas in the faint order, the conditions are always present, in the vivid order the conditions are often not present, but lie somewhere outside of the series. Seven separate characters, then, mark off these two orders of manifestations from one another.

§44. What is the meaning of this? The foregoing analysis was commenced in the belief that the proposition postulated by Philosophy, must affirm some ultimate classes of likenesses and unlikenesses, in which all other classes merge; and here we have found that all manifestations of the Unknowable are divisible into two such classes. What is the division equivalent to?

Obviously it corresponds to the division between *object* and *subject*. This profoundest of distinctions among the manifestations of the Unknowable, we recognize by grouping them into *self* and *not-self*. These faint manifestations, forming a continuous whole differing from the other in the quantity, quality, cohesion, and conditions of existence of its parts, we call the *ego;* and these vivid manifestations, indissolubly bound together in relatively-immense masses, and having independent conditions of existence, we call the *non-ego.* Or rather, more truly—each order of manifestations carries with it the irresistible implication of some power that manifests itself; and by the words *ego* and *non-ego* respectively, we mean the power that manifests itself in the faint forms, and the power that manifests itself in the vivid forms.

As we here see, these consolidated conceptions thus antithetically named, do not originate in some inscrutable way; but they have for their explanation the ultimate law of thought that is beyond appeal. The persistent consciousness of likeness or difference, is one which, by its very persistence, makes itself accepted; and one which transcends scepticism, since without it even doubt becomes impossible. And the primordial division of self from not-self, is a cumulative result of persistent consciousnesses of likenesses and differences among manifestations. Indeed, thought exists only through that kind of act which leads us, from moment to moment, to refer certain manifestations to the one class with which they have so many common attributes, and others to the other class with which they have common attributes equally numerous. And the myriad-fold repetition of these classings, bringing about the myriad-fold associations of each manifestation with those of its own class, brings about this union among the members of each class, and this disunion of the two classes.

Strictly speaking, this segregation of the manifestations and coalescence of them into two distinct wholes, is in great part spontaneous, and precedes all deliberate judgments; though it is indorsed by such judgments when they come to be made. For the manifestations of each order have not simply that kind of union implied by grouping them as individual objects of the same class; but, as we have seen, they have the much more intimate union implied by actual cohesion. This cohesive union exhibits itself before any conscious acts of classing take place. So that, in truth, these two contrasted orders of manifestations are substantially self-separated and self-consolidated. The members of each, by clinging to one another and parting from their opposites, themselves form these united wholes constituting object and subject. It is this self-union which gives to these wholes formed of them, their individualities as wholes, and that separateness from each other which transcends judgment; and judgment merely aids the predetermined segregation by assigning to their respective classes such manifestations as have not distinctly united themselves with the rest of their kind.

One further perpetually-repeated act of judgment there is, indeed, which strengthens this fundamental antithesis, and gives a vast extension to one term of it. We continually learn that while the conditions of occurrence of faint manifestations are always to be found, the conditions of occurrence of vivid manifestations are often not to be found. We also continually learn that vivid manifestations which have no perceivable antecedents among the vivid manifestations are like certain preceding ones which *had* perceivable antecedents among the vivid manifestations. Joining these two experiences together, there results the irresistible conception that some vivid manifestations have conditions of occurrence existing out of the current of vivid manifestations —existing as potential vivid manifestations capable of becoming actual. And so we are made vaguely conscious of an indefinitely-extended region of power or being, not merely separate from the current of faint manifestations constituting the *ego*, but lying beyond the current of vivid manifestations constituting the immediately-present portion of the *non-ego*.

§ 45. In a very imperfect way, passing over objections and omitting needful explanations, I have thus, in the nar-

row space that could properly be devoted to it, indicated the
essential nature and justification of that primordial proposition which Philosophy requires as a datum. I might, indeed, safely have assumed this ultimate truth; which Common Sense asserts, which every step in Science takes for
granted, and which no metaphysician ever for a moment succeeded in expelling from consciousness. Setting out with
the postulate that the manifestations of the Unknowable fall
into the two separate aggregates constituting the world of
consciousness and the world beyond consciousness, I might
have let the justification of this postulate depend on its sub-
sequently-proved congruity with every result of experience,
direct and indirect. But as all that follows proceeds upon
this postulate, it seemed desirable briefly to indicate its warrant, with the view of shutting out criticisms that might else
be made. It seemed desirable to show that this fundamental cognition is neither, as the idealist asserts, an illusion,
nor as the sceptic thinks, of doubtful worth, nor as is held
by the natural realist, an inexplicable intuition; but that it
is a legitimate deliverance of consciousness elaborating its
materials after the laws of its normal action. While, in
order of time, the establishment of this distinction precedes
all reasoning; and while, running through our mental structure as it does, we are debarred from reasoning about it without taking for granted its existence; analysis nevertheless
enables us to justify the assertion of its existence, by showing that it is also the outcome of a classification based on accumulated likenesses and accumulated differences. In other
words—Reasoning, which is itself but a formation of cohesions among manifestations, here strengthens, by the cohesions it forms, the cohesions which it finds already existing.

So much, then, for the data of Philosophy. In common
with Religion, Philosophy assumes the primordial *implication* of consciousness, which, as we saw in the last part, has
the deepest of all foundations. It assumes the validity of a
certain primordial *process* of consciousness, without which
inference is impossible, and without which there cannot even

be either affirmation or denial. And it assumes the validity of a certain primordial *product* of consciousness, which, though it originates in an earlier process, is also, in one sense, a product of this process, since by this process it is tested and stamped as genuine. In brief, our postulates are: —an Unknowable Power; the existence of knowable likenesses and differences among the manifestations of that Power; and a resulting segregation of the manifestations into those of subject and object.

Before proceeding with the substantial business of Philosophy—the complete unification of the knowledge partially unified by Science, a further preliminary is needed. The manifestations of the Unknowable, separated into the two divisions of self and not-self, are redivisible into certain most general forms, the reality of which Science, as well as Common Sense, from moment to moment assumes. In the chapter on "Ultimate Scientific Ideas," it was shown that we know nothing of these forms, considered in themselves. As, nevertheless, we must continue to use the words signifying them, it is needful to say what interpretations are to be put on these words.

———

CHAPTER III

SPACE, TIME, MATTER, MOTION, AND FORCE

§ 46. THAT sceptical state of mind which the criticisms of philosophy usually produce, is, in great measure, caused by the misinterpretation of words. A sense of universal illusion ordinarily follows the reading of metaphysics; and is strong in proportion as the argument has appeared conclusive. This sense of universal illusion would probably never have arisen, had the terms used been always rightly construed. Unfortunately, these terms have by association acquired meanings that are quite different from those given to them in philosophical discussions; and the ordinary meanings being unavoidably suggested, there results more or less of that dream-like idealism which is so incongruous with our instinctive convictions. The word *phenomenon* and its equivalent word *appearance,* are in great part to blame for this. In ordinary speech, these are uniformly employed in reference to visual perceptions. Habit, almost, if not quite, disables us from thinking of *appearance* except as something seen; and though *phenomenon* has a more generalized meaning, yet we cannot rid it of associations with *appearance,* which is its verbal equivalent. When, therefore, Philosophy proves that our knowledge of the external world can be but phenomenal—when it concludes that the things of which we are conscious are appearances; it inevitably arouses in us the notion of an illusiveness like that to which our visual perceptions are so liable in comparison with our tactual perceptions. Good pictures show us that the aspects of things may be very nearly simulated by colors on canvas. The looking-glass still more distinctly proves how deceptive is sight when unverified by touch. And the frequent cases in which we misinterpret the impressions made on our eyes, and think we see something which we do not see, further shake our faith in vision. So that the implication of uncertainty has infected the very word *appearance.* Hence, Philosophy, by giving it an extended meaning, leads us to think of all our senses as deceiving us in the same way that the eyes do; and so makes us feel ourselves floating in a world of phantasms. Had *phenomenon* and *appearance* no such misleading associations, little, if any, of this mental confusion would result. Or did we in place of them use the term *effect,* which is equally applicable to all impressions produced on consciousness through any of the senses, and which carries with it in thought the necessary correlative *cause,* with which it is equally real, we should be in little danger of falling into the insanities of idealism.

Such danger as there might still remain would disappear on making a further verbal correction. At present, the confusion resulting from the above misinterpretation, is made greater by an antithetical misinterpretation. We increase the seeming unreality of that phenonmenal existence which we can alone know, by contrasting it with a noumenal existence which we imagine would, if we could know it, be more truly real to us. But we delude ourselves with a verbal fiction. What is the meaning of the word *real?* This is the question which underlies every metaphysical inquiry; and the neglect of it is the remaining cause of the chronic antagonisms of metaphysicians. In the interpretation put on the word *real*, the discussions of philosophy retain one element of the vulgar conception of things, while they reject all its other elements; and create confusion by the inconsistency. The peasant, on contemplating an object, does not regard that which he contemplates as something in himself, but believes the thing of which he is conscious to be the external object—imagines that his consciousness extends to the very place where the object lies: to him the appearance and the reality are one and the same thing. The metaphysician, however, is convinced that consciousness cannot embrace the reality, but only the appearance of it; and so he transfers the appearance into consciousness and leaves the reality outside. This reality left outside of consciousness, he continues to think of much in the same way as the ignorant man thinks of the appearance. Though the reality is asserted to be out of consciousness, yet the *realness* ascribed to it is constantly spoken of as though it were a knowledge possessed apart from consciousness. It seems to be forgotten that the conception of reality can be nothing more than some mode of consciousness; and that the question to be considered is— What is the relation between this mode and other modes?

By reality we mean *persistence* in consciousness: a persistence that is either unconditional, as our consciousness of space, or that is conditional, as our consciousness of a body while grasping it. The real, as we conceive it, is distinguished solely by the test of persistence; for by this test we separate it from what we call the unreal. Between a person standing before us, and the idea of such a person, we discriminate by our ability to expel the idea from consciousness, and our inability, while looking at him, to expel the person from consciousness. And when in doubt as to the validity or illusiveness of some impression made upon us in the dusk, we settle the matter by observing whether the impression persists on closer observation; and we predicate reality if the persistence is complete. How truly persistence is what we mean by reality, is shown in the fact that when, after criticism has proved that the real as we are conscious of it is not the objectively real, the indefinite notion which we form of the objectively real, is of something which persists absolutely, under all changes of mode, form, or appearance. And the fact that we cannot form even an indefinite notion of the absolutely real, except as the absolutely persistent, clearly implies that persistence is our ultimate test of the real as present to consciousness.

Reality then, as we think it, being nothing more than persistence in consciousness, the result must be the same to us whether that which we perceive be the Unknowable itself, or an effect invariably wrought on us by the Unknowable. If, under constant conditions furnished by our constitutions, some Power of which the nature is beyond conception, always produces some mode of consciousness—if this mode of consciousness is as persistent as would be this Power were it in consciousness; the reality will be to consciousness as complete in the one case as in the other. Were Unconditioned Being itself present in thought, it could but be persistent; and if, instead, there is present Being conditioned by the forms of thought, but no less persistent, it must be to us no less real.

Hence there may be drawn these conclusions:—First, that we have an indefinite consciousness of an absolute reality transcending relations, which is produced by the absolute persistence in us of something which survives all changes of relation. Second, that we have a definite consciousness of relative reality, which unceasingly persists in us under one or other of its forms, and under each form so long as the conditions of presentation are fulfilled; and that the relative reality, being thus continuously persistent in us, is as real to us as would be the absolute reality could it be immediately known.   Third, that thought being possible only under relation, the relative reality can be conceived as such only in connection with an absolute reality; and the connection between the two being absolutely persistent in our consciousness, is real in the same sense as the terms it unites are real.

Thus then we may resume, with entire confidence, those realistic conceptions which philosophy at first sight seems to dissipate.   Though reality under the forms of our consciousness, is but a conditioned effect of the absolute reality, yet this conditioned effect standing in indissoluble relation with its unconditioned cause, and being equally persistent with it so long as the conditions persist, is, to the consciousness supplying those conditions, equally real.   The persistent impressions being the persistent results of a persistent cause, are for practical purposes the same to us as the cause itself; and may be habitually dealt with as its equivalents.   Somewhat in the same way that our visual perceptions, though merely symbols found to be the equivalents of tactual perceptions, are yet so identified with those tactual perceptions that we actually appear to see the solidity and hardness which we do but infer, and thus conceive as objects what are only the signs of objects; so, on a higher stage, do we deal with these relative realities as though they were absolutes instead of effects of the absolute.   And we may legitimately continue so to deal with them as long as the conclusions to which they help us are understood as relative realities and not absolute ones.

This general conclusion it now remains to interpret specifically, in its application to each of our ultimate scientific ideas.

§ 47.[1] We think in relations.   This is truly the form of all thought; and if there are any other forms, they must be

---

[1] For the psychological conclusions briefly set forth in this and the three sections following it, the justification will be found in the writer's "Principles of Psychology."

derived from this. We have seen (Chap. iii. Part I.) that the several ultimate modes of being cannot be known or conceived as they exist in themselves; that is, out of *relation* to our consciousness. We have seen, by analyzing the product of thought (§ 23), that it always consists of *relations;* and cannot include anything beyond the most general of these. On analyzing the process of thought, we found that cognition of the Absolute was impossible, because it presented neither *relation,* nor its elements—difference and likeness. Further, we found that not only Intelligence but Life itself, consists in the establishment of internal *relations* in correspondence with external relations. And lastly, it was shown that though by the relativity of our thought we are eternally debarred from knowing or conceiving Absolute Being; yet that this very *relativity* of our thought, necessitates that vague consciousness of Absolute Being which no mental effort can suppress. That *relation* is the universal form of thought, is thus a truth which all kinds of demonstration unite in proving.

By the transcendentalists, certain other phenomena of consciousness are regarded as forms of thought. Presuming that relation would be admitted by them to be a universal mental form, they would class with it two others as also universal. Were their hypothesis otherwise tenable, however, it must still be rejected if such alleged further forms are interpretable as generated by the primary form. If we think in relations, and if relations have certain universal forms, it is manifest that such universal forms of relations will become universal forms of our consciousness. And if these further universal forms are thus explicable, it is superfluous, and therefore unphilosophical, to assign them an independent origin. Now relations are of two orders—relations of sequence, and relations of co-existence; of which the one is original and the other derivative. The relation of sequence is given in every change of consciousness. The relation of co-existence, which cannot be originally given in a consciousness of which the states are serial, becomes distinguished only when it is found that certain relations of sequence have their terms presented in consciousness in either order with equal facility; while the others are presented only in one order. Relations of which the terms are not reversible, become recognized as sequences proper; while relations of which the terms occur indifferently in both directions, become recognized as co-existences. Endless experiences, which from moment to moment present both orders of these relations, render the distinction between them perfectly definite; and at the same time generate an abstract conception of each. The abstract of all sequences is Time. The abstract of all co-existences is Space. From the fact that in thought, Time is inseparable from sequence, and Space from co-existence, we do not here infer that Time and Space are original conditions of consciousness under which sequences and co-existences are known; but we infer that our conceptions of Time and Space are generated, as other abstracts are generated from other concretes: the only difference being, that the organization of experience has, in these cases, been going on throughout the entire evolution of intelligence.

This synthesis is confirmed by analysis. Our consciousness of Space is a consciousness of co-existent positions. Any limited portion of space can be conceived only by representing its limits as co-existing in certain relative positions; and each of its imagined boundaries, be it line or plane, can be thought of in no other way than as made up of coexistent positions in close proximity. And since a position is not an entity—since the congeries of positions which constitute any conceived portion of space, and mark its bounds, are not sensible existences; it follows that the co-existent positions which make up our consciousness of Space, are not co-existences in the full sense of the word (which implies realities as their terms), but are the blank forms of co-existences, left behind when the realities are absent; that is, are the abstracts of co-existences. The experiences out of which, during the evolution of intelligence, this abstract of all co-existences has been generated, are experiences of individual positions as ascertained by touch; and each of such experiences involves the resistance of an object touched, and the muscular tension which measures this resistance. By countless unlike muscular adjustments, involving unlike muscular tensions, different resisting positions are disclosed; and these, as they can be experienced in one order as readily as another, we regard as co-existing. But since, under other circumstances, the same muscular adjustments do not produce contact with resisting positions, there result the same states of consciousness, minus the resistances—blank forms of co-existence from which the co-existent objects before experienced are absent. And from a building up of these, too elaborate to be here detailed, results that abstract of all relations of co-existence which we call Space. It remains only to point out, as a thing which we must not forget, that the experiences from which the consciousness of Space arises, are experiences of *force*. A certain correlation of the muscular forces we ourselves exercise, is the index of each position as originally disclosed to us; and the resistance which makes us aware of something existing in that position, is an equivalent of the pressure we consciously exert. Thus, experiences of forces variously correlated, are those from which our consciousness of Space is abstracted.

That which we know as Space being thus shown, alike by its genesis and definition, to be purely relative, what are we to say of that which causes it? Is there an absolute Space which relative Space in some sort represents? Is Space in itself a form or condition of absolute existence, producing in our minds a corresponding form or condition of relative existence? These are unanswerable questions. Our conception of Space is produced by some mode of the Unknowable; and the complete unchangeableness of our conception of it simply implies a complete uniformity in the effects wrought by this mode of the Unknowable upon us. But therefore to call it a necessary mode of the Unknowable, is illegitimate. All we can assert is, that Space is a relative reality; that our consciousness of this unchanging relative reality implies an absolute reality equally unchanging in so far as we are concerned; and that the relative reality may be unhesitatingly accepted in thought as a valid basis for our reasonings: which, when rightly carried on, will bring us to truths that have a like relative reality—the only truths which concern us or can possibly be known to us.

Concerning Time, relative and absolute, a parallel argument leads to parallel conclusions. These are too obvious to need specifying in detail.

§ 48. Our conception of Matter, reduced to its simplest shape, is that of co-existent positions that offer resistance; as contrasted with our conception of Space, in which the co-existent positions offer no resistance. We think of Body as bounded by surfaces that resist; and as made up throughout of parts that resist. Mentally abstract the co-existent resistances, and the consciousness of Body disappears; leaving behind it the consciousness of Space. And since the group of co-existing resistent positions constituting a portion of matter, is uniformly capable of giving us impressions of resistance in combination with various muscular adjustments, according as we touch its near, its remote, its right, or its left side; it results that as different muscular adjustments habitually indicate different co-existences, we are obliged to conceive every portion of matter as containing more than one resistent position—that is, as occupying Space. Hence the necessity we are under of representing to ourselves the ultimate elements of Matter as being at once extended and resistent: this being the universal form of our sensible experiences of Matter, becomes the form which our conception of it cannot transcend, however minute the fragments which imaginary subdivisions produce. Of these two inseparable elements, the resistance is primary, and the extension secondary. Occupied extension, or Body, being distinguished in consciousness from unoccupied extension, or Space, by its resistance, this attribute must clearly have precedence in the genesis of the idea. Such a conclusion is, indeed, an

obvious corollary from that at which we arrived in the foregoing section. If, as was there contended, our consciousness of Space is a product of accumulated experiences, partly
our own but chiefly ancestral—if, as was pointed out, the
experiences from which our consciousness of Space is abstracted, can be received only through impressions of resistance made upon the organism; the necessary inference is,
that experiences of resistance being those from which the
conception of space is generated, the resistance-attribute of
Matter must be regarded as primordial and the space-attri-
bute as derivative. Whence it becomes manifest that our
experience of *force* is that out of which the idea of Matter
is built. Matter as opposing our muscular energies, being
immediately present to consciousness in terms of force; and
its occupancy of Space being known by an abstract of experiences originally given in terms of force; it follows that
forces, standing in certain correlations, form the whole content of our idea of Matter.

Such being our cognition of the relative reality, what are
we to say of the absolute reality? We can only say that it
is some mode of the Unknowable, related to the Matter we
know, as cause to effect. The relativity of our cognition of
Matter is shown alike by the above analysis, and by the
contradictions which are evolved when we deal with the cognition as an absolute one (§ 16). But, as we have lately
seen, though known to us only under relation, Matter is as
real in the true sense of that word, as it would be could we
know it out of relation; and further, the relative reality
which we know as Matter, is necessarily represented to the
mind as standing in a persistent or real relation to the absolute reality. We may therefore deliver ourselves over without hesitation, to those terms of thought which experience
has organized in us. We need not in our physical, chemical, or other researches, refrain from dealing with Matter as
made up of extended and resistent atoms; for this conception, necessarily resulting from our experiences of Matter, is
not less legitimate than the conception of aggregate masses

as extended and resistent. The atomic hypothesis, as well as the kindred hypothesis of an all-pervading ether consisting of molecules, is simply a necessary development of those universal forms which the actions of the Unknowable have wrought in us. The conclusions logically worked out by the aid of these hypotheses, are sure to be in harmony with all others which these same forms involve, and will have a relative truth that is equally complete.

§ 49. The conception of Motion as presented or represented in the developed consciousness, involves the conceptions of Space, of Time, and of Matter. A something that moves; a series of positions occupied in succession; and a group of co-existent positions united in thought with the successive ones—these are the constituents of the idea. And since, as we have seen, these are severally elaborated from experiences of *force* as given in certain correlations, it follows that from a further synthesis of such experiences, the idea of Motion is also elaborated. A certain other element in the idea, which is in truth its fundamental element (namely, the necessity which the moving body is under to go on changing its position), results immediately from the earliest experiences of force. Movements of different parts of the organism in relation to each other, are the first presented in consciousness. These, produced by the action of the muscles, necessitate reactions upon consciousness in the shape of sensations of muscular tension. Consequently, each stretching-out or drawing-in of a limb, is originally known as a series of muscular tensions, varying in intensity as the position of the limb changes. And this rudimentary consciousness of Motion, consisting of serial impressions of force, becomes inseparably united with the consciousness of Space and Time as fast as these are abstracted from further impressions of force. Or rather, out of this primitive conception of Motion, the adult conception of it is developed simultaneously with the development of the conceptions of Space and Time: all three being evolved from the more multiplied and varied impressions of muscular tension and objective resistance. Motion, as we know it, is thus traceable, in common with the other ultimate scientific ideas, to experiences of force.

That this relative reality answers to some absolute reality, it is needful only for form's sake to assert. What has been said above, respecting the Unknown Cause which produces in us the effects called Matter, Space, and Time, will apply, on simply changing the terms, to Motion.

§ 50. We come down then finally to Force, as the ultimate of ultimates. Though Space, Time, Matter, and Motion, are apparently all necessary data of intelligence, yet a psychological analysis (here indicated only in rude outline) shows us that these are either built up of, or abstracted from, experiences of Force. Matter and Motion, as we know them, are differently conditioned manifestations of Force. Space and Time, as we know them, are disclosed along with these different manifestations of Force as the conditions under which they are presented. Matter and Motion are concretes built up from the *contents* of various mental relations; while Space and Time are abstracts of the *forms* of these various relations. Deeper down than these, however, are the primordial experiences of Force, which, as occurring in consciousness in different combinations, supply at once the materials whence the forms of relations are generalized, and the related objects built up. A single impression of force is manifestly receivable by a sentient being devoid of mental forms: grant but sensibility, with no established power of thought, and a force producing some nervous change will still be presentable at the supposed seat of sensation. Though no single impression of force so received, could itself produce consciousness (which implies relations between different states), yet a multiplication of such impressions, differing in kind and degree, would give the materials for the establishment of relations, that is, of thought. And if such relations differed in their forms as well as in their contents, the impressions of such forms would be organized simultaneously with the impressions they contained. Thus all other modes of consciousness are derivable from experiences of Force; but experiences of Force are not derivable from anything else. Indeed, it needs but to remember that consciousness consists of changes, to see that the ultimate datum of consciousness must be that of which change is the manifestation; and that thus the force by which we ourselves produce changes, and which serves to symbolize the cause of changes in general, is the final disclosure of analysis.

It is a truism to say that the nature of this undecomposable element of our knowledge is inscrutable. If, to use an algebraic illustration, we represent Matter, Motion, and Force, by the symbols x, y, and z; then, we may ascertain the values of x and y in terms of z; but the value of z can never be found: z is the unknown quantity which must forever remain unknown; for the obvious reason that there is nothing in which its value can be expressed. It is within the possible reach of our intelligence to go on simplifying the equations of all phenomena, until the complex symbols which formulate them are reduced to certain functions of this ultimate symbol; but when we have done this, we have reached that limit which eternally divides science from nescience.

That this undecomposable mode of consciousness into which all other modes may be decomposed, cannot be itself the Power manifested to us through phenomena, has been already proved (§ 18). We saw that to assume an identity of nature between the cause of changes as it absolutely exists, and that cause of change of which we are conscious in our own muscular efforts, betrays us into alternative impossibilities of thought. Force, as we know it, can be regarded only as a certain conditioned effect of the Unconditioned Cause—as the relative reality indicating to us an Absolute Reality by which it is immediately produced. And here, indeed, we see even more clearly than before, how inevitable is that transfigured realism to which sceptical criticism finally brings us round. Getting rid of all complications, and contemplating pure Force, we are irresistibly compelled by the relativity of our thought to vaguely conceive some unknown force as the correlative of the known force. Noumenon and phenomenon are here presented in their primordial relation as two sides of the same change, of which we are obliged to regard the last as no less real than the first.

§ 51. In closing this exposition of the derivative data needed by Philosophy as the unifier of Science, we may properly glance at their relations to the primordial data, set forth in the last chapter.

An Unknown Cause of the known effects which we call phenomena, likenesses and differences among these known effects, and a segregation of the effects into subject and object—these are the postulates without which we cannot think. Within each of the segregated masses of manifestations, there are likenesses and differences involving secondary segregations, which have also become indispensable postulates. The vivid manifestations constituting the *non-ego* do not simply cohere, but their cohesions have certain invariable modes; and among the faint manifestations constituting the *ego,* which are products of the vivid, there exist corresponding modes of cohesion. These modes of cohesion under which manifestations are invariably presented, and therefore invariably represented, we call, when contemplated apart, Space and Time, and when contemplated along with the manifestations themselves, Matter and Motion. The ultimate natures of these modes are as unknown as is the ultimate nature of that which is manifested. But just the same warrant which we have for asserting that subject and object co-exist, we have for asserting that the vivid manifestations we call objective, exist under certain constant conditions, that are symbolized by these constant conditions among the manifestations we call subjective.

CHAPTER IV

THE INDESTRUCTIBILITY OF MATTER

§ 52. Not because the truth is unfamiliar, is it needful here to say something concerning the indestructibility of Matter; but partly because the symmetry of our argument demands the enunciation of this truth, and partly because the evidence on which it is accepted requires examination. Could it be shown, or could it with any rationality be even supposed, that Matter, either in its aggregates or in its units, ever became non-existent, there would be need either to ascertain under what conditions it became non-existent, or else to confess that Science and Philosophy are impossible. For if, instead of having to deal with fixed quantities and weights, we had to deal with quantities and weights which were apt, wholly or in part, to be annihilated, there would be introduced an incalculable element, fatal to all positive conclusions. Clearly, therefore, the proposition that matter is indestructible must be deliberately considered.

So far from being admitted as a self-evident truth, this would, in primitive times, have been rejected as a self-evident error. There was once universally current, a notion that things could vanish into absolute nothing, or arise out of absolute nothing. If we analyze early superstitions, or that faith in magic which was general in later times and even still survives among the uncultured, we find one of its postulates to be, that by some potent spell Matter can be called out of nonentity, and can be made non-existent. If men did not believe this in the strict sense of the word (which would imply that the process of creation or annihilation was clearly represented in consciousness), they still believed that they believed it; and how nearly, in their confused thoughts, the one was equivalent to the other, is shown by their conduct. Nor, indeed, have dark ages and inferior minds alone betrayed this belief. The current theology, in its teachings respecting the beginning and end of the world, is clearly pervaded by it; and it may be even questioned whether Shakespeare, in his poetical anticipation of a time when all things shall disappear and "leave not a wrack behind," was not under its influence. The gradual accumulation of experiences, however, and still more the organization of experiences, has tended slowly to reverse this conviction; until now, the doctrine that Matter is indestructible has become a commonplace. All the apparent proofs that something can come out of nothing, a wider knowledge has one by one cancelled. The comet that is suddenly discovered in the heavens and nightly waxes larger, is proved not to be a newly-created body, but a body that was until lately beyond the range of vision. The cloud which in the course of a few minutes forms in the sky, consists not of substance that has just begun to be, but of substance that previously existed in a more diffused and transparent form. And similarly with a crystal or precipitate in relation to the fluid depositing it. Conversely, the seeming annihilations of Matter turn out, on closer observation, to be only changes of state. It is found that the evaporated water, though it has become invisible, may be brought by condensation to its original shape. The discharged fowling-piece gives evidence that though the gunpowder has disappeared, there have appeared in place of it certain gases, which, in assuming a larger volume, have caused the explosion. Not, however, until the rise of quantitative chemistry, could the conclusion suggested by such experiences be harmonized with all the facts. When, having ascertained not only the combinations formed by various substances, but also the proportions in which they combine, chemists were enabled to account for the matter that had made its appearance or become invisible, scepticism was dissipated. And of the general conclusion thus reached, the exact analyses daily made, in which the same portion of matter is pursued through numerous disguises and finally separated, furnish never-ceasing confirmations.

Such has become the effect of this specific evidence, joined to that general evidence which the continued existence of familiar objects unceasingly gives us, that the indestructibility of Matter is now held by many to be a truth of which the negation is inconceivable.

§ 53. This last fact naturally raises the question, whether we have any higher warrant for this fundamental belief than the warrant of conscious induction. Before showing that we have a higher warrant, some explanations are needful.

The consciousness of logical necessity, is the consciousness that a certain conclusion is implicitly contained in certain premises explicitly stated. If, contrasting a young child and an adult, we see that this consciousness of logical necessity, absent from the one is present in the other, we are taught that there is a *growing up to* the recognition of certain necessary truths, merely by the unfolding of the inherited intellectual forms and faculties.

To state the case more specifically:—Before a truth can be known as necessary, two conditions must be fulfilled. There must be a mental structure capable of grasping the terms of the proposition and the relation alleged between them; and there must be such definite and deliberate mental representation of these terms, as makes possible a clear consciousness of this relation. Non-fulfilment of either condition may cause non-recognition of the necessity of the truth. Let us take cases.

The savage who cannot count the fingers on one hand, can frame no definite thought answering to the statement that 7 and 5 are 12; still less can he frame the consciousness that no other total is possible.

The boy adding up figures inattentively, says to himself that 7 and 5 are 11; and may repeatedly bring out a wrong result by repeatedly making this error.

Neither the non-recognition of the truth that 7 and 5 are

12, which in the savage results from undeveloped mental structure, nor the assertion, due to the boy's careless mental action, that they make 11, leads us to doubt the necessity of the relation between these two separately-existing numbers and the sum they make when existing together. Nor does failure from either cause to apprehend the necessity of this relation, make us hesitate to say that when its terms are distinctly represented in thought, its necessity will be seen; and that, apart from any multiplied experiences, this necessity becomes cognizable when structures and functions are so far developed that groups of 7 and 5 and 12 can be intellectually grasped.

Manifestly, then, there is a recognition of necessary truths, as such, which accompanies mental evolution. Along with acquirement of more complex faculty and more vivid imagination, there comes a power of perceiving to be necessary truths, what were before not recognized as truths at all. And there are ascending gradations in these recognitions. A boy who has intelligence enough to see that things which are equal to the same thing are equal to one another, may be unable to see that ratios which are severally equal to certain other ratios that are unequal to each other, are themselves unequal; though to a more-developed mind this last axiom is no less obviously necessary than the first.

All this, which holds of logical and mathematical truths, holds, with change of terms, of physical truths. There are necessary truths in Physics for the apprehension of which, also, a developed and disciplined intelligence is required; and before such intelligence arises, not only may there be failure to apprehend the necessity of them, but there may be vague beliefs in their contraries. Up to comparatively-recent times, all mankind were in this state of incapacity with respect to physical axioms; and the mass of mankind are so still. Various popular notions betray inability to form clear ideas of forces and their relations, or carelessness in thinking, or both. Effects are expected without causes of fit kinds; or effects extremely disproportionate to causes are

looked for; or causes are supposed to end without effects.[1]
But though many are incapable of grasping physical axioms,
it no more follows that physical axioms are not knowable
à priori by a developed intelligence, than it follows that
logical relations are not necessary, because undeveloped
intellects cannot perceive their necessity.

It is thus with the notions which have been current respecting the creation and annihilation of Matter. In the first
place, there has been a habitual confounding of two radi-
cally-different things—disappearance of Matter from that
place where it was lately perceived, and passage of Matter
from existence into non-existence. Only when there is
reached a power of discrimination beyond that possessed
by the uncultured, is there an avoidance of the confusion
between vanishing from the range of perception, and vanishing out of space altogether; and until this confusion is
avoided, the belief that Matter can be annihilated readily
obtains currency. In the second place, the currency of this
belief continues so long as there is not such power of introspection that it can be seen what happens when the attempt
is made to annihilate Matter in thought. But when, during
mental evolution, the vague ideas arising in a nervous structure imperfectly organized, are replaced by the clear ideas
arising in a definite nervous structure; this definite structure, molded by experience into correspondence with external phenomena, makes necessary in thought the relations
answering to absolute uniformities in things. Hence, among
others, the conception of the Indestructibility of Matter.

For careful self-analysis shows this to be a datum of con-

---

[1] I knew a lady who contended that a dress folded up tightly, weighed more
than when loosely folded up; and who, under this belief, had her trunks made
large that she might diminish the charge for freight! Another whom I know,
ascribes the feeling of lightness which accompanies vigor, to actual decrease of
weight; believes that by stepping gently, she can press less upon the ground;
and, when cross-questioned, asserts that, if placed in scales, she can make her-
self lighter by an act of will! Various popular notions betray like states of
mind—show, in the undisciplined, such inability to form ideas of forces and
their relations, or such randomness in thinking, or both, as incapacitates them
for grasping physical axioms, and makes them harbor numerous delusions respecting physical actions.

sciousness. Conceive the space before you to be cleared of all bodies save one. Now imagine the remaining one not to be removed from its place, but to lapse into nothing while standing in that place. You fail. The space which was solid you cannot conceive becoming empty, save by transfer of that which made it solid. What is termed the ultimate incompressibility of Matter, is an admitted law of thought. However small the bulk to which we conceive a piece of matter reduced, it is impossible to conceive it reduced into nothing. While we can represent to ourselves the parts of the matter as approximated, we cannot represent to ourselves the quantity of matter as made less. To do this would be to imagine some of the constituent parts compressed into nothing; which is no more possible than to imagine compression of the whole into nothing. Our inability to conceive Matter becoming non-existent, is immediately consequent on the nature of thought. Thought consists in the establishment of relations. There can be no relation established, and therefore no thought framed, when one of the related terms is absent from consciousness. Hence it is impossible to think of something becoming nothing, for the same reason that it is impossible to think of nothing becoming something—the reason, namely, that nothing cannot become an object of consciousness. The annihilation of Matter is unthinkable for the same reason that the creation of Matter is unthinkable.

It must be added that no experimental verification of the truth that Matter is indestructible, is possible without a tacit assumption of it. For all such verification implies weighing, and weighing implies that the matter forming the weight remains the same. In other words, the proof that certain matter dealt with in certain ways is unchanged in quantity, depends on the assumption that other matter, otherwise dealt with, is unchanged in quantity.

§ 54. That, however, which it most concerns us here to observe is the nature of the perceptions by which the permanence of Matter is perpetually illustrated to us. These perceptions, under all their forms, amount simply to this— that the *force* which a given quantity of matter exercises, remains always the same. This is the proof on which common sense and exact science alike rely. When, for example, an object known to have existed years since is said to exist still, by one who yesterday saw it, his assertion amounts to this— that an object which in past time wrought on his consciousness a certain group of changes, still exists, because a like group of changes has been again wrought on his consciousness: the continuance of the *power* thus to impress him, he holds to prove the continuance of the object. Even more clearly do we see that force is our ultimate measure of Matter, in those cases where the shape of the Matter has been changed. A piece of gold given to an artisan to be worked into an ornament, and which when brought back appears to be less, is placed in the scales; and if it balances a much smaller weight than it did in its rough state, we infer that much has been lost either in manipulation or by direct abstraction. Here the obvious postulate is, that the quantity of Matter is finally determinable by the quantity of gravitative force it manifests. And this is the kind of evidence on which Science bases its alleged induction that Matter is indestructible. Whenever a piece of substance lately visible and tangible, has been reduced to an invisible, intangible state, but is proved by the weight of the gas into which it has been transformed to be still existing; the assumption is that, though otherwise insensible to us, the amount of matter is the same if it still tends toward the Earth with the same force. Similarly, every case in which the weight of an element present in combination is inferred from the known weight of another element which it neutralizes, is a case in which the quantity of matter is expressed in terms of the quantity of chemical force it exerts; and in which this specific chemical force is assumed to be the correlative of a specific gravitative force.

Thus, then, by the Indestructibility of Matter, we really

mean the indestructibility of the *force* with which Matter affects us. As we become conscious of Matter only through that resistance which it opposes to our muscular energy, so do we become conscious of the permanence of Matter only through the permanence of this resistance; either as immediately or as mediately proved to us. And this truth is made manifest not only by analysis of the *à posteriori* cognition, but equally so by analysis of the *à priori* one.[1]

CHAPTER V

THE CONTINUITY OF MOTION

§ 55. ANOTHER general truth of the same order with the foregoing must here be specified. Like the Indestructibility of Matter, the Continuity of Motion, or, more strictly, of that something which has Motion for one of its sensible forms, is a proposition on the truth of which depends the possibility of exact Science, and therefore of a Philosophy which unifies the results of exact Science. Motions, visible and invisible, of masses and of molecules, form the larger half of the phenomena to be interpreted; and if such motions might either proceed from nothing or lapse into nothing, there could be no scientific interpretation of them.

This second fundamental truth, like the first, is by no means self-evident to primitive men or to the uncultured among ourselves. Contrariwise, to undeveloped minds the opposite seems self-evident. The facts that a stone thrown

------

[1] Lest he should not have observed it, the reader must be warned that the terms "*à priori* truth" and "necessary truth," as used in this work, are to be interpreted not in the old sense, as implying cognitions wholly independent of experiences, but as implying cognitions that have been rendered organic by immense accumulations of experiences, received partly by the individual, but mainly by all ancestral individuals whose nervous systems he inherits. On referring to the "Principles of Psychology" (§§ 426–433), it will be seen that the warrant alleged for one of these irreversible ultimate convictions is that, on the hypothesis of Evolution, it represents an immeasurably-greater accumulation of experiences than can be acquired by any single individual.

up soon loses its ascending motion, and that after the blow its fall gives to the Earth, it remains quiescent, apparently prove that the principle of activity[1] which the stone manifested may disappear absolutely. Accepting, without criticism, the dicta of unaided perception, to the effect that adjacent objects put in motion soon return to rest, all men once believed, and most believe still, that motion can pass into nothing; and ordinarily does so pass. But the establishment of certain facts having an opposite implication, led to inquiries which have gradually proved these appearances to be illusive. The discovery that the planets revolve round the Sun with undiminishing speed, raised the suspicion that a moving body, when not interfered with, will go on forever without change of velocity; and suggested the question whether bodies which lose their motion, do not at the same time communicate as much motion to other bodies. It was a familiar fact that a stone would glide further over a smooth surface, such as ice, presenting no small objects to which it could part with its motion by collision, than over a surface strewn with such small objects; and that a projectile would travel a far greater distance through a rare medium like air, than through a dense medium like water. Thus the primitive notion that moving bodies had an inherent tendency to lose their motion and finally stop—a notion of which the Greeks did not get rid, but which lasted till the time of Galileo—began to give way. It was further shaken by such experiments as those of Hooke, which proved that the spinning of a top continues long in proportion as it is prevented from communicating motion to surrounding matter.

To explain specifically how modern physicists interpret all disappearances and diminutions of visible motion, would require more knowledge than I possess and more space than I can spare. Here it must suffice to state, generally, that the molar motion which disappears when a bell is struck by

---

[1] Throughout this Chapter, I use this phrase, not with any metaphysical meaning, but merely to avoid foregone conclusions.

its clapper, reappears in the bell's vibrations and in the waves of air they produce; that when a moving mass is stopped by coming against a mass that is immovable, the motion which does not reappear in sound reappears as molecular motion; and that, similarly, when bodies rub against one another, the motion lost by friction is gained in the motion of molecules. But one aspect of this general truth, as it is displayed to us in the motions of masses, we must carefully contemplate; for otherwise the doctrine of the Continuity of Motion will be entirely misapprehended.

§ 56. As expressed by Newton, the first law of motion is that "every body must persevere in its state of rest, or of uniform motion in a straight line, unless it be compelled to change that state by forces impressed upon it."

With this truth may be associated the truth that a body describing a circular orbit round a centre which detains it by a tractive force, moves in that orbit with undiminished velocity.

The first of these abstract truths is never realized in the concrete, and the second of them is but approximately realized. Uniform motion in a straight line, implies the absence of a resisting medium; and it further implies the absence of forces, gravitative or other, exercised by neighboring masses: conditions never fulfilled. So, too, the maintenance of a circular orbit by any celestial body, implies both that there are no perturbing bodies, and that there is a certain exact adjustment between its velocity and the tractive force of its primary: neither requirement ever being conformed to. In all actual orbits, sensibly elliptical as they are, the velocity is sensibly variable. And along with great eccentricity there goes great variation.

To the case of celestial bodies which, moving in eccentric orbits, display at one time little motion and at another much motion, may be joined the case of the pendulum. With speed now increasing and now decreasing, the pendulum alternates between extremes at which motion ceases.

How shall we so conceive these allied phenomena as to express rightly the truth common to them? The first law of motion, nowhere literally fulfilled, is yet, in a sense, implied by these facts which seem at variance with it. Though in a circular orbit the direction of the motion is continually being changed, yet the velocity remains unchanged. Though in an elliptical orbit there is now acceleration and now retardation, yet the average speed is constant through successive revolutions. Though the pendulum comes to a momentary rest at the end of each swing, and then begins a reverse motion; yet the oscillation, considered as a whole, is continuous: friction and atmospheric resistance being absent, this alternation of states will go on forever.

What, then, do these cases show us in common? That which vision familiarizes us with in Motion, and that which has thus been made the dominant element in our conception of Motion, is not the element of which we can allege continuity. If we regard Motion simply as change of place; then the pendulum shows us both that the rate of this change may vary from instant to instant, and that, ceasing at intervals, it may be afresh initiated.

But if what we may call the translation-element in Motion is not continuous, what is continuous? If, watching like Galileo a swinging chandelier, we observe, not its isochronism, but the recurring reversal of its swing, we are impressed with the fact that though, at the end of each swing, the translation through space ceases, yet there is something which does not cease; for the translation recommences in the opposite direction. And on remembering that when a violent push was given to the chandelier it described a larger arc, and was a longer time before the resistance of the air destroyed its oscillations, we are shown that what continues to exist during these oscillations is some correlative of the muscular effort which put the chandelier in motion. The truth forced on our attention by these facts and inferences, is that translation through space is not itself an *existence;* and that hence the cessation of Motion, considered simply as translation, is not the cessation of an existence, but is the cessation of a certain *sign of an existence*—a sign occurring under certain conditions.

Still there remains a difficulty. If that element in the chandelier's motion of which alone we can allege continuity, is the correlative of the muscular effort which moved the chandelier, what becomes of this element at either extreme of the oscillation? Arrest the chandelier in the middle of its swing, and it gives a blow to the hand—exhibits some principle of activity such as muscular effort can give. But touch it at either turning point, and it displays no such principle of activity. This has disappeared just as much as the translation through space has disappeared. How, then, can it be alleged that though the Motion through space is not continuous, the principle of activity implied by the Motion is continuous?

Unquestionably the facts show that the principle of activity continues to exist under some form. When not perceptible it must be latent. How is it latent? A clew to the answer is gained on observing that though the chandelier when seized at the turning point of its swing, gives no impact in the direction of its late movement, it forthwith begins to pull in the opposite direction; and on observing, further, that its pull is great when the swing has been made extensive by a violent push. Hence the loss of visible activity at the highest point of the upward motion, is accompanied by the production of an invisible activity which generates the subsequent moton downward. To conceive this latent activity gained as an existence equal to the perceptible activity lost, is not easy; but we may help ourselves so to conceive it by considering cases of another class.

§ 57. When one who pushes against a door that has stuck fast, produces by great effort no motion, but eventually by a little greater effort bursts the door open, swinging it back against the wall and tumbling headlong into the room; he has evidence that a certain muscular strain which did not produce translation of matter through space, was yet equivalent to a certain amount of such translation. Again, when a railway-porter gradually stops a detached carriage by pulling at the buffer, he shows us that (supposing friction, etc., absent) the slowly-diminished motion of the carriage over a certain space, is the equivalent of the constant backward strain put upon the carriage while it is travelling through that space. Carrying with us the conception thus reached, we will now consider a case which makes it more definite.

When used as a plaything by boys, a ball fastened to the end of an India-rubber string yields a clear idea of the correlation between perceptible activity and latent activity. If, retaining one end of the string, a boy throws the ball from him horizontally, its motion is resisted by the increasing strain on the string; and the string, stretched more and more as the ball recedes, presently brings it to rest. Where now exists the principle of activity which the moving ball displayed? It exists in the strained thread of India-rubber. Under what form of changed molecular state it exists we need not ask. It suffices that the string is the seat of a tension generated by the motion of the ball, and equivalent to it. When the ball has been arrested, the stretched string begins to generate in it an opposite motion; and continues to accelerate that motion until the ball comes back to the point at which the stretching of the string commenced—a point at which, but for loss by atmospheric resistance and molecular redistribution, its velocity would be equal to the original velocity. Here the truth that the principle of activity, alternating between visible and invisible modes, does not cease to exist when the translation through space ceases to exist, is readily comprehensible; and it becomes easy to understand the corollary that at each point in the path of the ball, the quantity of its perceptible acivity, *plus* the quanity which is latent in the stretched string, yield a constant sum.

Aided by this illustration we can, in a general way, conceive what happens between bodies connected with one another, not by a stretched string, but by a traction exercised through what seems empty space. It matters not to our general conception that the intensity of this traction varies in a totally-different manner: decreasing as the square of the distance increases, but being practically constant for terrestrial distances. These differences being recognized, there is nevertheless to be recognized a truth common to both cases. The weight of something held in the hand shows that there exists between one body in space and another, a strain: this downward pull, ascribed to gravity, affects the hand as it might be affected by a stretched elastic string. Hence, when a body projected upward and gradually retarded by gravity, finally stops, we must regard the principle of activity manifested during its upward motion but disappearing at its turning-point, as having become latent in the strain between it and the Earth—a strain of which the quantity is to be conceived as the product of its intensity and the distance through which it acts. Carrying a step further our illustration of the stretched string will elucidate this. To simulate the action of gravity at terrestrial distances, let us imagine that when the attached moving body has stretched the elastic string to its limit, say at the distance of ten feet, a second like string could instantly be tied to the end of the first and to the body, which, continuing its course, stretched this second string to an equal length, and so on with a succession of such strings, till the body was arrested. Then, manifestly, the quantity of the principle of activity which the moving body had displayed, but which has now become latent in the series of stretched strings, is measured by the number of such strings similarly stretched—the number of feet through which this constant strain has been encountered, *and over which it still extends*. Now though we cannot conceive the tractive force of gravity to be exercised in a like way—though the gravitative action, utterly unknown in nature, is probably a *resultant* of actions pervading the ethereal medium; yet the above analogy suggests the belief that the principle of activity in a moving body arrested by gravity, has not ceased to exist, but has become so much imperceptible or latent activity in the medium occupying space, and that when the body falls, this is retransformed into its equivalent of perceptible activity. If we conceive the process at all, we must conceive it thus: otherwise, we have to conceive that a *power* is changed into a *space-relation*, and this is inconceivable.

Here, then, is the solution of the difficulty. The space-element of Motion is not in itself a thing. Change of position is not an existence, but the manifestation of an existence. This existence may cease to display itself as translation; but it can do so only by displaying itself as strain. And this principle of activity, now shown by translation, now by strain, and often by the two together, is alone that which in Motion we can call continuous.

§ 58. What is this principle of activity? Vision gives us no idea of it. If by a mirror we cast the image of an illuminated object on to a dark wall, and then suddenly changing the attitude of the mirror, make the reflected image pass from side to side, the image, if recognized as such, does not raise the thought that there is present in it a principle of activity. Before we can conceive the presence of this, we must regard the impression yielded through our eyes as symbolizing something tangible—something which offers resistance. Hence the principle of activity as known by sight, is inferential: visible translation suggests by association the presence of a principle of activity which would be appreciable by our skin and muscles did we lay hold of the body. Evidently, then, this principle of activity which Motion shows us, is the objective correlate of our subjective sense of effort. By pushing and pulling we get feelings which, generalized and abstracted, yield our ideas of resistance and tension. Now displayed by changing position and now by unchanging strain, this principle of activity is ultimately conceived by us under the single form of its equivalent muscular effort. So that the continuity of Motion, as well as the indestructibility of Matter, is really known to us in terms of Force.

§ 59. And now we reach the essential truth to be here especially noted. All proofs of the Continuity of Motion involve the postulate that the quantity of force is constant. Observe what results when we analyze the reasonings by which the Continuity of Motion, as here understood, is shown.

A particular planet can be identified only by its constant power to affect our visual organs in a special way. Further, such planet has not been *seen* to move by the astronomical observer; but its motion is *inferred* from a comparison of its present position with the position it before occupied. If rigorously examined, this comparison proves to be a comparison between the different impressions produced on him by the different adjustments of his observing instruments. And, manifestly, the validity of all the inferences drawn from these likenesses and unlikenesses, depends on the truth of the assumption that these masses of matter, celestial and terrestrial, will continue to affect his senses in exactly the same ways under the same conditions; and that no changes in their powers of affecting him can have arisen without force having been expended in working those changes. Going a step further back, it turns out that difference in the adjustment of his observing instrument, and by implication in the planet, is meaningless until shown to correspond with a certain calculated position which the planet must occupy, supposing that no motion has been lost. And if, finally, we examine the implied calculation, we find that it takes into account those accelerations and retardations which ellipticity of the orbit involves, as well as those variations of velocity caused by adjacent planets—we find, that is, that the motion is concluded to be indestructible not from the uniform velociy of the planet, but from the constant quantity of motion exhibited when allowance is made for the motion communicated to, or received from, other celestial bodies. And when we ask how this communicated motion is estimated, we discover that the estimate is based on certain laws of force; which laws, one and all, embody the postulate that force cannot be destroyed. Without the axiom that action and reaction are equal and opposite, astronomy could not make its exact predictions.

Similarly with the *à priori* conclusion that Motion is continuous. That which defies suppression in thought, is really the force which the motion indicates. We can imagine retardation to result from the action of external bodies. But to imagine this, is not possible without imagining abstraction of the force implied by the motion. We are obliged to conceive this force as impressed in the shape of reaction on the bodies that cause the arrest. And the motion communicated to them, we are compelled to regard, not as directly communicated, but as a product of the communicated force. We can mentally diminish the velocity or space-element of motion, by diffusing the momentum or force-element over a larger mass of matter; but the quantity of this force-element, which we regard as the cause of the motion, is unchangeable in thought.[1]

---

[1] It is needful to state that this exposition differs in its point of view from the expositions ordinarily given; and that some of the words employed, such as *strain,* have somewhat larger implications. Unable to learn anything about the nature of Force, physicists have, of late years, formulated ultimate physical truths in such ways as often tacitly to exclude the consciousness of Force: conceiving cause, as Hume proposed, in terms of antecedence and sequence only. "Potential energy," for example, is defined as constituted by such relations in space as permit masses to generate in one another certain motions, but as being in itself nothing. While this mode of conceiving the phenomena suffices for physical inquiries, it does not suffice for the purposes of philosophy. After referring to the "Principles of Psychology," §§ 347–350, the reader will understand what I mean by saying that since our ideas of Body, Space, Motion, are derived from our ideas of muscular tension, which are the ultimate symbols into which all our other mental symbols are interpretable, to formulate phenomena in the proximate terms of Body, Space, Motion, while discharging from the concepts the consciousness of Force, is to acknowledge the superstructure while ignoring the foundation.

CHAPTER VI

THE PERSISTENCE OF FORCE[1]

§ 60. IN THE foregoing two chapters, manifestations of force of two fundamentally-different classes have been dealt with—the force by which matter demonstrates itself to us as existing, and the force by which it demonstrates itself to us as acting.

Body is distinguishable from space by its power of affecting our senses, and, in the last resort, by its opposition to our efforts. We can conceive of body only by joining in thought extension and resistance: take away resistance, and there remains only space. In what way this force which produces space-occupancy is conditioned we do not know. The mode of force which is revealed to us only by opposition to our own powers, may be in essence the same with the mode of force which reveals itself by the changes it initiates in our consciousness. That the space a body occupies is in part determined by the degree of that activity possessed by its molecules which we call heat, is a familiar truth. Moreover, we know that such molecular rearrangement as occurs

---

[1] Some explanation of this title seems needful. In the text itself are given the reasons for using the word "force" instead of the word "energy"; and here I must say why I think "persistence" preferable to "conservation." Some two years ago (this was written in 1861) I expressed to my friend Prof. Huxley my dissatisfaction with the (then) current expression—"Conservation of Force": assigning as reasons, first, that the word "conservation" implies a conserver and an act of conserving; and, second, that it does not imply the existence of the force before the particular manifestation of it which is contemplated. And I may now add, as a further fault, the tacit assumption that, without some act of conservation, force would disappear. All these implications are at variance with the conception to be conveyed. In place of "conservation" Prof. Huxley suggested *persistence*. This meets most of the objections; and though it may be urged against it that it does not directly imply pre-existence of the force at any time manifested, yet no other word less faulty in this respect can be found. In the absence of a word specially coined for the purpose, it seems the best; and as such I adopt it.

in the change of water into ice, is accompanied by an evolution of force which may burst the containing vessel and give motion to the fragments. Nevertheless, the forms of our experience oblige us to distinguish between two modes of force; the one not a worker of change and the other a worker of change, actual or potential. The first of these—the space-occupying kind of force—has no specific name.

For the second kind of force, distinguishable as that by which change is either being caused or will be caused if counterbalancing forces are overcome, the specific name now accepted is "Energy." That which in the last chapter was spoken of as perceptible activity is called, by physicists, "actual energy"; and that which was called latent activity is called "potential energy." While including the mode of activity shown in molar motion, Energy includes also the several modes of activity into which molar motion is transformable—heat, light, etc. It is the common name for the power shown alike in the movements of masses and in the movements of molecules. To our perceptions this second kind of force differs from the first kind as being not intrinsic but extrinsic.

In aggregated matter as presented to sight and touch, this antithesis is, as above implied, much obscured. Especially in a compound substance, both the potential energy locked up in the chemically-combined molecules, and the actual energy made perceptible to us as heat, complicate the manifestations of intrinsic force by the manifestations of extrinsic force. But the antithesis here partially hidden, is clearly seen on reducing the data to their lowest terms—a unit of matter, or atom, and its motion. The force by which it exists is *passive but independent;* while the force by which it moves is *active but dependent* on its past and present relations to other atoms. These two cannot be identified in our thoughts. For as it is impossible to think of motion without something that moves; so it is impossible to think of energy without something possessing the energy.

While recognizing this fundamental distinction between

that *intrinsic* force by which body manifests itself as occupying space, and that *extrinsic* force distinguished as energy;
I here treat of them together as being alike persistent. And
I thus treat of them together partly for the reason that, in
our consciousness of them, there is the same essential element. The sense of effort is our subjective symbol for objective force in general, passive and active. Power of neutralizing that which we know as our own muscular strain, is the
ultimate element in our idea of body as distinguished from
space; and any energy which we can give to body, or receive
from it, is thought of as equal to a certain amount of muscular strain. The two consciousnesses differ essentially in
this, that the feeling of effort common to the two is in the
last case joined with consciousness of change of position,
but in the first case is not.[1]

There is, however, a further and more important reason
for here dealing with the truth that Force under each of
these forms persists. We have to examine its warrant.

§ 61. At the risk of trying the reader's patience, we must
reconsider the reasoning through which the indestructibility
of Matter and the continuity of Motion are established, that
we may see how impossible it is to arrive by parallel reasoning at the Persistence of Force.

In all three cases the question is one of quantity:—does
the Matter, or Motion, or Force, ever diminish in quantity?

---

[1] In respect to the fundamental distinction here made between the space-
occupying kind of force, and the kind of force shown by various modes of activity, I am, as in the last chapter, at issue with some of my scientific friends.
They do not admit that the conception of force is involved in the conception of
a unit of matter. From the psychological point of view, however, Matter, in all
its properties, is the unknown cause of the sensations it produces in us; of
which the one which remains when all the others are absent, is resistance to our
efforts—a resistance we are obliged to symbolize as the equivalent of the muscular force it opposes. In imagining a unit of matter we may not ignore this
symbol, by which alone a unit of matter can be figured in thought as an existence. It is not allowable to speak as though there remained a conception of
an existence when that conception has been eviscerated—deprived of the
element of thought by which it is distinguished from empty space. Divest the
conceived unit of matter of the objective correlate to our subjective sense of
effort, and the entire fabric of physical conceptions disappears.

Quantitative science implies measurement; and measurement implies a unit of measure. The units of measure from which all others of any exactness are derived, are units of linear extension. Our units of linear extension are the lengths of masses of matter, or the spaces between marks made on the masses; and we assume these lengths, or these spaces between marks, to remain unchanged while the temperature is unchanged. From the standard-measure preserved at Westminister, are derived the measures for trigonometrical surveys, for geodesy, the measurement of terrestrial arcs, and the calculations of astronomical distances, dimensions, etc., and therefore for Astronomy at large. Were these units of length, original and derived, irregularly variable, there could be no celestial dynamics; nor any of that verification yielded by it of the constancy of the celestial masses or of their energies. Hence, persistence of the space-occupying species of force cannot be proved; for the reason that it is tacitly assumed in every experiment or observation by which it is proposed to prove it. The like holds of the force distinguished as energy. The endeavor to establish this by measurement, takes for granted both the persistence of the intrinsic force by which body manifests itself as existing and the persistence of the extrinsic force by which body acts. For it is from these equal units of linear extension, through the medium of the equal-armed lever or scales, that we derive our equal units of weight, or gravitative force; and only by means of these can we make those quantitative comparisons by which the truths of exact science are reached. Throughout the investigations leading the chemist to the conclusion that of the carbon which has disappeared during combustion, no portion has been lost, what is his repeatedly-assigned proof? That afforded by the scales. In what terms is the verdict of the scales given? In grains—in units of weight—in units of gravitative force. And what is the total content of the verdict? That as many units of gravitative force as the carbon exhibited at first, it exhibits still. The validity of the inference, then, depends entirely upon

the constancy of the units of force. If the force with which
the portion of metal called a grain-weight, tends toward the
Earth, has varied, the inference that matter is indestructible
is vicious. Everything turns on the truth of the assumption
that the gravitation of the weights is persistent; and of this
no proof is assigned, or can be assigned. In the reasonings
of the astronomer there is a like implication; from which
we may draw the like conclusion. No problem in celestial
physics can be solved without the assumption of some unit
of force. This unit need not be, like a pound or a ton, one
of which we can take direct cognizance. It is requisite only
that the mutual attraction which some two of the bodies concerned exercise at a given distance, should be taken as one;
so that the other attractions with which the problem deals,
may be expressed in terms of this one. Such unit being
assumed, the motions which the respective masses will generate in each other in a given time, are calculated; and compounding these with the motions they already have, their
places at the end of that time are predicted. The prediction
is verified by observation. From this, either of two inferences may be drawn. Assuming the masses to be unchanged,
their energies, actual and potential, may be proved to be
undiminished; or assuming their energies to be undiminished, the masses may be proved unchanged. But the validity of one or other inference, depends wholly on the truth of
the assumption that the unit of force is unchanged. Let it
be supposed that the gravitation of the two bodies toward
each other at the given distance, has varied, and the conclusions drawn are no longer true. Nor is it only in their
concrete data that the reasonings of terrestrial and celestial
physics assume the Persistence of Force. The equality of
action and reaction is taken for granted from beginning to
end of either argument; and to assert that action and reaction are equal and opposite, is to assert that Force is persistent. The allegation really amounts to this, that there cannot be an isolated force beginning and ending in nothing;
but that any force manifested, implies an equal antecedent

force from which it is derived, and against which it is a reaction.

We might indeed be certain, even in the absence of any such analysis as the foregoing, that there must exist some principle which, as being the basis of science, cannot be established by science. All reasoned-out conclusions whatever must rest on some postulate. As before shown (§ 23), we cannot go on merging derivative truths in those wider and wider truths from which they are derived, without reaching at last a widest truth which can be merged in no other, or derived from no other. And whoever contemplates the relation in which it stands to the truths of science in general, will see that this truth transcending demonstration is the Persisence of Force.

§ 62. But now what is the force of which we predicate persistence? It is not the force we are immediately conscious of in our own muscular efforts; for this does not persist. As soon as an outstretched limb is relaxed, the sense of tension disappears. True, we assert that in the stone thrown or in the weight lifted, is exhibited the effect of this muscular tension; and that the force which has ceased to be present in our consciousness, exists elsewhere. But it does not exist elsewhere under any form cognizable by us. In § 18 we saw that though, on raising an object from the ground, we are obliged to think of its downward pull as equal and opposite to our upward pull; and though it is impossible to represent these as equal without representing them as like in kind; yet, since their likeness in kind would imply in the object a sensation of muscular tension, which cannot be ascribed to it, we are compelled to admit that force as it exists out of our consciousness, is not force as we know it. Hence the force of which we assert persistence is that Absolute Force of which we are indefinitely conscious as the necessary correlate of the force we know. By the Persistence of Force, we really mean the persistence of some Cause which transcends our knowledge and conception. In asserting it we assert an Unconditioned Reality, without beginning or end.

Thus, quite unexpectedly, we come down once more to that ultimate truth in which, as we saw, Religion and Science coalesce. On examining the data underlying a rational Theory of Things, we find them all at last resolvable into that datum without which consciousness was shown to be impossible—the continued existence of an Unknowable as the necessary correlative of the Knowable.

The sole truth which transcends experience by underlying it, is thus the Persistence of Force. This being the basis of experience, must be the basis of any scientific organization of experiences. To this an ultimate analysis brings us down; and on this a rational synthesis must build up.

CHAPTER VII

THE PERSISTENCE OF RELATIONS AMONG FORCES

§ 63. THE first deduction to be drawn from the ultimate universal truth that force persists, is that the relations among forces persist. Supposing a given manifestation of force, under a given form and given conditions, be either preceded by or succeeded by some other manifestation, it must, in all cases where the form and conditions are the same, be preceded by or succeeded by such other manifestation. Every antecedent mode of the Unknowable must have an invariable connection, quantitative and qualitative, with that mode of the Unknowable which we call its consequent.

For to say otherwise is to deny the persistence of force. If in any two cases there is exact likeness not only between those most conspicuous antecedents which we distinguish as the causes, but also between those accompanying antecedents which we call the conditions, we cannot affirm that the effects will differ, without affirming either that some force has come into existence or that some force has ceased to exist. If the co-operative forces in the one case are equal to those in the other, each to each, in distribution and amount; then it is impossible to conceive the product of their joint action in the one case as unlike that in the other, without conceiving one or more of the forces to have increased or diminished in quantity; and this is conceiving that force is not persistent.

To impress the truth here enunciated under its most abstract form, some illustrations will be desirable.

§ 64. Let two equal bullets be projected with equal forces; then, in equal times, equal distances must be travelled by them. The assertion that one of them will describe an assigned space sooner than the other, though their initial momenta were alike and they have been equally resisted (for if they are unequally resisted the antecedents differ), is an assertion that equal quantities of force have not done equal amounts of work; and this cannot be thought without thinking that some force has disappeared into nothing or arisen out of nothing. Assume, further, that during its flight, one of them has been drawn by the Earth a certain number of inches out of its original line of movement; then the other, which has moved the same distance in the same time, must have fallen just as far toward the Earth. No other result can be imagined without imagining that equal attractions acting for equal times, have produced unequal effects, which involves the inconceivable proposition that some action has been created or annihilated. Again, one of the bullets having penetrated the target to a certain depth, penetration by the other bullet to a smaller depth, unless caused by altered shape of the bullet or greater local density in the target, cannot be mentally represented. Such a modification of the consequents without modification of the antecedents, is thinkable only through the impossible thought that something has become nothing or nothing has become something. It is thus not with sequences only, but also with simultaneous changes and permanent co-existences. Given charges of powder alike in quantity and quality, fired from barrels of the same structure, and propelling bullets of equal weights, sizes and forms, similarly rammed down; and it is a necessary inference that the concomitant actions which make up the explosion, will bear to one another like relations of quantity and quality in the two cases. The proportions among the different products of combustion will be equal. The several amounts of force taken up in giving momentum to the bullet, heat to the gases, and sound on their escape, will preserve the same ratios. The quantities of light and smoke in the one case will be what they are in the other; and the two recoils will be alike. For no difference of proportion, or no difference of relation, among these concurrent phenomena can be imagined as arising, without imagining such difference of proportion or relation as arising uncaused—as arising by the creation or annihilation of force.

That which here holds between two cases must hold among any number of cases; and that which here holds between antecedents and consequents that are comparatively simple, must hold however involved the antecedents become and however involved the consequents become.

§ 65. Thus what we call uniformity of law, resolvable as we find it into the persistence of relations among forces, is an immediate corollary from the persistence of force. The general conclusion that there exist constant connections among phenomena, ordinarily regarded as an inductive conclusion only, is really a conclusion deducible from the ultimate datum of consciousness. Though, in saying this, we seem to be illegitimately inferring that what is true of the *ego* is also true of the *non-ego;* yet here this inference is legitimate. For that which we thus predicate as holding in common of *ego* and *non-ego,* is that which they have in common as being both existences. The assertion of an existence beyond consciousness, is itself an assertion that there is something beyond consciousness which persists; for persistence is nothing more than continued existence, and existence cannot be thought of as other than continued. And we cannot assert persistence of this something beyond consciousness, without asserting that the relations among its manifestation are persistent.

That uniformity of law thus follows inevitably from the persistence of force, will become more and more clear as we advance. The next chapter will indirectly supply abundant illustrations of it.

CHAPTER VIII

THE TRANSFORMATION AND EQUIVALENCE OF FORCES

§ 66. WHEN, to the unaided senses, Science began to add supplementary senses in the shape of measuring instruments, men began to perceive various phenomena which eyes and fingers could not distinguish. Of known forms of force, minuter manifestations became appreciable; and forms of force before unknown were rendered cognizable and measurable. Where forces had apparently ended in nothing, and had been carelessly supposed to have actually done so, instrumental observation proved that effects had in every instance been produced: the forces reappearing in new shapes. Hence there has at length arisen the inquiry whether the force displayed in each surrounding change, does not in the act of expenditure undergo metamorphosis into an equivalent amount of some other force or forces. And to this inquiry experiment is giving an affirmative answer, which becomes daily more decisive. Meyer, Joule, Grove and Helmholtz are more than any others to be credited with the clear enunciation of this doctrine. Let us glance at the evidence on which it rests.

Motion, wherever we can directly trace its genesis, we find to pre-exist as some other mode of force. Our own voluntary acts have always certain sensations of muscular tension as their antecedents. When, as in letting fall a relaxed limb, we are conscious of a bodily movement requiring no effort, the explanation is that the effort was exerted in raising the limb to the position whence it fell. In this case, as in the case of an inanimate body descending to the Earth, the force accumulated by the downward motion is just equal to the force previously expended in the act of elevation. Conversely, Motion that is arrested produces, under different circumstances, heat, electricity, magnetism, light. From the warming of the hands by rubbing them together, up to the ignition of a railway-brake by intense friction—from the lighting of detonating powder by percussion, up to the setting on fire a block of wood by a few blows from a steam-hammer; we have abundant instances in which heat arises as Motion ceases. It is uniformly found, that the heat generated is great in proportion as the Motion lost is great; and that to diminish the arrest of motion, by diminishing the friction, is to diminsh the quantity of heat evolved. The production of electricity by Motion is illustrated equally in the boy's experiment with rubbed sealing-wax, in the common electrical machine, and in the apparatus for exciting electricity by the escape of steam. Wherever there is friction between heterogeneous bodies, electrical disturbance is one of the consequences. Magnetism may result from Motion either immediately, as through percussion on iron, or mediately, as through electric currents previously generated by Motion. And similarly, Motion may create light; either directly, as in the minute incandescent fragments struck off by violent collisions, or indirectly, as through the electric spark. "Lastly, Motion may be again reproduced by the forces which have emanated from Motion; thus, the divergence of the electrometer, the revolution of the electrical wheel, the deflection of the magnetic needle, are when resulting from frictional electricity, palpable movements reproduced by the intermediate modes of force, which have themselves been originated by motion."

That mode of force which we distinguish as Heat, is now generally regarded by physicists as molecular motion—not motion as displayed in the changed relations of sensible masses to each other, but as occurring among the units of which such sensible masses consist. If we cease to think of Heat as that particular sensation given to us by bodies in certain conditions, and consider the phenomena otherwise presented by these bodies, we find that motion, either in them or in surrounding bodies, or in both, is all that we have evidence of. With one or two exceptions which are obstacles to every theory of Heat, heated bodies expand; and expansion can be interpreted only as a movement of the units of a mass in relation to each other. That so-called radiation through which anything of higher temperature than things around it, communicates Heat to them, is clearly a species of motion. Moreover, the evidence afforded by the thermometer that Heat thus diffuses itself, is simply a movement caused in the mercurial column. And that the molecular motion which we call Heat, may be transformed into visible motion, familiar proof is given by the steam-engine; in which "the piston and all its concomitant masses of matter are moved by the molecular dilatation of the vapor of water." Where Heat is absorbed without apparent result, modern inquiries show that decided though unobtrusive changes are produced: as on glass, the molecular state of which is so far changed by heat, that a polarized ray of light passing through it becomes visible, which it does not do when the glass is cold; or as on polished metallic surfaces, which are so far changed in structure by thermal radiations from objects very close to them, as to retain permanent impressions of such objects. The transformation of Heat into electricity, occurs when dissimilar metals touching each other are heated at the point of contact: electric currents being so induced. Solid, incombustible matter introduced into heated gas, as lime into the oxy-hydrogen flame, becomes incandescent; and so exhibits the conversion of Heat into light. The production of magnetism by Heat, if it cannot be proved to take place directly, may be proved to take place indirectly through the medium of electricity. And through the same medium may be established the correlation of Heat and chemical affinity—a correlation which is indeed implied by the marked influence that Heat exercises on chemical composition and decomposition.

The transformations of Electricity into other modes of force, are still more clearly demonstrable. Produced by the motion of heterogeneous bodies in contact, Electricity, through attractions and repulsions, will immediately reproduce motion in neighboring bodies. Now a current of Electricity generates magnetism in a bar of soft iron; and now the rotation of a permanent magnet generates currents of Electricity. Here we have a battery in which from the play of chemical affinities an electric current results; and there, in the adjacent cell, we have an electric current effecting chemical decomposition. In the conducting wire we witness the transformation of Electricity into heat; while in electric sparks and in the voltaic arc we see light produced. Atomic arrangement, too, is changed by Electricity: as instance the transfer of matter from pole to pole of a battery; the fractures caused by the disruptive discharge; the formation of crystals under the influence of electric currents. And whether, conversely, Electricity be or be not directly generated by rearrangement of the atoms of matter, it is at any rate indirectly so generated through the intermediation of magnetism.

How from Magnetism the other physical forces result, must be next briefly noted—briefly, because in each successive case the illustrations become in great part the obverse forms of those before given. That Magnetism produces motion is the ordinary evidence we have of its existence. In the magneto-electric machine we see a rotating magnet evolving electricity. And the electricity so evolved may immediately after exhibit itself as heat, light, or chemical affinity. Faraday's discovery of the effect of Magnetism on polarized light, as well as the discovery that change of mag-

netic state is accompanied by heat, point to further like connections. Lastly, various experiments show that the magnetization of a body alters its internal structure; and that
conversely, the alteration of its internal structure, as by
mechanical strain, alters its magnetic condition.

Improbable as it seemed, it is now proved that from
Light also may proceed the like variety of agencies. The
solar rays change the atomic arrangements of particular crystals. Certain mixed gases, which do not otherwise combine,
combine in the sunshine. In some compounds Light produces decomposition. Since the inquiries of photographers
have drawn attention to the subject, it has been shown that
"a vast number of substances, both elementary and compound, are notably affected by this agent, even those apparently the most unalterable in character, such as metals."
And when a daguerreotype plate is connected with a proper
apparatus "we get chemical action on the plate, electricity
circulating through the wires, magnetism in the coil, heat in
the helix, and motion in the needles."

The genesis of all other modes of force from Chemical
Action, scarcely needs pointing out. The ordinary accompaniment of chemical combination is heat; and when the
affinities are intense, light also is, under fit conditions, produced. Chemical changes involving alteration of bulk,
cause motion, both in the combining elements and in adjacent masses of matter: witness the propulsion of a bullet by
the explosion of gunpowder. In the galvanic battery we see
electricity resulting from chemical composition and decomposition. While through the medium of this electricity,
Chemical Action produces magnetism.

These facts, the larger part of which are culled from Mr.
Grove's work on "The Correlation of Physical Forces,"
show us that each force is transformable, directly or indirectly, into the others. In every change Force undergoes
metamorphosis; and from the new form or forms it assumes,
may subsequently result either the previous one or any of
the rest, in endless variety of order and combination. It is

further becoming manifest that the physical forces stand not simply in qualitative correlations with each other, but also in quantitative correlations. Besides proving that one mode of force may be transformed into another mode, experiments illustrate the truth that from a definite amount of one, definite amounts of others always arise. Ordinarily it is indeed difficult to show this; since it mostly happens that the transformation of any force is not into some one of the rest but into several of them: the proportions being determined by the ever-varying conditions. But in certain cases, positive results have been reached. Mr. Joule has ascertained that the fall of 772 lbs. through one foot, will raise the temperature of a pound of water one degree of Fahrenheit. The investigations of Dulong, Petit and Neumann, have proved a relation in amount between the affinities of combining bodies and the heat evolved during their combination. Between chemical action and voltaic electricity, a quantitative connection has also been established: Faraday's experiments implying that a specific measure of electricity is disengaged by a given measure of chemical action. The well-determined relations between the quantities of heat generated and water turned into steam, or still better the known expansion produced in steam by each additional degree of heat, may be cited in further evidence. Whence it is no longer doubted that among the several forms which force assumes, the quantitative relations are fixed. The conclusion tacitly agreed on by physicists, is, not only that the physical forces undergo metamorphoses, but that a certain amount of each is the constant equivalent of certain amounts of the others.

§ 67. Everywhere throughout the Cosmos this truth must invariably hold. Every successive change, or group of changes, going on in it, must be due to forces affiliable on the like or unlike forces previously existing; while from the forces exhibited in such change or changes must be derived others more or less transformed. And besides recognizing this necessary linking of the forces at any time manifested, with those preceding and succeeding them, we must recognize the amounts of these forces as determinate—as necessarily producing such and such quantities of results, and as necessarily limited to those quantities.

That unification of knowledge which is the business of Philosophy, is but little furthered by the establishment of this truth under its general form. We must trace it out under its leading special forms. Changes, and the accompanying transformations of forces, are everywhere in progress, from the movements of stars to the currents of our thoughts; and to comprehend, in any adequate way, the meaning of the great fact that forces, unceasingly metamorphosed, are nowhere increased or decreased, it is requisite for us to contemplate the various orders of changes going on around, for the purpose of ascertaining whence arise the forces they imply and what becomes of these forces. Of course if answerable at all, these questions can be answered only in the rudest way. We cannot hope to establish equivalence among the successive manifestations of force. The most we can hope is to establish a qualitative correlation that is indefinitely quantitative—quantitative to the extent of involving something like a due proportion between causes and effects. Let us, with the view of trying to do this, consider in succession the several classes of phenomena which the several concrete sciences deal with.

§ 68. The antecedents of those forces which our Solar System displays, belong to a past of which we can never have anything but inferential knowledge; and at present we cannot be said to have even this. Numerous and strong as are the reasons for believing the Nebular Hypothesis, we cannot yet regard it as more than a hypothesis. If, however, we assume that the matter composing the Solar System once existed in a diffused state, we have, in the gravitation of its parts, a force adequate to produce the motions now going on.

Masses of precipitated nebulous matter, moving toward their common centre of gravity through the resisting medium from which they were precipitated, will inevitably cause a general rotation, increasing in rapidity as the concentration progresses. So far as the evidence carries us, we perceive some quantitative relation between the motions so generated and the gravitative forces expended in generating them. The planets formed from that matter which has travelled the shortest distance toward the common centre of gravity, have the smallest velocities. Doubtless this is explicable on the teleological hypothesis; since it is a condition to equilibrium. But without insisting that this is beside the question, it will suffice to point out that the like cannot be said of the planetary rotations. No such final cause can be assigned for the rapid axial movement of Jupiter and Saturn, or the slow axial movement of Mercury. If, however, in pursuance of the doctrine of transformation, we look for the antecedents of these gyrations which all planets exhibit, the nebular hypothesis furnishes us with antecedents which bear manifest quantitative relations to the motions displayed. For the planets that turn on their axes with extreme rapidity, are those having great masses and large orbits—those, that is, of which the once diffused elements moved to their centres of gravity through immense spaces, and so acquired high velocities. While, conversely, the planets which rotate with the smallest velocities, are those formed out of the smallest nebulous rings—a relation still better shown by satellites.

"But what," it may be asked, "has in such case become of all that motion which brought about the aggregation of this diffused matter into solid bodies?" The answer is that it has been radiated in the form of heat and light; and this answer the evidence, so far as it goes, confirms. Geologists conclude that the heat of the Earth's still molten nucleus is but a remnant of the heat which once made molten the entire Earth. The mountainous surfaces of the Moon and of Venus (which alone are near enough to be scrutinized), indicating, as they do, crusts that have, like our own, been corrugated by contraction, imply that these bodies too have undergone refrigeration. Lastly, we have in the Sun a still-continued production of this heat and light, which must result from the arrest of diffused matter moving toward a common centre of gravity. Here also, as before, a quantitative relation is traceable. Among the bodies which make up the Solar System, those containing comparatively small amounts of matter whose centripetal motion has been destroyed, have already lost nearly all the produced heat: a result which their relatively larger surfaces have facilitated. But the Sun, a thousand times as great in mass as the largest planet, and having therefore to give off an enormously greater quantity of heat and light due to arrest of moving matter, is still radiating with great intensity.

§ 69. If we inquire the origin of those forces which have wrought the surface of our planet into its present shape, we find them traceable to the primordial source just assigned. Assuming the solar system to have arisen as above supposed, then geologic changes are either direct or indirect results of the unexpended heat caused by nebular condensation. These changes are commonly divided into igneous and aqueous— heads under which we may most conveniently consider them.

All those periodic disturbances which we call earthquakes, all those elevations and subsidences which they severally produce, all those accumulated effects of many such elevations and subsidences exhibited in ocean-basins, islands, continents, table-lands, mountain-chains, and all those formations which are distinguished as volcanic, geologists now regard as modifications of the Earth's crust produced by the still-molten matter occupying its interior. However untenable may be the details of M. Elie de Beaumont's theory, there is good reason to accept the general proposition that the disruptions and variations of level which take place at intervals on the terrestrial surface, are due to the progressive collapse of the Earth's solid envelope upon its cooling and contracting nucleus. Even supposing that volcanic eruptions, extrusions of igneous rock, and upheaved mountain-chains, could be otherwise satisfactorily accounted for, which they cannot; it would be impossible otherwise to account for those widespread elevations and depressions whence continents and oceans result. The conclusion to be drawn is, then, that the forces displayed in these so-called igneous changes, are derived positively or negatively from the unexpended heat of the Earth's interior. Such phenomena as the fusion or agglutination of sedimentary deposits, the warning of springs, the sublimation of metals into the fissures where we find them as ores, may be regarded as positive results of this residuary heat; while fractures of strata and alterations of level are its negative results, since they ensue on its escape. The original cause of all these effects is still, however, as it has been from the first, the gravitating movement of the Earth's matter toward the Earth's centre; seeing that to this is due both the internal heat itself and the collapse which takes place as it is radiated into space.

When we inquire under what forms previously existed the force which works out the geological changes classed as aqueous, the answer is less obvious. The effects of rain, of rivers, of winds, of waves, of marine currents, do not manifestly proceed from one general source. Analysis, nevertheless, proves to us that they have a common genesis. If we ask—Whence comes the power of the river-current, bearing sediment down to the sea? the reply is—The gravitation of water throughout the tract which this river drains. If we ask—How came the water to be dispersed over this tract? the reply is—It fell in the shape of rain. If we ask—How came the rain to be in that position whence it fell? the reply is—The vapor from which it was condensed was drifted there by the winds. If we ask—How came this vapor to be at that elevation? the reply is—It was raised by evaporation. And if we ask—What force thus raised it? the reply is—The sun's heat. Just that amount of gravitative force which the sun's heat overcame in raising the atoms of water, is given out again in the fall of those atoms to the same level. Hence the denudations effected by rain and rivers, during the descent of this condensed vapor to the level of the sea, are indirectly due to the sun's heat. Similarly with the winds that transport the vapor hither and thither. Consequent as atmospheric currents are on differences of temperature (either general, as between the equatorial and polar regions, or special, as between tracts of the Earth's surface of unlike physical characters), all such currents are due to that source from which the varying quantities of heat proceed. And if the winds thus originate, so too do the waves raised by them on the sea's surface. Whence it follows that whatever changes waves produce—the wearing away of shores, the breaking down of rocks into shingle, sand, and mud—are also traceable to the solar rays as their primary cause. The same may be said of ocean-currents. Generated as the larger ones are by the excess of heat which the ocean in tropical climates continually acquires from the Sun; and generated as the smaller ones are by minor local differences in the quantities of solar heat absorbed; it follows that the distribution of sediment and other geological processes which these marine currents effect, are affiliable upon the force which the sun radiates. The only aqueous agency otherwise originating is that of the tides—an agency which, equally with the others, is traceable to unexpended astronomical motion. But making allowance for the changes which this works, we reach the conclusion that the slow wearing down of continents and gradual filling up of seas, by rain, rivers, winds, waves, and ocean-streams, are the indirect effects of solar heat.

Thus the inference forced on us by the doctrine of transformation, that the forces which have molded and remolded the Earth's crust must have pre-existed under some other shape, presents no difficulty if nebular genesis be granted; since this presupposes certain forces that are both adequate to the results, and cannot be expended without producing the results. We see that while the geological changes classed as igneous, arise from the still-progressing motion of the Earth's substance to its centre of gravity; the antagonistic changes classed as aqueous, arise from the still-progressing motion of the Sun's substance toward its centre of gravity— a motion which, transformed into heat and radiated to us, is here retransformed, directly into motions of the gaseous and liquid matters on the Earth's surface, and indirectly into motions of the solid matters.

§ 70. That the forces exhibited in vital actions, vegetal and animal, are similarly derived, is so obvious a deduction from the facts of organic chemistry, that it will meet with ready acceptance from readers acquainted with these facts. Let us note first the physiological generalizations; and then the generalizations which they necessitate.

Plant-life is all directly or indirectly dependent on the heat and light of the sun—directly dependent in the immense majority of plants, and indirectly dependent in plants which, as the fungi, flourish in the dark: since these, growing as they do at the expense of decaying organic matter, mediately draw their forces from the same original source. Each plant owes the carbon and hydrogen of which it mainly consists, to the carbonic acid and water contained in the surrounding air and earth. The carbonic acid and water must, however, be decomposed before their carbon and hydrogen can be assimilated. To overcome the powerful affinities which hold their elements together, requires the expenditure of force; and this force is supplied by the Sun. In what manner the decomposition is effected we do not know. But we know that when, under fit conditions, plants are exposed to the Sun's rays, they give off oxygen and accumulate carbon and hydrogen. In darkness this process ceases. It ceases too when the quantities of light and heat received are greatly reduced, as in winter. Conversely, it is active when the light and heat are great, as in summer. And the like relation is seen in the fact that while plant-life is luxuriant in the tropics, it diminishes in temperate regions, and disappears as we approach the poles. Thus the irresistable inference is, that the forces by which plants abstract the materials of their tissues from surrounding inorganic compounds—the forces by which they grow and carry on their functions—are forces that previously existed as solar radiations.

That animal life is immediately or mediately dependent on vegetal life is a familiar truth; and that, in the main, the processes of animal life are opposite to those of vegetal life is a truth long current among men of science. Chemically considered, vegetal life is chiefly a process of de-oxidation, and animal life chiefly a process of oxidation: chiefly, we must say, because in so far as plants are expenders of force for the purposes of organization, they are oxidizers (as is shown by the exhalation of carbonic acid during the night); and animals, in some of their minor processes, are probably de-oxidizers. But with this qualification, the general truth is that while the plant, decomposing carbonic acid and water and liberating oxygen, builds up the detained carbon and hydrogen (along with a little nitrogen and small quantities of other elements elsewhere obtained) into branches, leaves, and seeds; the animal, consuming these branches, leaves, and seeds, and absorbing oxygen, recomposes carbonic acid and water, together with certain nitrogenous compounds in minor amounts. And while the decomposition effected by the plant, is at the expense of certain forces emanating from the sun, which are employed in overcoming the affinities of carbon and hydrogen for the oxygen united with them; the recomposition effected by the animal, is at the profit of these forces, which are liberated during the combination of such elements. Thus the movements, internal and external, of the animal, are reappearances in new forms of a power absorbed by the plant under the shape of light and heat. Just as, in the manner above explained, the solar forces expended in raising vapor from the sea's surface, are given out again in the fall of rain and rivers to the same level, and in the accompanying trans-

fer of solid matters; so, the solar forces that in the plant
raised certain chemical elements to a condition of unstable
equilibrium, are given out again in the actions of the animal
during the fall of these elements to a condition of stable
equilibrium.

Besides thus tracing a qualitative correlation between
these two great orders of organic activity, as well as between
both of them and inorganic agencies, we may rudely trace a
quantitative correlation. Where vegetal life is abundant,
we usually find abundant animal life; and as we advance
from torrid to temperate and frigid climates, the two decrease together. Speaking generally, the animals of each
class reach a larger size in regions where vegetation is abundant, than in those where it is sparse. And further, there
is a tolerably apparent connection between the quantity of
energy which each species of animal expends, and the quantity of force which the nutriment it absorbs gives out during
oxidation.

Certain phenomena of development in both plants and
animals illustrate still more directly the ultimate truth enunciated. Pursuing the suggestion made by Mr. Grove, in the
first edition of his work on the "Correlation of the Physical
Forces," that a connection probably exists between the forces
classed as vital and those classed as physical, Dr. Carpenter
has pointed out that such a connection is clearly exhibited
during incubation. The transformation of the unorganized
contents of an egg into the organized chick, is altogether a
question of heat: withhold heat and the process does not
commence; supply heat and it goes on while the temperature is maintained, but ceases when the egg is allowed to
cool. The developmental changes can be completed only
by keeping the temperature with tolerable constancy at a
definite height for a definite time; that is—only by supplying a definite quantity of heat. In the metamorphoses of
insects we may discern parallel facts. Experiments show
not only that the hatching of their eggs is determined by
temperature, but also that the evolution of the pupa into the

imago is similarly determined; and may be immensely accelerated or retarded according as heat is artificially supplied
or withheld. It will suffice just to add that the germina-
tion of plants presents like relations of cause and effect—
relations so similar that detail is superfluous.

Thus then the various changes exhibited to us by the
organic creation, whether considered as a whole, or in its two
great divisions, or in its individual members, conform, so
far as we can ascertain, to the general principle. Where, as
in the transformation of an egg into a chick, we can investi-
gate the phenomena apart from all complications, we find
that the force manifested in the process of organization,
involves expenditure of a pre-existing force. Where it is
not, as in the egg or the chrysalis, merely the change of a
fixed quantity of matter into a new shape, but where, as in
the growing plant or animal, we have an incorporation of
matter existing outside, there is still a pre-existing external
force at the cost of which this incorporation is effected.
And where, as in the higher division of organisms, there
remain, over and above the forces expended in organization,
certain surplus forces expended in movement, these too are
indirectly derived from this same pre-existing external force.

§ 71. Even after all that has been said in the foregoing
part of this work, many will be alarmed by the assertion,
that the forces which we distinguish as mental, come within
the same generalization. Yet there is no alternative but to
make this assertion: the facts which justify, or rather which
necessitate it, being abundant and conspicuous. They fall
into the following groups.

All impressions from moment to moment made on our
organs of sense, stand in direct correlation with physical
forces existing externally. The modes of consciousness
called pressure, motion, sound, light, heat, are effects produced in us by agencies which, as otherwise expended,
crush or fracture pieces of matter, generate vibrations in
surrounding objects, cause chemical combinations, and re-

duce substances from a solid to a liquid form. Hence if we regard the changes of relative position, of aggregation, or of chemical state, thus arising, as being transformed manifestations of the agencies from which they arise; so must we regard the sensations which such agencies produce in us, as new forms of the forces producing them. Any hesitation to admit that, between the physical forces and the sensations there exists a correlation like that between the physical forces themselves, must disappear on remembering how the one correlation, like the other, is not qualitative only but quantitative. Masses of matter which, by scales or dynamometer, are shown to differ greatly in weight, differ as greatly in the feelings of pressure they produce on our bodies. In arresting moving objects, the strains we are conscious of are proportionate to the momenta of such objects as otherwise measured. Under like conditions the impressions of sounds given to us by vibrating strings, bells, or columns of air, are found to vary in strength with the amount of force applied. Fluids or solids proved to be markedly contrasted in temperature by the different degrees of expansion they produce in the mercurial column, produce in us correspondingly different degrees of the sensation of heat. And similarly unlike intensities in our impressions of light, answer to unlike effects as measured by photometers.

Besides the correlation and equivalence between external physical forces, and the mental forces generated by them in us under the form of sensations, there is a correlation and equivalence between sensations and those physical forces which, in the shape of bodily actions, result from them. The feelings we distinguish as light, heat, sound, odor, taste, pressure, etc., do not die away without immediate results; but are invariably followed by other manifestations of force. In addition to the excitements of secreting organs, that are in some cases traceable, there arises a contraction of the involuntary muscles, or of the voluntary muscles, or of both. Sensations increase the action of the heart—slightly when they are slight; markedly when they are marked; and recent physiological inquiries imply not only that contraction of the heart is excited by every sensation, but also that the muscular fibres throughout the whole vascular system, are at the same time more or less contracted. The respiratory muscles, too, are stimulated into greater activity by sensations. The rate of breathing is visibly and audibly augmented both by pleasurable and painful impressions on the nerves, when these reach any intensity. It has even of late been shown that inspiration becomes more frequent on transition from darkness into sunshine—a result probably due to the increased amount of direct and indirect nervous stimulation involved. When the quantity of sensation is great, it generates contractions of the voluntary muscles, as well as of the involuntary ones. Unusual excitement of the nerves of touch, as by tickling, is followed by almost uncontrollable movements of the limbs. Violent pains cause violent struggles. The start that succeeds a loud sound, the wry face produced by the taste of anything extremely disagreeable, the jerk with which the hand or foot is snatched out of water that is very hot, are instances of the transformation of feeling into motion; and in these cases, as in all others, it is manifest that the quantity of bodily action is proportionate to the quantity of sensation. Even where from pride there is a suppression of the screams and groans expressive of great pain (also indirect results of muscular contraction), we may still see in the clinching of the hands, the knitting of the brows, and the setting of the teeth, that the bodily actions developed are as great, though less obtrusive in their results. If we take emotions instead of sensations, we find the correlation and equivalence equally manifest. Not only are the modes of consciousness directly produced in us by physical forces, retransformable into physical forces under the form of muscular motions and the changes they initiate; but the like is true of those modes of consciousness which are not directly produced in us by the physical forces. Emotions of moderate intensity, like sensations of moderate intensity generate little beyond excitement of the heart and vascular system, joined sometimes with increased action of glandular organs. But as the emotions rise in strength, the muscles of the face, body, and limbs, begin to move. Of examples may be mentioned the frowns, dilated nostrils, and stampings of anger; the contracted brows, and wrung hands, of grief; the smiles and leaps of joy; and the frantic struggle of terror or despair. Passing over certain apparent, but only apparent, exceptions, we see that whatever be the kind of emotion, there is a manifest relation between its amount, and the amount of muscular action induced: alike from the erect carriage and elastic step of exhilaration, up to the dancings of immense delight, and from the fidgetiness of impatience up to the almost convulsive movements accompanying great mental agony. To these several orders of evidence must be joined the further one, that between our feelings and those voluntary motions into which they are transformed, there comes the sensation of muscular tension, standing in manifest correlation with both—a correlation that is distinctly quantitative: the sense of strain varying, other things equal, directly as the quantity of momentum generated.

"But how," it may be asked, "can we interpret by the law of correlation the genesis of those thoughts and feelings which, instead of following external stimuli, arise spontaneously? Between the indignation caused by an insult, and the loud sounds or violent acts that follow, the alleged connection may hold; but whence come the crowd of ideas and the mass of feelings that expend themselves in these demonstrations? They are clearly not equivalents of the sensations produced by the words on the ears; for the same words, otherwise arranged, would not have caused them. The thing said bears to the mental action it excites, much the same relation that the pulling of a trigger bears to the subsequent explosion—does not produce the power, but merely liberates it. Whence then arises this immense amount of nervous energy which a whisper or a glance may call forth?" The reply is, that the immediate correlates of these and other such modes of consciousness, are not to be found in the agencies acting on us externally, but in certain internal agencies. The forces called vital, which we have seen to be correlates of the forces called physical, are the immediate sources of these thoughts and feelings; and are expended in producing them. The proofs of this are various. Here are some of them. It is a conspicuous fact that mental action is contingent on the presence of a certain nervous apparatus; and that, greatly obscured as it is by numerous and involved conditions, a general relation may be traced between the size of this apparatus and the quantity of mental action as measured by its results. Further, this apparatus has a particular chemical constitution on which its activity depends; and there is one element in it between the amount of which and the amount of function performed, there is an ascertained connection: the proportion of phosphorus present in the brain being the smallest in infancy, old age and idiocy, and the greatest during the prime of life. Note next, that the evolution of thought and emotion varies, other things equal, with the supply of blood to the brain. On the one hand, a cessation of the cerebral circulation, from arrest of the heart's action, immediately entails unconsciousness. On the other hand, excess of cerebral circulation (unless it is such as to cause undue pressure) results in an exitement rising finally to delirium, Not the quantity only, but also the condition of the blood passing through the nervous system, influences the mental manifestations. The arterial currents must be duly aerated, to produce the normal amount of cerebration. At the one extreme, we find that if the blood is not allowed to exchange its carbonic acid for oxygen, there results asphyxia, with its accompanying stoppage of ideas and feelings. While at the other extreme, we find that by the inspiration of nitrous oxide, there is produced an excessive, and indeed irrepressible, nervous activity. Besides the connection between the development of the mental forces and the presence of sufficient oxygen in the cerebral arteries, there is a kindred connection between the development of the mental forces and the presence in the cerebral arteries of certain other elements. There must be supplied special materials for the nutrition of the nervous centres, as well as for their oxidation. And how what we may call the quantity of consciousness, is, other things equal, determined by the constituents of the blood, is unmistakably seen in the exaltation that follows when certain chemical compounds, as alcohol and the vegeto-alkalies, are added to it. The gentle exhilaration which tea and coffee create, is familiar to all; and though the gorgeous imaginations and intense feelings of happiness produced by opium and hashish, have been experienced by few (in this country at least), the testimony of those who have experienced them is sufficiently conclusive. Yet another proof that the genesis of the mental energies is immediately dependent on chemical change, is afforded by the fact, that the effete products separated from the blood by the kidneys, vary in character with the amount of cerebral action. Excessive activity of mind is habitually accompanied by the excretion of an unusual quantity of the alkaline phosphates. Conditions of abnormal nervous excitement bring on analogous effects. And the "peculiar odor of the insane," implying as it does morbid products in the perspiration, shows a connection between insanity and a special composition of the circulating fluids—a composition which, whether regarded as cause or consequence, equally implies correlation of the mental and the physical forces. Lastly we have to note that this correlation too, is, so far as we can trace it, quantitative. Provided the conditions to nervous action are not infringed on, and the concomitants are the same, there is a tolerably constant ratio between the amounts of the antecedents and consequents. Within the implied limits, nervous stimulants and anæsthetics produce effects on the thoughts and feelings, proportionate to the quantities administered. And conversely, where the thoughts and feelings form the initial term of the relation, the degree of reaction on the bodily energies is great, in proportion as they

are great: reaching in extreme cases a total prostration
of physique.

Various classes of facts thus unite to prove that the law
of metamorphosis, which holds among the physical forces,
holds equally between them and the mental forces. Those
modes of the Unknowable which we call motion, heat, light,
chemical affinity, etc., are alike transformable into each
other, and into those modes of the Unknowable which we
distinguish as sensation, emotion, thought: these, in their
turns, being directly or indirectly retransformable into the
original shapes. That no idea or feeling arises, save as a
result of some physical force expended in producing it, is
fast becoming a commonplace of science; and whoever duly
weighs the evidence will see, that nothing but an overwhelming bias in favor of a preconceived theory can explain
its non-acceptance. How this metamorphosis takes place—
how a force existing as motion, heat, or light, can become a
mode of consciousness—how it is possible for aerial vibrations to generate the sensation we call sound, or for the
forces liberated by chemical changes in the brain to give
rise to emotion—these are mysteries which it is impossible
to fathom. But they are not profounder mysteries than the
transformations of the physical forces into each other. They
are not more completely beyond our comprehension than
the natures of Mind and Matter. They have simply the
same insolubility as all other ultimate questions. We can
learn nothing more than that here is one of the uniformities
in the order of phenomena.

§ 72. If the general law of transformation and equivalence holds of the forces we class as vital and mental, it
must hold also of those which we class as social. Whatever
takes place in a society is due to organic or inorganic agencies, or to a combination of the two—results either from the
undirected physical forces around, from these physical forces
as directed by men, or from the forces of the men themselves. No change can occur in its organization, its modes

of activity, or the effects it produces on the face of the Earth, but what proceeds, mediately or immediately, from these. Let us consider first the correlation between the phenomena which societies display, and the vital phenomena.

Social power and life varies, other things equal, with the population. Though different races, differing widely in their fitness for combination, show us that the forces manifested in a society are not necessarily proportionate to the number of people; yet we see that, under given conditions, the forces manifested are confined within the limits which the number of people imposes. A small society, no matter how superior the character of its members, cannot exhibit the same quantity of social action as a large one. The production and distribution of commodities must be on a comparatively small scale. A multitudinous press, a prolific literature, or a massive political agitation, is not possible. And there can be but a small total of results in the shape of art-products and scientific discoveries. The correlation of the social with the physical forces through the intermediation of the vital ones, is, however, most clearly shown in the different amounts of activity displayed by the same society according as its members are supplied with different amounts of force from the external world. In the effects of good and bad harvests we yearly see this relation illustrated. A greatly deficient yield of wheat is soon followed by a diminution of business. Factories are worked half-time, or closed entirely; railway traffic falls; retailers find their sales much lessened; house-building is almost suspended; and if the scarcity rises to famine, a thinning of the population still more diminishes the industrial vivacity. Conversely, an unusually abundant harvest, occurring under conditons not otherwise unfavorable, both excites the old producing and distributing agencies and sets up new ones. The surplus social energy finds vent in speculative enterprises. Capital seeking investment carries out inventions that have been lying unutilized. Labor is expended in opening new channels of communication. There is increased encouragement to those who furnish the luxuries of life and minister to the æsthetic faculties. There are more marriages, and a greater rate of increase in population. Thus the social organism grows larger, more complex, and more active. When, as happens with most civilized nations, the whole of the materials for subsistence are not drawn from the area inhabited, but are partly imported, the people are still supported by certain harvests elsewhere grown at the expense of certain physical forces. Our own cotton-spinners and weavers supply the most conspicuous instance of a section in one nation living, in great part, on imported commodities, purchased by the labor they expend on other imported commodities. But though the social activities of Lancashire are due chiefly to materials not drawn from our own soil, they are none the less evolved from physical forces elsewhere stored up in fit forms and then brought here.

If we ask whence come these physical forces from which, through the intermediation of the vital forces, the social forces arise, the reply is of course as heretofore—the solar radiations. Based as the life of a society is on animal and vegetal products; and dependent as these animal and vegetal products are on the light and heat of the sun; it follows that the changes going on in societies are effects of forces having a common origin with those which produce all the other orders of changes that have been analyzed. Not only is the force expended by the horse harnessed to the plow, and by the laborer guiding it, derived from the same reservoir as is the force of the falling cataract and the roaring hurricane; but to this same reservoir are eventually traceable those subtler and more complex manifestations of force which humanity, as socially embodied, evolves. The assertion is a startling one, and by many will be thought ludicrous; but it is an unavoidable deduction which cannot here be passed over.

Of the physical forces that are directly transformed into social ones, the like is to be said. Currents of air and water, which before the use of steam were the only agencies brought in aid of muscular effort for the performance of industrial processes, are, as we have seen, generated by the heat of the sun. And the inanimate power that now, to so vast an extent, supplements human labor, is similarly derived. The late George Stephenson was one of the first to recognize the fact that the force impelling his locomotive, originally emanated from the sun. Step by step we go back —from the motion of the piston to the evaporation of the water; thence to the heat evolved during the oxidation of coal; thence to the assimilation of carbon by the plants of whose imbedded remains coal consists; thence to the carbonic acid from which their carbon was obtained; and thence to the rays of light that deoxidized this carbonic acid. Solar forces millions of years ago expended on the Earth's vegetation, and since locked up beneath its surface, now smelt the metals required for our machines, turn the lathes by which the machines are shaped, work them when put together, and distribute the fabrics they produce. And in so far as economy of labor makes possible the support of a larger population; gives a surplus of human power that would else be absorbed in manual occupations; and facilitates the development of higher kinds of activity; it is clear that these social forces which are directly correlated with physical forces anciently derived from the sun, are only less important than those whose correlates are the vital forces recently derived from it.

§ 73. Regarded as an induction, the doctrine set forth in this chapter will most likely be met by a demurrer. Many who admit that among physical phenomena at least, transformation of forces is now established, will probably say that inquiry has not yet gone far enough to enable us to predicate equivalence. And in respect of the forces classed as vital, mental, and social, the evidence assigned, however little to be explained away, they will consider by no means conclusive even of transformation, much less of equivalence.

To those who think thus, it must now however be pointed

out, that the universal truth above illustrated under its various aspects, is a necessary corollary from the persistence of force. Setting out with the proposition that force can neither come into existence, nor cease to exist, the several foregoing general conclusions inevitably follow. Each manifestation of force can be interpreted only as the effect of some antecedent force: no matter whether it be an inorganic action, an animal movement, a thought, or a feeling. Either this must be conceded, or else it must be asserted that our successive states of consciousness are self-created. Either mental energies, as well as bodily ones, are quantitatively correlated to certain energies expended in their production, and to certain other energies which they initiate; or else nothing must become something and something must become nothing. The alternatives are, to deny the persistence of force, or to admit that every physical and psychical change is generated by certain antecedent forces, and that from given amounts of such forces neither more nor less of such physical and psychical changes can result. And since the persistence of force, being a datum of consciousness, cannot be denied, its unavoidable corollory must be accepted. This corollary cannot indeed be made more certain by accumulating illustrations. The truth as arrived at deductively, cannot be inductively confirmed. For every one of such facts as those above detailed, is established only through the indirect assumption of that persistence of force, from which it really follows as a direct consequence. The most exact proof of correlation and equivalence which it is possible to reach by experimental inquiry, is that based on measurement of the forces expended and the forces produced. But, as was shown in the last chapter, any such process of measurement implies the use of some unit of force which is assumed to remain constant; and for this assumption there can be no warrant but that it is a corollary from the persistence of force. How then can any reasoning based on this corollary, prove the equally direct corollary that when a given quantity of force ceases to exist under one form, an equal

quantity must come into existence under some other form
or forms? Clearly the *à priori* truth expressed in this last
corollary, cannot be more firmly established by any *à posteriori* proofs which the first corollary helps us to.

"What then," it may be asked, "is the use of these
investigations by which transformation and equivalence of
forces is sought to be established as an inductive truth?
Surely it will not be alleged that they are useless. Yet if
the correlation cannot be made more certain by them than
it is already, does not their uselessness necessarily follow?"
No. They are of value as disclosing the many particular
implications which the general truth does not specify. They
are of value as teaching us how much of one mode of force
is the equivalent of so much of another mode. They are of
value as determining under what conditions each metamorphosis occurs. And they are of value as leading us to
inquire in what shape the remnant of force has escaped,
when the apparent results are not equivalent to the cause.

CHAPTER IX

THE DIRECTION OF MOTION

§ 74. THE Absolute Cause of changes, no matter what
may be their special natures, is not less incomprehensible in
respect of the unity or duality of its action, than in all other
respects. We cannot decide between the alternative suppositions, that phenomena are due to the variously-condi-
tioned workings of a single force, and that they are due to
the conflict of two forces. Whether, as some contend, everything is explicable on the hypothesis of universal pressure,
whence what we call tension results differentially from inequalities of pressure in opposite directions; or whether, as
might be with equal propriety contended, things are to be
explained on the hypothesis of universal tension, from which
pressure is a differential result; or whether, as most physicists hold, pressure and tension everywhere co-exist; are

questions which it is impossible to settle. Each of these three suppositions makes the facts comprehensible, only by postulating an inconceivability. To assume a universal pressure, confessedly requires us to assume an infinite plenum—an unlimited space full of something which is everywhere pressed by something beyond; and this assumption cannot be mentally realized. That universal tension is the immediate agency to which phenomena are due, is an idea open to a parallel and equally fatal objection. And however verbally intelligible may be the proposition that pressure and tension everywhere co-exist, yet we cannot truly represent to ourselves one ultimate unit of matter as drawing another while resisting it.

Nevertheless, this last belief is one which we are compelled to entertain. Matter cannot be conceived except as manifesting forces of attraction and repulsion. Body is distinguished in our consciousness from Space, by its opposition to our muscular energies; and this opposition we feel under the twofold form of a cohesion that hinders our efforts to rend, and a resistance that hinders our efforts to compress. Without resistance there can be merely empty extension. Without cohesion there can be no resistance. Probably this conception of antagonistic forces, is originally derived from the antagonism of our flexor and extensor muscles. But be this as it may, we are obliged to think of all objects as made up of parts that attract and repel each other; since this is the form of our experience of all objects.

By a higher abstraction results the conception of attractive and repulsive forces pervading space. We cannot dissociate force from occupied extension, or occupied extension from force; because we have never an immediate consciousness of either in the absence of the other. Nevertheless, we have abundant proof that force is exercised through what appears to our senses a vacuity. Mentally to represent this exercise, we are hence obliged to fill the apparent vacuity with a species of matter—an ethereal medium. The constitution we assign to this ethereal medium, however, like the constitution we assign to solid substance, is necessarily an abstract of the impressions received from tangible bodies. The opposition to pressure which a tangible body offers to us, is not shown in one direction only, but in all directions; and so likewise is its tenacity. Suppose countless lines radiating from its centre on every side, and it resists along each of these lines and coheres along each of these lines. Hence the constitution of those ultimate units through the instrumentality of which phenomena are interpreted. Be they atoms of ponderable matter or molecules of ether, the properties we conceive them to possess are nothing else than these perceptible properties idealized. Centres of force attracting and repelling each other in all directions, are simply insensible portions of matter having the endowments common to sensible portions of matter—endowments of which we cannot by any mental effort divest them. In brief, they are the invariable elements of the conception of matter, abstracted from its variable elements —size, form, quality, etc. And so to interpret manifestations of force which cannot be tactually experienced, we use the terms of thought supplied by our tactual experiences; and this for the sufficient reason that we must use these or none.

After all that has been before shown, and after the hint given above, it needs scarcely be said that these universally co-existent forces of attraction and repulsion, must not be taken as realities, but as our symbols of the reality. They are the forms under which the workings of the Unknowable are cognizable by us—modes of the Unconditioned as presented under the conditions of our consciousness. But while knowing that the ideas thus generated in us are not absolutely true, we may unreservedly surrender ourselves to them as relatively true; and may proceed to evolve a series of deductions having a like relative truth.

§ 75. From universally co-existent forces of attraction and repulsion, there result certain laws of direction of all movement. Where attractive forces alone are concerned, or rather are alone appreciable, movement takes place in the direction of their resultant; which may, in a sense, be called the line of greatest traction. Where repulsive forces alone are concerned, or rather are alone appreciable, movement takes place along their resultant; which is usually known as the line of least resistance. And where both attractive and repulsive forces are concerned, or are appreciable, movement takes place along the resultant of all the tractions and resistances. Strictly speaking, this last is the sole law; since, by the hypothesis, both forces are everywhere in action. But very frequently the one kind of force is so immensely in excess that the effect of the other kind may be left out of consideration. Practically we may say that a body falling to the Earth, follows the line of greatest traction; since, though the resistance of the air must, if the body be irregular, cause some divergence from this line (quite perceptible with feathers and leaves), yet ordinarily the divergence is so slight that we may omit it. In the same manner, though the course taken by the steam from an exploding boiler differs somewhat from that which it would take were gravitation out of the question; yet, as gravitation affects its course infinitesimally, we are justified in asserting that the escaping steam follows the line of least resistance. Motion then, we may say, always follows the line of greatest traction, or the line of least resistance, or the resultant of the two: bearing in mind that though the last is alone strictly true, the others are in many cases sufficiently near the truth for practical purposes.

Movement set up in any direction is itself a cause of further movement in that direction, since it is the embodiment of a surplus force in that direction. This holds equally with the transit of matter through space, the transit of matter through matter, and the transit through matter of any kind of vibration. In the case of matter moving through space, this principle is expressed in the law of inertia—a law on which the calculations of physical astronomy are wholly based. In the case of matter moving through matter, we trace the same truth under the familiar experience that any breach made by one solid through another, or any channel formed by a fluid through a solid, becomes a route along which, other things equal, subsequent movements of like nature take place. And in the case of motion passing through matter under the form of an impulse communicated from part to part, the facts of magnetization go to show that the establishment of undulations along certain lines, determines their continuance along those lines.

It further follows from the conditions, that the direction of movement can rarely if ever be perfectly straight. For matter in motion to pursue continuously the exact line in which it sets out, the forces of attraction and repulsion must be symmetrically disposed around its path; and the chances against this are infinitely great. The impossibility of making an absolutely true edge to a bar of metal—the fact that all which can be done by the best mechanical appliances, is to reduce the irregularities of such an edge to amounts that cannot be perceived without magnifiers—sufficiently exemplifies how, in consequence of the unsymmetrical distribution of forces around the line of movement, the movement is rendered more or less indirect. It may be well to add that in proportion as the forces at work are numerous and varied, the curve a moving body describes is necessarily complex: witness the contrast between the flight of an arrow and the gyrations of a stick tossed about by breakers.

As a step toward unification of knowledge we have now to trace these general laws throughout the various orders of changes which the Cosmos exhibits. We have to note how every motion takes place along the line of greatest traction, of least resistance, or of their resultant; how the setting up of motion along a certain line, becomes a cause of its continuance along that line; how, nevertheless, change of relations to external forces, always renders this line indirect; and how the degree of its indirectness increases with every addition to the number of influences at work.

§ 76. If we assume the first stage in nebular condensation to be the precipitation into flocculi of denser matter previously diffused through a rarer medium (a supposition both physically justified, and in harmony with certain astronomical observations), we shall find that nebular motion is interpretable in pursuance of the above general laws. Each portion of such vapor-like matter must begin to move toward the common centre of gravity. The tractive forces which would of themselves carry it in a straight line to the centre of gravity, are opposed by the resistant forces of the medium through which it is drawn. The direction of movement must be the resultant of these—a resultant which, in consequence of the unsymmetrical form of the flocculus, must be a curve directed, not to the centre of gravity, but toward one side of it. And it may be readily shown that in an aggregation of such flucculi, severally thus moving, there must, by composition of forces, eventually result a rotation of the whole nebula in one direction.

Merely noting this hypothetical illustration for the purpose of showing how the law applies to the case of nebular evolution, supposing it to have taken place, let us pass to the phenomena of the Solar System as now exhibited. Here the general principles above set forth are every instant exemplified. Each planet and satellite has a momentum which would, if acting alone, carry it forward in the direction it is at any instant pursuing. This momentum hence acts as a resistance to motion in any other direction. Each planet and satellite, however, is drawn by a force which, if unopposed, would take it in a straight line toward its primary. And the resultant of these two forces is that curve which it describes—a curve manifestly consequent on the unsymmetrical distribution of the forces around its path. This path, when more closely examined, supplies us with further illustrations. For it is not an exact circle or ellipse; which it would be were the tangential and centripetal forces the only ones concerned. Adjacent members of the Solar System, ever varying in their relative positions, cause what we call perturbations; that is, slight divergences in various directions from that circle or ellipse which the two chief forces would produce. These perturbations severally show us in minor degrees, how the line of movement is the resultant of all the forces engaged; and how this line becomes more complicated in proportion as the forces are multiplied. If instead of the motions of the planets and satellites as wholes, we consider the motions of their parts, we meet with comparatively complex illustrations. Every portion of the Earth's substance in its daily rotation, describes a curve which is in the main a resultant of that resistance which checks its nearer approach to the centre of gravity, that momentum which would carry it off at a tangent, and those forces of gravitation and cohesion which keep it from being so carried off. If this axial motion be compounded with the orbital motion, the course of each part is seen to be a much more involved one. And we find it to have a still greater complication on taking into account that lunar attraction which mainly produces the tides and the precession of the equinoxes.

§ 77. We come next to terrestrial changes: present ones as observed, and past ones as inferred by geologists. Let us set out with the hourly-occurring alterations in the Earth's atmosphere; descend to the slower alterations in progress on its surface; and then to the still slower ones going on beneath.

Masses of air, absorbing heat from surfaces warmed by the sun, expand, and so lessen the weight of the atmospheric columns of which they are parts. Hence they offer to adjacent atmosphere columns, diminished lateral resistance; and these, moving in the directions of the diminished resistance, displace the expanded air; while this, pursuing an upward course, displays a motion along that line in which there is least pressure. When again, by the ascent of such heated masses from extended areas like the torrid zone, there is produced at the upper surface of the atmosphere, a protuberance beyond the limits of equilibrium—when the air forming this protuberance begins to overflow laterally toward the poles; it does so because, while the tractive force of the Earth is nearly the same, the lateral resistance is greatly diminished. And throughout the course of each current thus generated, as well as throughout the course of each counter-current flowing into the vacuum that is left, the direction is always the resultant of the Earth's tractive force and the resistance offered by the surrounding masses of air: modified only by conflict with other currents similarly determined, and by collision with prominences on the Earth's crust. The movements of water, in both its gaseous and liquid states, furnish further examples. In conformity with the mechanical theory of heat, it may be shown that evaporation is the escape of particles of water in the direction of least resistance; and that as the resistance (which is due to the pressure of the water diffused in a gaseous state) diminishes, the evaporation increases. Conversely, that rushing together of particles called condensation, which takes place when any portion of atmospheric vapor has its temperature much lowered, may be interpreted as a diminution of the mutual pressure among the condensing particles, while the pressure of surrounding particles remains the same; and so is a motion taking place in the direction of lessened resistance. In the course followed by the resulting rain-drops, we have one of the simplest instances of the joint effect of the two antagonist forces. The Earth's attraction, and the resistance of atmospheric currents ever varying in direction and intensity, give as their resultants, lines which incline to the horizon in countless different degrees and undergo perpetual variations. More clearly still is the law exemplified by these same rain-drops when they reach the ground. In the course they take while trickling over its surface, in every rill, in every larger stream, and in every river, we see them descending as straight as the antagonism of surrounding objects permits. From moment to moment, the motion of water toward the Earth's centre is opposed by the solid matter around and under it; and from moment to moment its route is the resultant of the lines of greatest traction and least resistance. So far from a cascade furnishing, as it seems to do, an exception, it furnishes but another illustration. For though all solid obstacles to a vertical fall of the water are removed, yet the water's horizontal momentum is an obstacle; and the parabola in which the stream leaps from the projecting ledge, is generated by the combined gravitation and momentum. It may be well just to draw attention to the degree of complexity here produced in the line of movement by the variety of forces at work.

In atmospheric currents, and still more clearly in water-courses (to which might be added ocean-streams), the route followed is too complex to be defined, save as a curve of three dimensions with an ever varying equation.

The Earth's solid crust undergoes changes that supply another group of illustrations. The denudation of lands and the depositing of the removed sediment in new strata at the bottoms of seas and lakes, is a process throughout which motion is obviously determined in the same way as is that of the water effecting the transport. Again, though we have no direct inductive proof that the forces classed as igneous, expend themselves along lines of least resistance; yet what little we know of them is in harmony with the belief that they do so. Earthquakes continually revisit the same localities, and special tracts undergo for long periods together successive elevations or subsidences—facts which imply that already-fractured portions of the Earth's crust are those most prone to yield under the pressure caused by further contractions. The distribution of volcanoes along certain lines, as well as the frequent recurrence of eruptions from the same vents, are facts of like meaning.

§ 78. That organic growth takes place in the direction of least resistance, is a proposition that has been set forth and illustrated by Mr. James Hinton, in the "Medico-Chirurgical Review" for October, 1858. After detailing a few of the early observations which led him to this generalization, he formulates it thus:—

"Organic form is the result of motion."

"Motion takes the direction of least resistance."

"Therefore organic form is the result of motion in the direction of least resistance."

After an elucidation and defence of this position, Mr. Hinton proceeds to interpret, in conformity with it, sundry phenomena of development. Speaking of plants he says:—

"The formation of the root furnishes a beautiful illustration of the law of least resistance, for it grows by insinuating itself, cell by cell, through the interstices of the soil; it is by such minute additions that it increases, winding and twisting whithersoever the obstacles it meets in its path determine, and growing there most, where the nutritive materials are added to it most abundantly. As we look on the roots of a mighty tree, it appears to us as if they had forced themselves with giant violence into the solid earth. But it is not so; they were led on gently, cell added to cell, softly as the dews descended, and the loosened earth made way. Once formed, indeed, they expand with an enormous power, but the spongy condition of the growing radicles utterly forbids the supposition that they are forced into the earth. Is it not probable, indeed, that the enlargement of the roots already formed may crack the surrounding soil, and help to make the interstices into which the new rootlets grow?". . .

"Throughout almost the whole of organic nature the spiral form is more or less distinctly marked. Now, motion under resistance takes a spiral direction, as may be seen by the motion of a body rising or falling through water. A bubble rising rapidly in water describes a spiral closely resembling a corkscrew, and a body of moderate specific gravity dropped into water may be seen to fall in a curved direction, the spiral tendency of which may be distinctly observed. . . . In this prevailing spiral form of organic bodies, therefore, it appears to me, that there is presented a strong *prima facie* case for the view I have maintained. . . . The spiral form of the branches of many trees is very apparent, and the universally spiral arrangement of the leaves around the stem of plants needs only to be referred to. . . . The heart commences as a spiral turn, and in its perfect form a manifest spiral may be traced through the left ventricle, right ventricle, right auricle, left auricle and appendix. And what is the spiral turn in which the heart commences but a necessary result of the lengthening, under a limit, of the cellular mass of which it then consists?" . . .

"Every one must have noticed the peculiar curling up of the young leaves of the common fern. The appearance is as if the leaf were rolled up, but in truth this form is merely a phenomenon of growth. The curvature results from the increase of the leaf, it is only another form of the wrinkling up, or turning at right angles by extension under limit."

"The rolling up or imbrication of the petals in many flower-buds is a similar thing; at an early period the small petals may be seen lying side by side, afterward growing within the capsule, they become folded round one another." . . .

"If a flower-bud be opened at a sufficiently early period, the stamens will be found as if molded in the cavity between the pistil and the corolla, which cavity the anthers exactly fill; the stalks lengthen at an after period. I have noticed also in a few instances, that in those flowers in which the petals are imbricated, or twisted together, the pistil is tapering as growing up between the petals; in some flowers which have the petals so arranged in the bud as to form a dome (as the hawthorn; *e.g.*), the pistil is flattened at the apex, and in the bud occupies a space precisely limited by the stamens below, and the inclosing petals above and at the sides. I have not, however, satisfied myself that this holds good in all cases."

Without indorsing all Mr. Hinton's illustrations, to some

of which exception might be taken, his conclusion may be accepted as a large instalment of the truth. It is, however, to be remarked, that in the case of organic growth, as in all other cases, the line of movement is in strictness the resultant of tractive and resistant forces; and that the tractive forces here form so considerable an element that the formula is scarcely complete without them. The shapes of plants are manifestly modified by gravitation: the direction of each branch is not what it would have been were the tractive force of the Earth absent; and every flower and leaf is somewhat altered in the course of development by the weight of its parts. Though in animals, such effects are less conspicuous, yet the instances in which flexible organs have their directions in great measure determined by gravity, justify the assertion that throughout the whole organism the forms of parts must be affected by this force.

The organic movements which constitute growth, are not, however, the only organic movements to be interpreted. There are also those which constitute function. And throughout these the same general principles are discernible. That the vessels along which blood, lymph, bile, and all the secretions, find their ways, are channels of least resistance, is a fact almost too conspicuous to be named as an illustration. Less conspicuous, however, is the truth, that the currents setting along these vessels are affected by the tractive force of the Earth: witness varicose veins; witness the relief to an inflamed part obtained by raising it; witness the congestion of head and face produced by stooping. And in the fact that dropsy in the legs gets greater by day and decreases at night, while, conversely, that œdematous fulness under the eyes common in debility, grows worse during the hours of reclining and decreases after getting up, shows us how the transudation of fluid through the walls of the capillaries, varies according as change of position changes the effect of gravity in different parts of the body.

It may be well in passing just to note the bearing of the

principle on the development of species. From a dynamic point of view, "natural selection" implies structural changes along lines of least resistance. The multiplication of any kind of plant or animal in localities that are favorable to it, is a growth where the antagonistic forces are less than elsewhere. And the preservation of varieties that succeed better than their allies in coping with surrounding conditions, is the continuance of vital movement in those directions where the obstacles to it are most eluded.

§ 79. Throughout the phenomena of mind the law enunciated is not so readily established. In a large part of them, as those of thought and emotion, there is no perceptible movement. Even in sensation and volition, which show us in one part of the body an effect produced by a force applied to another part, the intermediate movement is inferential rather than visible. Such indeed are the difficulties that it is not possible here to do more than briefly indicate the proofs which might be given did space permit.

Supposing the various forces throughout an organism to be previously in equilibrium, then any part which becomes the seat of a further force, added or liberated, must be one from which the force, being resisted by smaller forces around, will initiate motion toward some other part of the organism. If elsewhere in the organism there is a point at which force is being expended, and which so is becoming minus a force which it before had, instead of plus a force which it before had not, and thus is made a point at which the reaction against surrounding forces is diminished; then, manifestly, a motion taking place between the first and the last of these points is a motion along the line of least resistance. Now a sensation implies a force added to, or evolved in, that part of the organism which is its seat; while a mechanical movement implies an expenditure or loss of force in that part of the organism which is its seat. Hence if, as we find to be the fact, motion is habitually propagated from those parts of an organism to which the external world adds

forces in the shape of nervous impressions, to those parts
of an organism which react on the external world through
muscular contractions, it is simply a fulfilment of the
law above enunciated. From this general conclusion we
may pass to a more special one. When there is anything in the circumstances of an animal's life, involving
that a sensation in one particular place is habitually followed by a contraction in another particular place—when
there is thus a frequently-repeated motion through the
organism between these places; what must be the result
as respects the line along which the motions take place?
Restoration of equilibrium between the points at which the
forces have been increased and decreased, must take place
through some channel. If this channel is affected by the
discharge—if the obstructive action of the tissues traversed,
involves any reaction upon them, deducting from their obstructive power; then a subsequent motion between these
two points will meet with less resistance along this channel
than the previous motion met with; and will consequently
take this channel still more decidedly. If so, every repetition will further diminish the resistance offered by this
route; and hence will gradually be formed between the two
a permanent line of communication, differing greatly from
the surrounding tissue in respect of the ease with which
force traverses it. We see, therefore, that if between a
particular impression and a particular motion associated
with it, there is established a connection producing what is
called reflex action, the law that motion follows the line of
least resistance, and that, if the conditions remain constant,
resistance in any direction is diminished by motion occurring in that direction, supplies an explanation. Without
further details it will be manifest that a like interpretation
may be given to the succession of all other nervous changes.
If in the surrounding world there are objects, attributes, or
actions that usually occur together, the effects severally
produced by them in the organism will become so connected
by those repetitions which we call experience, that they also

will occur together. In proportion to the frequency with which any external connection of phenonema is experienced, will be the strength of the answering internal connection of nervous states. Thus there will arise all degrees of cohesion among nervous states, as there are all degrees of commonness among the surrounding co-existences and sequences that generate them: whence must result a general correspondence between associated ideas and associated actions in the environment.[1]

The relation between emotions and actions may be similarly construed. As a first illustration let us observe what happens with emotions that are undirected by volitions. These, like feelings in general, expend themselves in generating organic changes, and chiefly in muscular contractions. As was pointed out in the last chapter, there result movements of the involuntary and voluntary muscles, that are great in proportion as the emotions are strong. It remains here to be pointed out, however, that the order in which these muscles are affected is explicable only on the principle above set forth. Thus, a pleasurable or painful state of mind of but slight intensity, does little more than increase the pulsations of the heart. Why? For the reason that the relation between nervous excitement and vascular contraction, being common to every genus and species of feeling, is the one of most frequent repetition; that hence the nervous connection is, in the way above shown, the one which offers the least resistance to a discharge; and is therefore the one along which a feeble force produces motion. A sentiment or passion that is somewhat stronger, affects not only the heart but the muscles of the face, and especially those around the mouth. Here the like explanation applies; since these muscles, being both comparatively small, and, for purposes of speech, perpetually used, offer less

---

[1] This paragraph is a restatement, somewhat amplified, of an idea set forth in the "Medico-Chirurgical Review" for January, 1859 (pp. 189 and 190); and contains the germ of the intended fifth part of the "Principles of Psychology," which was withheld for the reasons given in the preface to that work.

resistance than other voluntary muscles to the nervo-motor force. By a further increase of emotion the respiratory and vocal muscles become perceptibly excited. Finally, under strong passion, the muscles in general of the trunk and limbs are violently contracted. Without saying that the facts can be thus interpreted in all their details (a task requiring data impossible to obtain) it may be safely said that the order of excitation is from muscles that are small and frequently acted on, to those which are larger and less frequently acted on. The single instance of laughter, which is an undirected discharge of feeling that affects first the muscles round the mouth, then those of the vocal and respiratory apparatus, then those of the limbs, and then those of the spine;[1] suffices to show that when no special route is opened for it, a force evolved in the nervous centres produces motion along channels which offer the least resistance, and if it is too great to escape by these, produces motion along channels offering successively greater resistance.

Probably it will be thought impossible to extend this reasoning so as to include volitions. Yet we are not without evidence that the transition from special desires to special muscular acts, confirms to the same principle. It may be shown that the mental antecedents of a voluntary movement, are antecedents which temporarily make the line along which this movement takes place, the line of least resistance. For a volition, suggested as it necessarily is by some previous thought connected with it by associations that determine the transition, is itself a representation of the movements that are willed, and of their sequences. But to represent in consciousness certain of our own movements is partially to arouse the sensations accompanying such movements, inclusive of those of muscular tension—is partially to excite the appropriate motor-nerves and all the other nerves implicated. That is to say, the volition is itself an incipient discharge along a line which previous experiences

---

[1] For details see a paper on "The Physiology of Laughter," published in "Macmillan's Magazine" for March, 1860.

have rendered a line of least resistance. And the passing of volition into action is simply a completion of the discharge.

One corollary from this must be noted before proceeding; namely, that the particular set of muscular movements by which any object of desire is reached, are movements implying the smallest total of forces to be overcome. As each feeling generates motion along the line of least resistance, it is tolerably clear that a group of feelings, constituting a more or less complex desire, will generate motion along a series of lines of least resistance. That is to say, the desired end will be achieved with the smallest expenditure of effort. Should it be objected that through want of knowledge or want of skill, a man often pursues the more laborious of two courses, and so overcomes a larger total of opposing forces than was necessary; the reply is, that relatively to his mental state the course he takes is that which presents the fewest difficulties. Though there is another which in the abstract is easier, yet his ignorance of it, or inability to adopt it, is, physically considered, the existence of an insuperable obstacle to the discharge of his energies in that direction. Experience obtained by himself, or communicated by others, has not established in him such channels of nervous communication as are required to make this better course the course of least resistance to him.

§ 80. As in individual animals, inclusive of man, motion follows lines of least resistance, it is to be inferred that among aggregations of men, the like will hold good. The changes in a society, being due to the joint actions of its members, the courses of such changes will be determined as are those of all other changes wrought by composition of forces.

Thus when we contemplate a society as an organism, and observe the direction of its growth, we find this direction to be that in which the average of opposing forces is the least. Its units have energies to be expended in self-maintenance and reproduction. These energies are met by various environing energies that are antagonistic to them—those of geological origin, those of climate, of wild animals, of other human races with whom they are at enmity or in competition. And the tracts the society spreads over, are those in which there is the smallest total antagonism. Or, reducing the matter to its ultimate terms, we may say that these social units have jointly and severally to preserve themselves and their offspring from those inorganic and organic forces which are ever tending to destroy them (either indirectly by oxidation and by undue abstraction of heat, or directly by bodily mutilation); that these forces are either counteracted by others, which are available in the shape of food, clothing, habitations, and appliances of defense, or are, as far as may be, eluded; and that population spreads in whichever directions there is the readiest escape from these forces, or the least exertion in obtaining the materials for resisting them, or both. For these reasons it happens that fertile valleys where water and vegetal produce abound, are early peopled. Sea-shores, too, supplying a large amount of easily-gathered food, are lines along which mankind have commonly spread.

The general fact that, so far as we can judge from the traces left by them, large societies first appeared in those tropical regions where the fruits of the earth are obtainable with comparatively little exertion, and where the cost of maintaining bodily heat is but slight, is a fact of like meaning. And to these instances may be added the allied one daily furnished by emigration; which we see going on toward countries presenting the fewest obstacles to the self-preservation of individuals, and therefore to national growth. Similarly with that resistance to the movements of a society which neighboring societies offer. Each of the tribes or nations inhabiting any region, increases in numbers until it outgrows its means of subsistence. In each there is thus a force ever pressing outward on to adjacent areas—a force antagonized by like forces in the tribes or nations occupying those areas. And the ever-recurring wars that result—the conquests of weaker tribes or nations, and the over-running of their territories by the victors, are instances of social movements taking place in the directions of least resistance. Nor do the conquered peoples, when they escape extermination or enslavement, fail to show us movements that are similarly determined. For migrating as they do to less fertile regions—taking refuge in deserts or among mountains—moving in a direction where the resistance to social growth is comparatively great; they still do this only under an excess of pressure in all other directions: the physical obstacles to self-preservation they encounter being really less than the obstacles offered by the enemies from whom they fly.

Internal social movements may also be thus interpreted. Localities naturally fitted for producing particular commodities—that is, localities in which such commodities are got at the least cost of force—that is, localites in which the desires for these commodities meet with the least resistance; become localities especially devoted to the obtainment of these commodities. Where soil and climate render wheat a profitable crop, or a crop from which the greatest amount of life-sustaining power is gained by a given quantity of effort, the growth of wheat becomes the dominant industry. Where wheat cannot be economically produced, oats, or rye, or maize, or rice, or potatoes, is the agricultural staple. Along sea-shores men support themselves with least effort by catching fish; and hence choose fishing as an occupation. And in places that are rich in coal or metallic ores, the population, finding that labor devoted to the raising of these materials brings a larger return of food and clothing than when otherwise directed, becomes a population of miners. This last instance introduces us to the phenomena of exchange; which equally illustrate the general law. For the practice of barter begins as soon as it facilitates the fulfilment of men's desires, by diminishing the exertion needed to reach the objects of those desires. When instead of growing his own corn, weaving his own cloth, sewing his own shoes, each man began to confine himself to farming, or weaving, or shoemaking; it was because each found it more laborious to make everything he wanted, than to make a great quantity of one thing and barter the surplus for the rest: by exchange, each procured the necessaries of life without encountering so much resistance. Moreover, in deciding what commodity to produce, each citizen was, as he is at the present day, guided in the same manner. For besides those local conditions which determine whole sections of a society toward the industries easiest for them, there are also individual conditions and individual aptitudes which to each citizen render certain occupations preferable; and in choosing those forms of activity which their special circumstances and faculties dictate, these social units are severally moving toward the objects of their desires in the directions which present to them the fewest obstacles. The process of transfer which commerce presupposes, supplies another series of examples. So long as the forces to be overcome in procuring any necessary of life in the district where it is consumed, are less than the forces to be overcome in procuring it from an adjacent district, exchange does not take place. But when the adjacent district produces it with an economy that is not outbalanced by cost of transit—when the distance is so small and the route so easy that the labor of conveyance plus the labor of production is less than the labor of production in the consuming district, transfer commences. Movement in the direction of least resistance is also seen in the establishment of the channels along which intercourse takes place. At the outset, when goods are carried on the backs of men and horses, the paths chosen are those which combine shortness with levelness and freedom from obstacles—those which are achieved with the smallest exertion. And in the subsequent formation of each highway, the course taken is that which deviates horizontally from a straight line so far only as is needful to avoid vertical deviations entailing greater labor in draught. The smallest total of obstructive forces determines the route, even in seemingly exceptional cases; as where a detour is made to avoid the opposition of a landowner. All subsequent improvements, ending in macadamized roads, canals, and railways, which reduce the antagonism of friction and gravity to a minimum, exemplify the same truth. After there comes to be a choice of roads between one point and another, we still see that the road chosen is that along which the cost of transit is the least: cost being the measure of resistance. Even where, time being a consideration, the more expensive route is followed, it is so because the loss of time involves loss of force. When, division of labor having been carried to a considerable extent and means of communication made easy, there arises a marked localization of industries, the relative growths of the populations devoted to them may be interpreted on the same principle. The influx of people to each industrial centre, as well as the rate of multiplication of those already inhabiting it, is determined by the payment for labor; that is—by the quantity of commodities which a given amount of effort will obtain. To say that artisans flock to places where, in consequence of facilities for production, an extra proportion of produce can be given in the shape of wages; is to say that they flock to places where there are the smallest obstacles to the support of themselves and families. Hence, the rapid increase of number which occurs in such places, is really a social growth at points where the opposing forces are the least.

Nor is the law less clearly to be traced in those functional changes daily going on. The flow of capital into businesses yielding the largest returns; the buying in the cheapest market and selling in the dearest; the introduction of more economical modes of manufacture; the development of better agencies for distribution; and all those variations in the currents of trade that are noted in our newspapers and telegrams from hour to hour; exhibit movement taking place in directions where it is met by the smallest total of opposing forces. For if we analyze each of these changes— if instead of interest on capital we read surplus of products

which remains after maintenance of laborers; if we so interpret large interest or large surplus to imply labor expended
with the greatest results; and if labor expended with the
greatest results means muscular action so directed as to
evade obstacles as far as possible; we see that all these
commercial phenomena are complicated motions set up
along lines of least resistance.

Objections of two opposite kinds will perhaps be made
to these sociological applications of the law. By some it
may be said that the term force as here used, is used metaphorically—that to speak of men as *impelled* in certain directions by certain desires, is a figure of speech and not the
statement of a physical fact. The reply is, that the foregoing illustrations are to be interpreted literally, and that
the processes described *are* physical ones. The pressure of
hunger is an actual force—a sensation implying some state
of nervous tension; and the muscular action which the
sensation prompts is really a discharge of it in the shape
of bodily motion—a discharge which, on analyzing the
mental acts involved, will be found to follow lines of least
resistance. Hence the motions of a society whose members
are impelled by this or any other desire, are actually, and
not metaphorically, to be understood in the manner shown.
An opposite objection may possibly be, that the several
illustrations given are elaborated truisms; and that the law
of direction of motion being once recognized, the fact that
social movements, in common with all others, must conform
to it, follows inevitably. To this it may be rejoined, that
a mere abstract assertion that social movements must do
this, would carry no conviction to the majority; and that
it is needful to show *how* they do it. For social phenomena
to be unified with phenomena of simpler kinds, it is requisite that such generalizations as those of political economy
shall be reduced to equivalent propositions expressed in
terms of force and motion.

Social movements of these various orders severally conform to the two derivative principles named at the outset.

In the first place we may observe how, once set up in given directions, such movements, like all others, tend to continue in these directions. A commercial mania or panic, a current of commodities, a social custom, a political agitation, or a popular delusion, maintains its course for a long time after its original source has ceased; and requires antagonistic forces to arrest it. In the second place it is to be noted that in proportion to the complexity of social forces is the tortuousness of social movements. The involved series of muscular contractions gone through by the artisan, that he may get the wherewithal to buy a loaf lying at the baker's next door, show us how extreme becomes the indirectness of motion when the agencies at work become very numerous—a truth still better illustrated by the more public social actions; as those which end in bringing a successful man of business, toward the close of his life, into Parliament.

§ 81. And now of the general truth set forth in this chapter, as of that dealt with in the last, let us ask—what is our ultimate evidence? Must we accept it simply as an empirical generalization? or may it be established as a corollary from a still deeper truth? The reader will anticipate the answer. We shall find it deducible from that datum of consciousness which underlies all science.

Suppose several tractive forces, variously directed, to be acting on a given body. By what is known among mathematicians as the composition of forces, there may be found for any two of these, a single force of such amount and direction as to produce on the body an exactly equal effect. If in the direction of each of them there be drawn a straight line, and if the lengths of these two straight lines be made proportionate to the amounts of the forces; and if from the end of each line there be drawn a line parallel to the other, so as to complete a parallelogram; then the diagonal of this parallelogram represents the amount and direction of a force that is equivalent to the two. Such a resultant force, as it is called, may be found for any pair of forces throughout the group. Similarly, for any pair of such resultants a single resultant may be found. And by repeating this course, all of them may be reduced to two. If these two are equal and opposite—that is, if there is no line of greatest traction, motion does not take place. If they are opposite but not equal, motion takes place in the direction of the greater. And if they are neither equal nor opposite, motion takes place in the direction of their resultant. For in either of these cases there is an unantagonized force in one direction. And this residuary force that is not neutralized by an opposing one, must move the body in the direction in which it is acting. To assert the contrary is to assert that a force can be expended without effect—without generating an equivalent force; and by so implying that force can cease to exist, this involves a denial of the persistence of force. It needs scarcely be added that if in place of tractions we take resistances, the argument equally holds; and that it holds also where both tractions and resistances are concerned. Thus the law that motion follows the line of greatest traction, or the line of least resistance, or the resultant of the two, is a necessary deduction from that primordial truth which transcends proof.

Reduce the proposition to its simplest form, and it becomes still more obviously consequent on the persistence of force. Suppose two weights suspended over a pulley or from the ends of an equal-armed lever; or better still—suppose two men pulling against each other. In such cases we say that the heavier weight will descend, and that the stronger man will draw the weaker toward him. But now, if we are asked how we know which is the heavier weight or the stronger man; we can only reply that it is the one producing motion in the direction of its pull. Our only evidence of excess of force is the movement it produces. But if of two opposing tractions we can know one as greater than the other only by the motion it generates in its own direction, then the assertion that motion occurs in the direction of greatest traction is a truism. When, going a step further back, we seek a warrant for the assumption that of the two conflicting forces, that is the greater which produces motion in its own direction, we find no other than the consciousness that such part of the greater force as is unneutralized by the lesser, must produce its effect—the consciousness that this residuary force cannot disappear, but must manifest itself in some equivalent change—the consciousness that force is persistent. Here, too, as before, it may be remarked that no amount of varied illustrations, like those of which this chapter mainly consists, can give greater certainty to the conclusion thus immediately drawn from the ultimate datum of consciousness. For in all cases, as in the simple ones just given, we can identify the greatest force only by the resulting motion. It is impossible for us ever to get evidence of the occurrence of motion in any other direction that that of the greatest force; since our measure of relative greatness among forces is their relative power of generating motion. And clearly, while the comparative greatness of forces is thus determined, no multiplication of instances can add certainty to a law of direction of movement which follows immediately from the persistence of force.

From this same primordial truth, too, may be deduced the principle that motion once set up along any line, becomes itself a cause of subsequent motion along that line. The mechanical axiom that, if left to itself, matter moving in any direction will continue in that direction with undiminished velocity, is but an indirect assertion of the persistence of force; since it is an assertion that the force manifested in the transfer of a body along a certain length of a certain line in a certain time, cannot disappear without producing some equal manifestation—a manifestation which, in the absence of conflicting forces, must be a further transfer in the same direction at the same velocity. In the case of matter traversing matter the like inference is necessitated. Here indeed the actions are much more complicated. A liquid that follows a certain channel through or over a solid, as water along the Earth's surface, loses part of its motion in the shape of heat, through friction and collision with the matters forming its bed. A further amount of its motion may be absorbed in overcoming forces which it liberates; as when it loosens a mass which falls into, and blocks up, its channel. But after these deductions by transformation into other modes of force, any further deduction from the motion of the water is at the expense of a reaction on the channel, which by so much diminishes its obstructive power: such reaction being shown in the motion acquired by the detached portions which are carried away. The cutting out of river-courses is a perpetual illustration of this truth. Still more involved is the case of motion passing through matter by impulse from part to part; as a nervous discharge through animal tissue. Some chemical change may be wrought along the route traversed, which may render it less fit than before for conveying a current. Or the motion may itself be in part metamorphosed into some obstructive form of force; as in metals, the conducting power of which is, for the time, decreased by the heat which the passage of electricity itself generates. The real question is, however, what structural modification, if any, is produced throughout the matter traversed, apart from *incidental* disturbing forces—apart from everything but the *necessary* resistance of the matter: that, namely, which results from the inertia of its units. If we confine our attention to that part of the motion which, escaping transformation, continues its course, then it is a corollary from the persistence of force that as much of this remaining motion as is taken up in changing the positions of the units, must leave these by so much less able to obstruct subsequent motion in the same direction.

Thus in all the changes heretofore and at present displayed by the Solar System; in all those that have gone on and are still going on in the Earth's crust; in all processes of organic development and function; in all mental actions and the effects they work on the body; and in all modifications of structure and activity in societies; the implied movements are of necessity determined in the manner above set forth. Wherever we see motion, its direction must be that of the greatest force. Wherever we see the greatest force to be acting in a given direction, in that direction motion must ensue. These are not truths holding only of one class, or of some classes, of phenomena; but they are among those universal truths by which our knowledge of phenomena in general is unified.

CHAPTER X

THE RHYTHM OF MOTION

§ 82. WHEN the pennant of a vessel lying becalmed first shows the coming breeze, it does so by gentle undulations that travel from its fixed to its free end. Presently the sails begin to flap; and their blows against the mast increase in rapidity as the breeze rises. Even when, being fully bellied out, they are in great part steadied by the strain of the yards and cordage, their free edges tremble with each stronger gust. And should there come a gale, the jar that is felt on laying hold of the shrouds shows that the rigging vibrates; while the rush and whistle of the wind prove that in it, also, rapid undulations are generated. Ashore the conflict between the current of air and the things it meets results in a like rhythmical action. The leaves all shiver in the blast; each branch oscillates; and every exposed tree sways to and fro. The blades of grass and dried bents in the meadows, and still better the stalks in the neighboring cornfields, exhibit the same rising and falling movement. Nor do the more stable objects fail to do the like, though in a less manifest fashion; as witness the shudder that may be felt throughout a house during the paroxysms of a violent storm. Streams of water produce in opposing objects the same general effects as do streams of air. Submerged weeds growing in the middle of a brook undulate from end to end. Branches brought down by the last flood, and left entangled at the bottom where the current is rapid, are thrown into a state of up and down movement that is slow or quick in proportion as they are large or small; and where, as in great rivers like the Mississippi, whole trees are thus held, the name "sawyers," by which they are locally known, sufficiently describes the rhythm produced in them. Note again the effect of the antagonism between the current and its channel. In shallow places, where the action of the bottom on the water flowing over it is visible, we see a ripple produced—a series of undulations. And if we study the action and reaction going on between the moving fluid and its banks, we still find the principle illustrated, though in a different way. For in every rivulet, as in the mapped-out course of every great river, the bends of the stream from side to side throughout its tortuous course constitute a lateral undulation—an undulation so inevitable that even an artificially straightened channel is eventually changed into a serpentine one. Analogous phenomena may be observed where the water is stationary and the solid matter moving. A stick drawn laterally through the water with much force, proves by the throb which it communicates to the hand that it is in a state of vibration. Even where the moving body is massive, it only requires that great force should be applied to get a sensible effect of like kind: instance the screw of a screw-steamer, which instead of a smooth rotation falls into a rapid rhythm that sends a tremor through the whole vessel. The sound which results when a bow is drawn over a violin-string, shows us vibrations produced by the movement of a solid over a solid. In lathes and planing machines, the attempt to take off a thick shaving causes a violent jar of the whole apparatus, and the production of a series of waves on the iron or wood that is cut. Every boy in scraping his slate-pencil finds it scarcely possible to help making a ridged surface. If you roll a ball along the ground or over the ice, there is always more or less up and down movement—a movement that is visible while the velocity is considerable, but becomes too small and rapid to be seen by the unaided eye as the velocity diminishes. However smooth the rails, and however perfectly built the carriages, a railway train inevitably gets into oscillations, both lateral and vertical. Even where moving matter is suddenly arrested by collision, the law is still illustrated; for both the body striking and the body struck are made to tremble; and trembling is rhythmical movement. Little as we habitually observe it, it is yet certain that the impulses our actions impress from moment to moment on surrounding objects, are propagated through them in vibrations. It needs but to look through a telescope of high power, to be convinced that each pulsation of the heart gives a jar to the whole room. If we pass to motions of another order—those namely which take place in the ethereal medium—we still find the same thing. Every fresh discovery confirms the hypothesis that light consists of undulations. The rays of heat, too, are now found to have a like fundamental nature: their undulations differing from those of light only in their comparative lengths. Nor do the movements of electricity fail to furnish us with an illustration; though one of a different order. The northern aurora may often be observed to pulsate with waves of greater brightness; and the electric discharge through a vacuum shows us by its stratified appearance that the current is not uniform, but comes in gushes of greater and lesser intensity. Should it be said that at any rate there are some motions, as those of projectiles, which are not rhythmical, the reply is, that the exception is apparent only; and that these motions would be rhythmical if they were not interrupted. It is common to assert that the trajectory of a cannon ball is a parabola; and it is true that (omitting atmospheric resistance) the curve described differs so slightly from a parabola that it may practically be regarded as one. But, strictly speaking, it is a portion of an extremely eccentric ellipse, having the Earth's centre of gravity for its remoter focus; and but for its arrest by the substance of the Earth, the cannon ball would travel round that focus and return to the point whence it started; again to repeat this slow rhythm. Indeed, while seeming at first sight to do the reverse, the discharge of a cannon furnishes one of the best illustrations of the principle enunciated. The explosion produces violent undulations in the surrounding air. The whiz of the shot, as it flies toward its mark, is due to another series of atmospheric undulations. And the movement to and from the Earth's centre, which the cannon ball is beginning to perform, being checked by solid matter, is transformed into a rhythm of another order; namely, the vibration which the blow sends through neighboring bodies.[1]

Rhythm is very generally not simple but compound. There are usually at work various forces, causing undulations differing in rapidity; and hence it continually happens that besides the primary rhythms there are secondary rhythms, produced by the periodic coincidence and antagonism of the primary ones. Double, triple, and even quadruple rhythms, are thus generated. One of the simplest instances is afforded by what in acoustics are known as "beats": recurring intervals of sound and silence which are perceived when two notes of nearly the same pitch are struck together; and which are due to the alternate correspondence and antagonism of the atmospheric waves. In like manner the various phenomena due to what is called interference of light, severally result from the periodic agreement and disagreement of ethereal undulations—undulations which, by alternately intensifying and neutralizing each other, produce intervals of increased and diminished light. On the sea-shore may be noted sundry instances of compound rhythm. We have that of the tides, in which the daily rise and fall undergoes a fortnightly increase and decrease, due to the alternate coincidence and antagonism

---

[1] After having for some years supposed myself alone in the belief that all motion is rhythmical, I discovered that my friend Professor Tyndall also held this doctrine.

of the solar and lunar attractions. We have again that which is perpetually furnished by the surface of the sea: every large wave bearing smaller ones on its sides, and these still smaller ones; with the result that each flake of foam, along with the portion of water bearing it, undergoes minor ascents and descents of several orders while it is being raised and lowered by the greater billows. A quite different and very interesting example of compound rhythm, occurs in the little rills which, at low tide, run over the sand out of the shingle banks above. Where the channel of one of these is narrow, and the stream runs strongly, the sand at the bottom is raised into a series of ridges corresponding to the ripple of the water. On watching for a short time, it will be seen that these ridges are being raised higher and the ripple growing stronger; until at length, the action becoming violent, the whole series of ridges is suddenly swept away, the stream runs smoothly, and the process commences afresh. Instances of still more complex rhythms might be added; but they will come more appropriately in connection with the several kinds of cosmical changes, hereafter to be dealt with.

From the ensemble of the facts as above set forth, it will be seen that rhythm results wherever there is a conflict of forces not in equilibrium. If the antagonist forces at any point are balanced, there is rest; and in the absence of motion there can of course be no rhythm. But if instead of a balance there is an excess of force in one direction—if, as necessarily follows, motion is set up in that direction; then for that motion to continue uniformly in that direction, it is requisite that the moving matter should, notwithstanding its unceasing change of place, present unchanging relations to the sources of force by which its motion is produced and opposed. This however is impossible. Every further transfer through space must alter the ratio between the forces concerned—must increase or decrease the predominance of one force over the other—must prevent uniformity of movement. And if the movement cannot be uniform, then, in the absence of acceleration or retardation continued through infinite time and space (results which cannot be conceived) the only alternative is rhythm.

A secondary conclusion must not be omitted. In the last chapter we saw that motion is never absolutely rectilinear; and here it remains to be added that, as a consequence, rhythm is necessarily incomplete. A truly rectilinear rhythm can arise only when the opposing forces are in exactly the same line; and the probabilities against this are infinitely great. To generate a perfectly circular rhythm, the two forces concerned must be exactly at right angles to each other, and must have exactly a certain ratio; and against this the probabilities are likewise infinitely great. All other proportions and directions of the two forces will produce an ellipse of greater or less eccentricity. And when, as indeed always happens, above two forces are engaged, the curve described must be more complex; and cannot exactly repeat itself. So that in fact throughout nature, this action and reaction of forces never brings about a complete return to a previous state. Where the movement is much involved, and especially where it is that of some aggregate whose units are partially independent, anything like a regular curve is no longer traceable; we see nothing more than a general oscillation. And on the completion of any periodic movement, the degree in which the state arrived at differs from the state departed from, is usually marked in proportion as the influences at work are numerous.

§ 83. That spiral arrangement so general among the more diffused nebulæ—an arrangement which must be assumed by matter moving toward a centre of gravity through a resisting medium—shows us the progressive establishment of revolution, and therefore of rhythm, in those remote spaces which the nebulæ occupy. Double stars, moving round common centres of gravity in periods some of which are now ascertained, exhibit settled rhythmical actions in distant parts of our sidereal system. And another fact which, though of a different order, has a like general significance, is furnished by variable stars—stars which alternately brighten and fade.

The periodicities of the planets, satellites, and comets, are so familiar that it would be inexcusable to name them, were it not needful here to point out that they are so many grand illustrations of this general law of movement. But besides the revolutions of these bodies in their orbits (all more or less eccentric) and their rotations on their axes, the Solar System presents us with various rhythms of a less manifest and more complex kind. In each planet and satellite there is the revolution of the nodes—a slow change in the position of the orbit-plane, which after completing itself commences afresh. There is the gradual alteration in the length of the axis major of the orbit; and also of its eccentricity: both of which are rhythmical alike in the sense that they alternate between maxima and minima, and in the sense that the progress from one extreme to the other is not uniform, but is made with fluctuating velocity. Then, too, there is the revolution of the line of apsides, which in course of time moves round the heavens—not regularly, but through complex oscillations. And further we have variations in the directions of the planetary axes—that known as nutation, and that larger gyration which, in the case of the Earth, causes the precession of the equinoxes. These rhythms, already more or less compound, are compounded with each other. Such an instance as the secular acceleration and retardation of the moon, consequent on the varying eccentricity of the Earth's orbit, is one of the simplest. Another, having more important consequences, results from the changing direction of the axes of rotation in planets whose orbits are decidedly eccentric. Every planet, during a certain long period, presents more of its northern than of its southern hemisphere to the sun at the time of its nearest approach to him; and then again, during a like period, presents more of its southern hemisphere than of its northern—a recurring coincidence which, though causing in some planets no sensible alterations of climate, involves in the case of the Earth an epoch of 21,000 years, during which each hemisphere goes through a cycle of temperate seasons, and seasons that are extreme in their heat and cold. Nor is this all. There is even a variation of this variation. For the summers and winters of the whole Earth become more or less strongly contrasted, as the eccentricity of its orbit increases and decreases. Hence during increase of the eccentricity, the epochs of moderately contrasted seasons and epochs of strongly contrasted seasons, through which alternately each hemisphere passes, must grow more and more different in the degrees of their contrasts; and contrariwise during decrease of the eccentricity. So that in the quantity of light and heat which any portion of the Earth receives from the sun, there goes on a quadruple rhythm: that of day and night; that of summer and winter; that due to the changing position of the axis at perihelion and aphelion, taking 21,000 years to complete; and that involved by the variation of the orbit's eccentricity, gone through in millions of years.

§ 84. Those terrestrial processes whose dependence on the solar heat is direct, of course exhibit a rhythm that corresponds to the periodically changing amount of heat which each part of the Earth receives. The simplest, though the least obtrusive, instance is supplied by the magnetic variations. In these there is a diurnal increase and decrease, an annual increase and decrease, and a decennial increase and decrease; the latter answering to a period during which the solar spots become alternately abundant and scarce: besides which known variations there are probably others corresponding with the astronomical cycles just described. More obvious examples are furnished by the movements of the ocean and the atmosphere. Marine currents from the equator to the poles above, and from the poles to the equator beneath, show us an unceasing backward and forward motion throughout this vast mass of water—a motion varying in amount according to the seasons, and compounded with smaller like motions of local origin. The similarly-caused general currents in the air, have similar annual variations similarly modified. Irregular as they are in detail, we still see in the monsoons and other tropical atmospheric disturbances, or even in our own equinoctial gales and spring east winds, a periodicity sufficiently decided. Again, we have an alternation of times during which evaporation predominates with times during which condensation predominates: shown in the tropics by strongly marked rainy seasons and seasons of drought, and in the temperate zones by corresponding changes of which the periodicity, though less definite, is still traceable. The diffusion and precipitation of water, besides the slow alternations answering to different parts of the year, furnish us with examples of rhythm of a more rapid kind. During wet weather, lasting, let us say, over some weeks, the tendency to condense, though greater than the tendency to evaporate, does not show itself in continuous rain; but the period is made up of rainy days and days that are wholly or partially fair. Nor is it in this rude alternation only that the law is manifested. During any day throughout this wet weather a minor rhythm is traceable; and especially so when the tendencies to evaporate and to condense are nearly balanced. Among mountains this minor rhythm and its causes may be studied to great advantage. Moist winds, which do not precipitate their contained water in passing over the comparatively warm lowlands, lose so much heat when they reach the cold mountain peaks, that condensation rapidly takes place. Water, however, in passing from the gaseous to the fluid state, gives out a considerable amount of heat; and hence the resulting clouds are warmer than the air that precipitates them, and much warmer than the high rocky surfaces round which they fold themselves. Hence in the course of the storm, these high rocky surfaces are raised in temperature, partly by radiation from the enwrapping cloud, partly by contact of the falling rain-drops. Giving off more heat than before, they no longer lower so greatly the temperature of the air passing over them; and so cease to precipitate its contained water. The clouds break; the sky begins to clear; and a gleam of sunshine promises that the day is going to be fine. But the small supply of heat which the cold mountain's sides have received, is soon lost: especially when the dispersion of the clouds permits free radiation into space. Very soon, therefore, these elevated surfaces, becoming as cold as at first (or perhaps even colder in virtue of the evaporation set up), begin again to condense the vapor in the air above; and there comes another storm, followed by the same effects as before. In lowland regions this action and reaction is usually less conspicuous, because the contrast of temperatures is less marked. Even here, however, it may be traced; and that not only on showery days, but on days of continuous rain; for in these we do not see uniformity: always there are fits of harder and gentler rain that are probably caused as above explained.

Of course these meteorologic rhythms involve something corresponding to them in the changes wrought by wind and water on the Earth's surface. Variations in the quantities of sediment brought down by rivers that rise and fall with the seasons, must cause variations in the resulting strata— alternations of color or quality in the successive laminæ. Beds formed from the detritus of shores worn down and carried away by the waves, must similarly show periodic differences answering to the periodic winds of the locality. In so far as frost influences the rate of denudation, its recurrence is a factor in the rhythm of sedimentary deposits. And the geological changes produced by glaciers and icebergs must similarly have their alternating periods of greater and less intensity.

There is evidence also that modifications in the Earth's crust due to igneous action have a certain periodicity. Volcanic eruptions are not continuous but intermittent, and as far as the data enable us to judge, have a certain average rate of recurrence; which rate of recurrence is complicated by rising into epochs of greater activity and falling into epochs of comparative quiescence. So too is it with earthquakes and the elevations or depressions caused by them. At the mouth of the Mississippi, the alternation of strata gives decisive proof of successive sinkings of the surface, that have taken place at tolerably equal intervals. Everywhere, in the extensive groups of comfortable strata that imply small subsidences recurring with a certain average frequency, we see a rhythm in the action and reaction between the Earth's crust and its molten contents—a rhythm compounded with those slower ones shown in the termination of groups of strata, and the commencement of other groups not conformable to them. There is even reason for suspecting a geological periodicity that is immensely slower and far wider in its effects; namely, an alternation of those vast upheavals and submergences by which continents are produced where there were oceans, and oceans where there were continents. For supposing, as we may fairly do, that the Earth's crust is throughout of tolerably equal thickness, it is manifest that such portions of it as become most depressed below the average level, must have their inner surfaces most exposed to the currents of molten matter circulating within, and will therefore undergo a larger amount of what may be called igneous denudation; while, conversely the withdrawal of the inner surfaces from these currents where the Earth's crust is most elevated will cause a thickening more or less compensating the aqueous denudation going on externally. Hence those depressed areas over which the deepest oceans lie, being gradually thinned beneath and not covered by much sedimentary deposit above, will become areas of least resistance, and will then begin to yield to the upward pressure of the Earth's contents; whence will result, throughout such areas, long continued elevations, ceasing only when the reverse state of things has been brought about. Whether this speculation be well or ill founded, does not however affect the general conclusion. Apart from it we have sufficient evidence that geologic processes are rhythmical.

§ 85. Perhaps nowhere are the illustrations of rhythm so numerous and so manifest as among the phenomena of life. Plants do not, indeed, usually show us any decided periodicities, save those determined by day and night and by the seasons. But in animals we have a great variety of movements in which the alternation of opposite extremes goes on with all degrees of rapidity. The swallowing of food is effected by a wave of constriction passing along the œsophagus; its digestion is accompanied by a muscular action of the stomach that is also undulatory; and the peristaltic motion of the intestines is of like nature. The blood obtained from this food is propelled not in a uniform current but in pulses; and it is aerated by lungs that alternately contract and expand. All locomotion results from oscillating movements: even where it is apparently continuous, as in many minute forms, the microscope proves the vibration of cilia to be the agency by which the creature is moved smoothly forward.

Primary rhythms of the organic actions are compounded with secondary ones of longer duration. These various modes of activity have their recurring periods of increase and decrease. We see this in the periodic need for food, and in the periodic need for repose. Each meal induces a more rapid rhythmic action of the digestive organs; the pulsation of the heart is accelerated; and the inspirations become more frequent. During sleep, on the contrary, these several movements slacken. So that in the course of the twenty-four hours, those small undulations of which the different kinds of organic action are constituted, undergo one long wave of increase and decrease, complicated with several minor waves. Experiments have shown that there are still slower rises and falls of functional activity. Waste and assimilation are not balanced by every meal, but one or other maintains for some time a slight excess; so that a person in ordinary health is found to undergo an increase and decrease of weight during recurring intervals of tolerable equality. Besides these regular periods there are still longer and comparatively irregular ones; namely, those alternations of greater and less vigor, which even healthy people experience. So inevitable are these oscillations that even men in training cannot be kept stationary at their highest power, but when they have reached it begin to retrograde. Further evidence of rhythm in the vital movements is furnished by invalids. Sundry disorders are named from the intermittent character of their symptoms. Even where the periodicity is not very marked, it is mostly traceable. Patients rarely if ever get uniformly worse; and convalescents have usually their days of partial relapse or of less decided advance.

Aggregates of living creatures illustrate the general truth in other ways. If each species of organism be regarded as a whole, it displays two kinds of rhythm. Life as it exists in all the members of such species, is an extremely complex kind of movement, more or less distinct from the kinds of movement which constitute life in other species. In each individual of the species, this extremely complex kind of movement begins, rises to its climax, declines, and ceases in death. And every successive generation thus exhibits a wave of that peculiar activity characterizing the species as a whole. The other form of rhythm is to be traced in that variation of number which each tribe of animals and plants is ever undergoing. Throughout the unceasing conflict between the tendency of a species to increase and the antagonistic tendencies, there is never an equilibrium: one always predominates. In the case even of a cultivated plant or domesticated animal, where artificial means are used to maintain the supply at a uniform level, we still see that oscillations of abundance and scarcity cannot be avoided. And among the creatures uncared for by man, such oscillations are usually more marked. After a race of organisms has been greatly thinned by enemies or lack of food, its surviving members become more favorably circumstanced than usual. During the decline in their numbers their food has grown relatively more abundant; while their enemies have diminished from want of prey. The conditions thus remain for some time favorable to their increase; and they multiply rapidly. By and by their food is rendered relatively scarce, at the same time that their enemies have become more numerous; and the destroying influences being thus in excess, their number begins to diminish again. Yet one more rhythm, extremely slow in its action, may be traced in the phenomena of Life, contemplated under their most general aspect. The researches of paleontologists show that there have been going on, during the vast period of which our sedimentary rocks bear record, successive changes of organic forms. Species have appeared, become abundant, and then disappeared. Genera, at first constituted of but few species, have for a time gone on growing more multiform; and then have begun to decline in the number of their subdivisions: leaving at last but one or two representatives, or none at all. During longer epochs whole orders have thus arisen, culminated, and dwindled away. And even those wider divisions containing many orders have similarly undergone a gradual rise, a high tide, and a long-continued ebb. The stalked *Crinoidea,* for example, which, during the carboniferous epoch, became abundant, have almost disappeared: only a single species being extant. Once a large family of mollusks, the *Brachiopoda* have now become rare. The shelled Cephalopods, at one time dominant among the inhabitants of the ocean, both in number of forms and of individuals, are in our day nearly extinct. And after an "age of reptiles," there has come an age in which reptiles have been in great measure supplanted by mammals. Whether these vast rises and falls of different kinds of life ever undergo anything approaching to repetitions (which they may possibly do in correspondence with those vast cycles of elevation and subsidence that produce continents and oceans), it is sufficiently clear that Life on the Earth has not progressed uniformly, but in immense undulations.

§ 86. It is not manifest that the changes of consciousness are in any sense rhythmical. Yet here, too, analysis proves both that the mental state existing at any moment is not uniform, but is decomposable into rapid oscillations; and also that mental states pass through longer intervals of increasing and decreasing intensity.

Though while attending to any single sensation, or any group of related sensations constituting the consciousness of an object, we seem to remain for the time in a persistent and homogeneous condition of mind, a careful self-examination shows that this apparently unbroken mental state is in truth traversed by a number of minor states, in which various other sensations and perceptions are rapidly presented and disappear. From the admitted fact that thinking consists in the establishment of relations, it is a necessary corollary that the maintenance of consciousness in any one state to the entire exclusion of other states, would be a cessation of thought, that is, of consciousness. So that any seemingly continuous feeling, say of pressure, really consists of portions of that feeling perpetually recurring after the momentary intrusion of other feelings and ideas—quick thoughts concerning the place where it is felt, the external object producing it, its consequences, and other things suggested by association. Thus there is going on an extremely rapid departure from, and return to, that particular mental state which we regard as persistent. Besides the evidence of rhythm in consciousness which direct analysis thus affords, we may gather further evidence from the correlation between feeling and movement. Sensations and emotions expend themselves in producing muscular contractions. If a sensation or emotion were strictly continuous, there would be a continuous discharge along those motor nerves acted upon. But so far as experiments with arti-

ficial stimuli enable us to judge, a continuous discharge
along the nerve leading to a muscle does not contract it: a
broken discharge is required—a rapid succession of shocks.
Hence muscular contraction presupposes that rhythmic state
of consciousness which direct observation discloses. A much
more conspicuous rhythm, having longer waves, is seen during the outflow of emotion into dancing, poetry, and music.
The current of mental energy that shows itself in these
modes of bodily action, is not continuous, but falls into a
succession of pulses. The measure of a dance is produced
by the alternation of strong muscular contractions with
weaker ones; and, save in measures of the simplest order
such as are found among barbarians and children, this
alternation is compounded with longer rises and falls in
the degree of muscular excitement. Poetry is a form of
speech which results when the emphasis is regularly recurrent; that is, when the muscular effort of pronunciation has
definite periods of greater and less intensity—periods that
are complicated with others of like nature answering to the
successive verses. Music, in still more various ways, exemplifies the law. There are the recurring bars, in each
of which there is a primary and a secondary beat. There
is the alternate increase and decrease of muscular strain,
implied by the ascents and descents to the higher and
lower notes—ascents and descents composed of smaller
waves, breaking the rises and falls of the larger ones,
in a mode peculiar to each melody. And then we have,
further, the alternation of *piano* and *forte* passages. That
these several kinds of rhythm, characterizing æsthetic expression, are not, in the common sense of the word, artificial, but are intenser forms of an undulatory movement
habitually generated by feeling in its bodily discharge, is
shown by the fact that they are all traceable in ordinary
speech; which in every sentence has its primary and secondary emphases, and its cadence containing a chief rise
and fall complicated with subordinate rises and falls; and
which is accompanied by a more or less oscillatory action

of the limbs when the emotion is great. Still longer undulations may be observed by every one, in himself and in others, on occasions of extreme pleasure or extreme pain. Note, in the first place, that pain having its origin in bodily disorder, is nearly always perceptibly rhythmical. During hours in which it never actually ceases, it has its variations of intensity—fits or paroxysms; and then after these hours of suffering there usually come hours of comparative ease. Moral pain has the like smaller and larger waves. One possessed by intense grief does not utter continuous moans, or shed tears with an equable rapidity; but these signs of passion come in recurring bursts. Then after a time, during which such stronger and weaker waves of emotion alternate, there comes a calm—a time of comparative deadness; to which again succeeds another interval, when dull sorrow rises afresh into acute anguish, with its series of paroxysms. Similarly in great delight, especially as manifested by children who have its display less under control, there are visible variations in the intensity of feeling shown—fits of laughter and dancing about, separated by pauses in which smiles, and other slight manifestations of pleasure, suffice to discharge the lessened excitement. Nor are there wanting evidences of mental undulations greater in length than any of these—undulations which take weeks, or months, or years, to complete themselves. We continually hear of moods which recur at intervals. Very many persons have their epochs of vivacity and depression. There are periods of industry following periods of idleness; and times at which particular subjects or tastes are cultivated with zeal, alternating with times at which they are neglected. Respecting which slow oscillations, the only qualification to be made is, that being affected by numerous influences, they are comparatively irregular.

§ 87. In nomadic societies the changes of place, determined as they usually are by exhaustion or failure of the supply of food, are periodic; and in many cases show a recurrence answering to the seasons. Each tribe that has become in some degree fixed in its locality, goes on increasing, till, under the pressures of unsatisfied desires, there results migration of some part of it to a new region—a process repeated at intervals. From such excesses of population, and such successive waves of migration, come conflicts with other tribes; which are also increasing and tending to diffuse themselves. This antagonism, like all others, results not in a uniform motion, but in an intermittent one. War, exhaustion, recoil—peace, prosperity, and renewed aggression:—see here the alternation more or less discernible in the military activities of both savage and civilized nations. And irregular as is this rhythm, it is not more so than the different sizes of the societies, and the extremely involved causes of variation in their strengths, would lead us to anticipate.

Passing from external to internal changes, we meet with this backward and forward movement under many forms. In the currents of commerce it is especially conspicuous. Exchange during early times is almost wholly carried on at fairs, held at long intervals in the chief centres of population. The flux and reflux of people and commodities which each of these exhibits, becomes more frequent as national development leads to greater social activity. The more rapid rhythm of weekly markets begins to supersede the slow rhythm of fairs. And eventually the process of exchange becomes at certain places so active, as to bring about daily meetings of buyers and sellers—a daily wave of accumulation and distribution of cotton, or corn, or capital. If from exchange we turn to production and consumption, we see undulations, much longer indeed in their periods, but almost equally obvious. Supply and demand are never completely adapted to each other; but each of them, from time to time in excess, leads presently to an excess of the other. Farmers who have one season produced wheat very abundantly, are disgusted with the consequent low price; and next season, sowing a much smaller quantity, bring to market a deficient crop; whence follows a converse effect. Consumption undergoes parallel undulations that need not be specified. The balancing of supplies between different districts, too, entails analogous oscillations. A place at which some necessary of life is scarce, becomes a place to which currents of it are set up from other places where it is relatively abundant; and these currents from all sides lead to a wave of accumulation where they meet—a glut: whence follows a recoil—a partial return of the currents. But the undulatory character of these actions is perhaps best seen in the rises and falls of prices. These, given in numerical measures which may be tabulated and reduced to diagrams, shows us in the clearest manner how commercial movements are compounded of oscillations of various magnitudes. The price of consols or the price of wheat, as thus represented, is seen to undergo vast ascents and descents whose highest and lowest points are reached only in the course of years. These largest waves of variation are broken by others extending over periods of perhaps many months. On these again come others having a week or two's duration. And were the changes marked in greater detail, we should have the smaller undulations that take place each day, and the still smaller ones which brokers telegraph from hour to hour. The whole outline would show a complication like that of a vast ocean-swell, on whose surface there rise large billows, which themselves bear waves of moderate size, covered by wavelets, that are roughened by a minute ripple. Similar diagrammatic representations of births, marriages, and deaths, of disease, of crime, of pauperism, exhibit involved conflicts of rhythmical motions throughout society under these several aspects.

There are like characteristics in social changes of a more complex kind. Both in England and among Continental nations, the action and reaction of political progress have come to be generally recognized. Religion, besides its occasional revivals of smaller magnitude, has its long periods of exaltation and depression—generations of belief and self-mortification, following generations of indifference and laxity. There are poetical epochs, and epochs in which the sense of the beautiful seems almost dormant. Philosophy, after having been a while predominant, lapses for a long season into neglect; and then again slowly revives. Each science has its eras of deductive reasoning, and its eras when attention is chiefly directed to collecting and colligating facts. And how in such minor but more obtrusive phenomena as those of fashion, there are ever going on oscillations from one extreme to the other, is a trite observation.

As may be foreseen, social rhythms well illustrate the irregularity that results from combination of many causes. Where the variations are those of one simple element in national life, as the supply of a particular commodity, we do indeed witness a return, after many involved movements, to a previous condition—the price may become what it was before: implying a like relative abundance. But where the action is one into which many factors enter, there is never a recurrence of exactly the same state. A political reaction never brings round just the old form of things. The rationalism of the present day differs widely from the rationalism of the last century. And though fashion from time to time revives extinct types of dress, these always reappear with decided modifications.

§ 88. The universality of this principle suggests a question like that raised in foregoing cases. Rhythm being manifested in all forms of movement, we have reason to suspect that it is determined by some primordial condition to action in general. The tacit implication is that it is deducible from the persistence of force. This we shall find to be the fact.

When the prong of a tuning-fork is pulled on one side by the finger, a certain extra tension is produced among its cohering particles; which resist any force that draws them out of their state of equilibrium. As much force as the finger exerts in pulling the prong aside, so much opposing force is brought into play among the cohering particles. Hence, when the prong is liberated, it is urged back by a force equal to that used in deflecting it. When, therefore, the prong reaches its original position, the force impressed on it during its recoil, has generated in it a corresponding amount of momentum—an amount of momentum nearly equivalent, that is, to the force originally impressed (nearly, we must say, because a certain portion has gone in communicating motion to the air, and a certain other portion has been transformed into heat). This momentum carries the prong beyond the position of rest, nearly as far as it was originally drawn in the reverse direction; until at length, being gradually used up in producing an opposing tension among the particles, it is all lost. The opposing tension into which the expended momentum has been transformed, then generates a second recoil; and so on continually—the vibration eventually ceasing only because at each movement a certain amount of force goes in creating atmospheric and ethereal undulations. Now it needs but to contemplate this repeated action and reaction, to see that it is, like every action and reaction, a consequence of the persistence of force. The force exerted by the finger in bending the prong cannot disappear. Under what form then does it exist? It exists under the form of that cohesive tension which it has generated among the particles. This cohesive tension cannot cease without an equivalent result. What is its equivalent result? The momentum generated in the prong while being carried back to its position of rest. This momentum too—what becomes of it? It must either continue as momentum, or produce some correlative force of equal amount. It cannot continue as momentum, since change of place is resisted by the cohesion of the parts; and thus it gradually disappears by being transformed into tension among these parts. This is retransformed into the equivalent momentum; and so on continuously. If instead of motion that is directly antagonized by the cohesion of matter, we consider motion through space, the same truth presents itself under another form. Though here no opposing force seems at work, and therefore no cause of rhythm is apparent, yet its own accumulated momentum must eventually carry the moving body beyond the body attracting it; and so must become a force at variance with that which generated it. From this conflict, rhythm necessarily results as in the foregoing case. The force embodied as momentum in a given direction, cannot be destroyed; and if it eventually disappears, it reappears in the reaction on the retarding body; which begins afresh to draw the now arrested mass back from its aphelion. The only conditions under which there could be absence of rhythm—the only conditions, that is, under which there could be a continuous motion through space in the same straight line forever, would be the existence of an infinity void of everything but the moving body. And neither of these conditions can be represented in thought. Infinity is inconceivable; and so also is a motion which never had a commencement in some pre-existing source of power.

Thus, then, rhythm is a necessary characteristic of all motion. Given the co-existence everywhere of antagonist forces—a postulate which, as we have seen, is necessitated by the form of our experience—and rhythm is an inevitable corollary from the persistence of force.

[NOTE.—In the "Edinburgh Review" for January, 1884, there was an antagonistic criticism of this work. The writer of the criticism, Lord Grimthorpe, made much of the exception furnished by non-periodic comets to the law above set forth. I was about to admit this exception when, on looking into the matter, I found no need for doing so. Though five or six cometary orbits are said to be hyperbolic, yet, as I learn from one who has paid special attention to comets (having tabulated the directions of their aphelia), "no such orbit has, I believe, been computed for a well-observed comet." Hence the probability that all the orbits are ellipses is overwhelming. Ellipses and hyperbolas have countless varieties of forms, but there is only one form of parabola; or, to speak literally, all parabolas are similar, while there are infinitely numerous dissimilar ellipses and dissimilar hyperbolas. Consequently, anything coming to the Sun from a great distance must have one exact amount of proper motion to produce a parabola: all other amounts would give hyperbolas or ellipses. And if there are no hyperbolic orbits, then it is infinity to one that all the orbits are elliptical.]

CHAPTER XI

§ 89. LET us pause a while to consider how far the contents of the foregoing chapters go toward forming a body of knowledge such as was defined at the outset as constituting Philosophy.

In respect of its generality, the proposition enunciated and exemplified in each chapter, is of the required kind—is a proposition transcending those class-limits which Science, as currently understood, recognizes. "The Indestructibility of Matter" is a truth not belonging to mechanics more than to chemistry, a truth assumed alike by molecular physics and the physics that deals with sensible masses, a truth which the astronomer and the biologist equally take for granted. Not merely do those divisions of Science which deal with the movements of celestial and terrestrial bodies postulate "The Continuity of Motion," but it is no less postulated in the physicist's investigations into the phenomena of light and heat, and is tacitly, if not avowedly, implied in the generalizations of the higher sciences. So, too, "The Persistence of Force," involved in each of the preceding propositions, is co-extensive with them, as is also its corollary, "The Persistence of Relations among Forces." These are not truths of a high generality, but they are universal truths. Passing to the deductions drawn from them, we see the same thing. That force is transformable, and that between its correlates there exist quantitative equivalences, are ultimate facts not to be classed with those of mechanics, or thermology, or electricity, or magnetism; but they are illustrated throughout phenomena of every order, up to those of mind and society. Similarly, the law that motion follows the line of least resistance or the line of greatest traction or the resultant of the two, we found to be an all-pervading law; conformed to alike by each planet in its orbit, and by the moving matters, aërial, liquid, and solid, on its surface—conformed to no less by every organic movement and process than by every inorganic movement and process. And so likewise, in the chapter just closed, it has been shown that rhythm is exhibited universally, from the slow gyrations of double stars down to the inconceivably rapid oscillations of molecules—from such terrestrial changes as those of recurrent glacial epochs and gradually alternating elevations and subsidences, down to those of the winds and tides and waves; and is no less conspicuous in the functions of living organisms, from the pulsations of the heart up to the paroxysms of the emotions.

Thus these truths have the character which constitutes them parts of Philosophy, properly so called. They are truths which unify concrete phenomena belonging to all divisions of Nature; and so must be components of that complete, coherent conception of things which Philosophy seeks.

§ 90. But now what parts do these truths play in forming such a conception? Does any one of them singly convey an idea of the Cosmos: meaning by this word the totality of the manifestations of the Unknowable? Do all of them taken together yield us an adequate idea of this kind? Do they even when thought of in combination compose anything like such an idea? To each of these questions the answer must be—No.

Neither these truths nor any other such truths, separately or jointly, constitute that integrated knowledge in which only Philosophy finds its goal. It has been supposed by one thinker that when Science has succeeded in reducing all more complex laws to some most simple law, as of molecular action, knowledge will have reached its limit. Another authority has tacitly asserted that all minor facts are so merged in the major fact that the force everywhere in action is nowhere lost, that to express this is to express "the constitution of the universe." But either conclusion implies a misapprehension of the problem.

For these are all analytical truths, and no analytical truth—no number of analytical truths—will make up that synthesis of thought which alone can be an interpretation of the synthesis of things. The decomposition of phenomena into their elements, is but a preparation for understanding phenomena in their state of composition, as actually manifested. To have ascertained the laws of the factors is not at all to have ascertained the laws of their co-operation. The question is, not how any factor, Matter or Motion or Force, behaves by itself, or under some imagined simple conditions; nor is it even how one factor behaves under the complicated conditions of actual existence. The thing to be expressed is the joint product of the factors under all its various aspects. Only when we can formulate the total process, have we gained that knowledge of it which Philosophy aspires to. A clear comprehension of this matter is important enough to justify some further exposition.

§ 91. Suppose a chemist, a geologist, and a biologist, have given the deepest explanations furnished by their respective sciences, of the processes going on in a burning candle, in a region changed by earthquake, and in a growing plant. To the assertion that their explanations are not the deepest possible, they will probably rejoin—"What would you have? What remains to be said of combustion when light and heat and the dissipation of substance have all been traced down to the liberation of molecular motion as their common cause? When all the actions accompanying an earthquake are explained as consequent upon the slow loss of the Earth's internal heat, how is it possible to go lower? When the influence of light on the oscillations of molecules has been proved to account for vegetal growth, what is the imaginable further rationale?

You ask for a synthesis. You say that knowledge does not end in the resolution of phenomena into the actions of certain factors, each conforming to ascertained laws; but that the laws of the factors having been ascertained, there comes the chief problem—to show how from their joint action result the phenomena in all their complexity. Well, do not the above interpretations satisfy this requirement? Do we not, starting with the molecular motions of the elements concerned in combustion, build up synthetically an explanation of the light, and the heat, and the produced gases, and the movements of the produced gases? Do we not, setting out from the still-continued radiation of its heat, construct by synthesis a clear conception of the Earths' nucleus as contracting, its crust as collapsing, as becoming shaken and fissured and contorted and burst through by lava? And is it not the same with the chemical changes and accumulation of matter in the growing plant"?

To all which the reply is, that the ultimate interpretation to be reached by Philosophy, is a universal synthesis comprehending and consolidating such special syntheses. The synthetic explanations which Science gives, even up to the most general, are more or less independent of one another. Though they may have like elements in them, they are not united by the likeness of their essential structures. Is it to be supposed that in the burning candle, in the quaking Earth, and in the organism that is increasing, the processes as wholes are unrelated to one another? If it is admitted that each of the factors concerned always operates in conformity to a law, is it to be concluded that their co-operation conforms to no law? These various changes, artificial and natural, organic and inorganic, which for convenience' sake we distinguish, are not from the highest point of view to be distinguished; for they are all changes going on in the same Cosmos, and forming parts of one vast transformation. The play of forces is essentially the same in principle throughout the whole region explored by our intelligence; and though, varying infinitely in their proportions and combinations, they work out results everywhere more or less different, and often seeming to have no kinship, yet there cannot but be among these results a fundamental community. The question to be answered is—What is the common element in the histories of all concrete processes?

§ 92. To resume, then, we have now to seek a law of composition of phenomena, co-extensive with those laws of their components set forth in the foregoing chapters. Having seen that matter is indestructible, motion continuous, and force persistent—having seen that forces are everywhere undergoing transformation, and that motion, always following the line of least resistance, is invariably rhythmic, it remains to discover the similarly-invariable formula expressing the combined consequences of the actions thus separately formulated.

What must be the general character of such a formula? It must be one that specifies the course of the changes undergone by both the matter and the motion. Every transformation implies rearrangement of component parts; and a definition of it, while saying what has happened to the sensible or insensible portions of substance concerned, must also say what has happened to the movements, sensible or insensible, which the rearrangement of parts implies. Further, unless the transformation always goes on in the same way and at the same rate, the formula must specify the conditions under which it commences, ceases, and is reversed.

The law we seek, therefore, must be the law of *the continuous redistribution of matter and motion*. Absolute rest and permanence do not exist. Every object, no less than the aggregate of all objects, undergoes from instant to instant some alteration of state. Gradually, or quickly it is receiving motion or losing motion, while some or all of its parts are simultaneously changing their relations to one another. And the question to be answered is—What dynamic principle, true of the metamorphosis as a whole and in its details, expresses these ever-changing relations?

This chapter has served its purpose if it has indicated the nature of the ultimate problem. The discussion on which we are now to enter, may fitly open with a new presentation of this problem, carrying with it the clear implication that a Philosophy, rightly so-called, can come into existence only by solving the problem.

CHAPTER XII

EVOLUTION AND DISSOLUTION

§ 93. An entire history of anything must include its appearance out of the imperceptible and its disappearance into the imperceptible. Be it a single object or the whole universe, any account which begins with it in a concrete form, or leaves off with it in a concrete form, is incomplete; since there remains an era of its knowable existence undescribed and unexplained. Admitting, or rather asserting, that knowledge is limited to the phenomenal, we have, by implication, asserted that the sphere of knowledge is co-extensive with the phenomenal—co-extensive with all modes of the Unknowable that can affect consciousness. Hence, wherever we now find Being so conditioned as to act on our senses, there arise the questions—how came it thus conditioned? and how will it cease to be thus conditioned? Unless on the assumption that it acquired a sensible form at the moment of perception, and lost its sensible form the moment after perception, it must have had an antecedent existence under this sensible form, and will have a subsequent existence under this sensible form. These preceding and succeeding existences under sensible forms, are possible subjects of knowledge; and knowledge has obviously not reached its limits until it has united the past, present and future histories into a whole.

The sayings and doings of daily life imply more or less such knowledge, actual or potential, of states which have gone before and of states which will come after; and, indeed, the greater part of our knowledge involves these elements. Knowing any man personally, implies having before seen him under a shape much the same as his present shape; and knowing him simply as a man, implies the inferred antecedent states of infancy, childhood and youth. Though the man's future is not known specifically, it is known generally: the facts that he will die and that his body will decay, are facts which complete in outline the changes to be hereafter gone through by him. So with all the objects around. The pre-existence under concrete forms of the woollens, silks, and cottons we wear, we can trace some distance back. We are certain that our furniture consists of matter which was aggregated by trees within these few generations. Even of the stones composing the walls of the house, we are able to say that years or centuries ago, they formed parts of some stratum imbedded in the earth. Moreover, respecting the hereafter of the wearable fabrics, the furniture, and the walls, we can assert thus much, that they are all in process of decay, and in periods of various lengths will lose their present coherent shapes. This general information which all men gain concerning the past and future careers of surrounding things, Science has extended, and continues unceasingly to extend. To the biography of the individual man, it adds an intra-uterine biography beginning with him as a microscopic germ; and it follows out his ultimate changes until it finds his body resolved into the gaseous products of decomposition. Not stopping short at the sheep's back and the caterpillar's cocoon, it identifies in wool and silk the nitrogenous matters absorbed by the sheep and the caterpillar from plants. The substance of a plant's leaves, in common with the wood from which furniture is made, it again traces back to the vegetal assimilation of gases from the air and of certain minerals from the soil. And inquiring whence came the stratum of stone that was quarried to build the house, it finds that this was once a loose sediment deposited in an estuary or on the sea bottom.

If, then, the past and the future of each object, is a sphere of possible knowledge; and if intellectual progress consists largely, if not mainly, in widening our acquaintance with this past and this future; it is obvious that we have not acquired all the information within the grasp of our intelligence until we can, in some way or other, express the whole past and the whole future of each object and the aggregate of objects. Usually able, as we are, to say of any visible tangible thing how it came to have its present shape and consistence; we are fully possessed with the conviction that, setting out abruptly as we do with some substance which already had a concrete form, our history is incomplete: the thing had a history preceding the state with which we started. Hence our Theory of Things, considered individually or in their totality, is confessedly imperfect so long as any past or future portions of their sensible existences are unaccounted for.

May it not be inferred that Philosophy has to formulate this passage from the imperceptible into the perceptible, and again from the perceptible into the imperceptible? Is it not clear that this general law of the redistribution of matter and motion, which we lately saw is required to unify the various kinds of changes, must also be one that unifies the successive changes which sensible existences, separately and together, pass through? Only by some formula combining these characters can knowledge be reduced to a coherent whole.

§ 94. Already in the foregoing paragraphs the outline of such a formula is foreshadowed. Already in recognizing the fact that Science, tracing back the genealogies of various objects, finds their components were once in diffused states, and, pursuing their histories forward, finds diffused states will be again assumed by them, we have recognized the fact that the formula must be one comprehending the two opposite processes of concentration and diffusion. And already in thus describing the general nature of the formula, we have approached a specific expression of it. The change from a diffused, imperceptible state, to a concentrated, perceptible state, is an integration of matter and concomitant dissipation of motion; and the change from a concentrated, perceptible state, to a diffused, imperceptible state, is an absorption of motion and concomitant disintegration of matter. These are truisms. Constituent parts cannot aggregate without losing some of their relative motion; and they cannot separate without more relative motion being given to them. We are not concerned here with any motion which the components of a mass have with respect to other masses: we are concerned only with the motion they have with respect to one another. Confining our attention to this internal motion, and to the matter possessing it, the axiom which we have to recognize is that a progressing consolidation involves a decrease of internal motion; and that increase of internal motion involves a progressing unconsolidation.

When taken together, the two opposite processes thus formulated constitute the history of every sensible existence, under its simplest form. Loss of motion and consequent integration, eventually followed by gain of motion and consequent disintegration—see here a statement comprehensive of the entire series of changes passed through: comprehensive in an extremely general way, as any statement which holds of sensible existences at large must be; but still, comprehensive in the sense that all the changes gone through fall within it. This will probably be thought too sweeping an assertion; but we shall quickly find it justified.

§ 95. For here we have to note the further all-important fact, that every change undergone by every sensible existence, is a change in one or other of these two opposite directions. Apparently an aggregate which has passed out of some originally discrete state into a concrete state, thereafter remains for an indefinite period without undergoing further integration, and without beginning to disintegrate. But this is untrue. All things are growing or decaying, accumulating matter or wearing away, integrating or disintegrating. All things are varying in their temperatures, contracting or expanding, integrating or disintegrating. Both the quantity of matter contained in an aggregate, and the quantity of motion contained in it, increase or decrease; and increase or decrease of either is an advance toward greater diffusion or greater concentration. Continued losses or gains of substance, however slow, imply ultimate disappearance or indefinite enlargement; and losses or gains of the insensible motion we call heat, will, if continued, produce complete integration or complete disintegration. The sun's rays falling on a cold mass, augmenting the molecular motions throughout it, and causing it to occupy more space, are beginning a process which if carried far will disintegrate the mass into liquid, and if carried further will disintegrate the liquid into gas; and the diminution of bulk which a volume of gas undergoes as it parts with some of its molecular motion, is a diminution which, if the loss of molecular motion proceeds, will presently be followed by liquefaction and eventually by solidification. And since there is no such thing as an absolutely constant temperature, the necessary inference is that every aggregate is at every moment progressing toward either greater concentration or greater diffusion.

Not only does all change consisting in the addition or subtraction of matter come under this head; and not only does this head include all change called thermal expansion or contraction; but it is also, in a general way, comprehensive of all change distinguished as transposition. Every internal redistribution which leaves the component molecules or the constituent portions of a mass differently placed with respect to one another, is sure to be at the same time a progress toward integration or toward disintegration—is sure to have altered in some degree the total space occupied. For when the parts have been moved relatively to one another, the chances are infinity to one that their average distances from the common centre of the aggregate are no longer the same. Hence whatever be the special character of the redistribution—be it that of superficial accretion or detachment, be it that of general expansion or contraction, be it that of rearrangement, it is always an advance in integration or disintegration. It is always this, though it may at the same time be something further.

§ 96. A general idea of these universal actions under their simplest aspects having been obtained, we may now consider them under certain relatively complex aspects. Changes toward greater concentration or greater diffusion, nearly always proceed after a manner much more involved than that above described. Thus far we have supposed one or other of the two opposite processes to go on alone—we have supposed an aggregate to be either losing motion and integrating or gaining motion and disintegrating. But though it is true that every change furthers one or other of these processes, it is not true that either process is ever wholly unqualified by the other. For each aggregate is at all times both gaining motion and losing motion.

Every mass from a grain of sand to a planet, radiates heat to other masses, and absorbs heat radiated by other masses; and in so far as it does the one it becomes integrated, while in so far as it does the other it becomes disintegrated. Ordinarily in inorganic objects this double process works but unobtrusive effects. Only in a few cases, among which that of a cloud is the most familiar, does the conflict produce rapid and marked transformations. One of these floating bodies of vapor expands and dissipates, if the amount of molecular motion it receives from the Sun and Earth, exceeds that which it loses by radiation into space and toward adjacent surfaces; while, contrariwise, if, drifting over cold mountain tops, it radiates to them much more heat than it receives, the loss of molecular motion is followed by increasing integration of the vapor, ending in the aggregation of it into liquid and the fall of rain. Here, as elsewhere, the integration or the disintegration is a differential result.

In living aggregates, and more especially those classed as animals, these conflicting processes go on with great activity under several forms. There is not merely what we may call the passive integration of matter, that results in inanimate objects from simple molecular attractions; but there is an active integration of it under the form of food. In addition to that passive superficial disintegration which inanimate objects suffer from external agents, animals produce in themselves active internal disintegration, by absorbing such agents into their substance. While, like inorganic aggregates, they passively give off and receive motion, they are also active absorbers of motion latent in food, and active expenders of that motion. But notwithstanding this complication of the two processes, and the immense exaltation of the conflict between them, it remains true that there is always a differential progress toward either integration or disintegration. During the earlier part of the cycle of changes, the integration predominates—there goes on what we call growth. The middle part of the cycle is usually characterized, not by equilibrium between the integrating and disintegrating processes, but by alternate excesses of them. And the cycle closes with a period in which the disintegration, beginning to predominate, eventually puts a stop to integration, and undoes what integration had originally done. At no moment are assimilation and waste so balanced that no increase or decrease of mass is going on. Even in cases where one part is growing while other parts are dwindling, and even in cases where different parts are differently exposed to external sources of motion so that some are expanding while others are contracting, the truth still holds. For the chances are infinity to one against these opposite changes balancing one another; and if they do not balance one another, the aggregate as a whole is integrating or disintegrating.

Everywhere and to the last, therefore, the change at any moment going on forms a part of one or other of the two processes. While the general history of every aggregate is definable as a change from a diffused imperceptible state to a concentrated perceptible state, and again to a diffused imperceptible state; every detail of the history is definable as a part of either the one change or the other. This, then, must be that universal law of redistribution of matter and motion, which serves at once to unify the seemingly diverse groups of changes, as well as the entire course of each group.

§ 97. The processes thus everywhere in antagonism, and everywhere gaining now a temporary and now a more or less permanent triumph the one over the other, we call Evolution and Dissolution. Evolution under its simplest and most general aspect is the integration of matter and concomitant dissipation of motion; while Dissolution is the absorption of motion and concomitant disintegration of matter.

These titles are by no means all that is desirable; or rather we may say that while the last answers its purpose tolerably well, the first is open to grave objections. Evolution has other meanings, some of which are incongruous with, and some even directly opposed to, the meaning here given to it. The evolution of a gas is literally an absorption of motion and disintegration of matter, which is exactly the reverse of that which we here call Evolution is—that which we here call Dissolution. As ordinarily understood, to evolve is to unfold, to open and expand, to throw out, to emit; whereas, as we understand it, the act of evolving, though it implies increase of a concrete aggregate, and in so far an expansion of it, implies that its component matter has passed from a more diffused to a more concentrated state—has contracted. The antithetical word Involution would much more truly express the nature of the process; and would, indeed, describe better the secondary characters of the process which we shall have to deal with presently. We are obliged, however, notwithstanding the liabilities to confusion that must result from these unlike and even contradictory meanings, to use Evolution as antithetical to Dissolution. The word is now so widely recognized as signifying, not, indeed, the general process above described, but sundry of the most conspicuous varieties of it, and certain of its secondary but most remarkable accompaniments, that we cannot now substitute another word. All we can do is carefully to define the interpretation to be given to it.

While, then, we shall by Dissolution everywhere mean the process tacitly implied by its ordinary meaning—the absorption of motion and disintegration of matter; we shall everywhere mean by Evolution, the process which is always an integration of matter and dissipation of motion, but which, as we shall now see, is in most cases much more than this.

_____

CHAPTER XIII

SIMPLE AND COMPOUND EVOLUTION

§ 98. WHERE the only forces at work are those directly tending to produce aggregation or diffusion, the whole history of an aggregate will comprise no more than the approaches of its components toward their common centre and their recessions from their common centre. The process of Evolution, including nothing beyond what was described at the outset of the last chapter, will be simple.

Again, in cases where the forces which cause movements toward a common centre are greatly in excess of all other forces, any changes additional to those constituting aggregation will be comparatively insignificant—there will be integration scarcely at all modified by further kinds of redistribution.

Or if, because of the smallness of the mass to be integrated, or because of the little motion the mass receives from without in return for the motion it loses, the integration proceeds rapidly; there will similarly be wrought but insignificant effects on the integrating mass by incident forces, even though these are considerable.

But when, conversely, the integration, is but slow; either because the quantity of motion contained in the aggregate is relatively great; or because, though the quantity of motion which each part possesses is not relatively great, the large size of the aggregate prevents easy dissipation of the motion; or because, though motion is rapidly lost more motion is rapidly received; then, other forces will cause in the aggregate appreciable modifications. Along with the change constituting integration, there will take place supplementary changes. The Evolution, instead of being simple, will be compound.

The several propositions thus briefly enunciated require some explanation.

§ 99. So long as a body moves freely through space, every force that acts on it produces an equivalent in the shape of some change in its motion. No matter how high its velocity, the slightest lateral traction or resistance causes it to deviate from its line of movement—causes it to move toward the new source of traction or away from the new source of resistance, just as much as it would do had it no other motion. And the effect of the perturbing influence goes on accumulating in the ratio of the squares of the times during which its action continues uniform. This same body, however, will, if it is united in certain ways with other bodies, cease to be movable by small incident forces. When it is held fast by gravitation or cohesion, these small incident forces, instead of giving it some relative motion through space, are otherwise dissipated.

What here holds of masses, holds, in a qualified way, of the sensible parts of masses, and of molecules. As the sensible parts of a mass, and the molecules of a mass, are, by virtue of their aggregation, not perfectly free, it is not true of each of them, as of a body moving through space, that every incident force produces an equivalent change of position: part of the force goes in working other changes. But in proportion as the parts or the molecules are feebly bound together, incident forces effect marked rearrangements among them. At the one extreme, where the integration is so slight that the parts, sensible or insensible, are almost independent, they are almost completely amenable to every additional action; and along with the concentration going on there go on other redistributions. Contrariwise, where the parts have approached within such small distances that what we call the attraction of cohesion is great, additional actions, unless intense, cease to have much power to cause secondary rearrangements. The firmly-united parts no longer readily change their relative positions in obedience to small perturbing influences; but each small perturbing influence usually does little or nothing more than temporarily modify the insensible molecular motions.

How may we best express this difference in the most general terms? An aggregate that is widely diffused, or but little integrated, is an aggregate that contains a large quantity of motion—actual or potential or both. An aggregate that has become completely integrated or dense, is one that contains comparatively little motion: most of the motion its parts once had has been lost during the integration that has rendered it dense. Hence, other things equal, in proportion to the quantity of motion which an aggregate contains will be the quantity of secondary change in the arrangement of its parts that accompanies the primary change in their arrangement. Hence also, other things equal, in proportion to the time during which the internal motion is retained, will be the quantity of this secondary redistribution that accompanies the primary redistribution. It matters not how these conditions are fulfilled. Whether the internal motion continues great because the components are of a kind that will not readily aggregate, or because surrounding conditions prevent them from parting with their motion, or because the loss of their motion is impeded by the size of the aggregate they form, or because they directly or indirectly obtain more motion in place of that which they lose; it throughout remains true that much retained internal motion must render secondary redistributions facile, and that long retention of it must make possible an accumulation of such secondary redistributions. Conversely, the non-fulfilment of these conditions, however caused, entails opposite results. Be it that the components of the aggregate have special aptitudes to integrate quickly, or be it that the smallness of the aggregate formed of them permits the easy escape of their motion, or be it that they receive little or no motion in exchange for that which they part with; it alike holds that but little secondary redistribution can accompany the primary redistribution constituting their integration.

These abstract propositions will not be fully understood without illustrations. Let us, before studying simple and compound Evolution as thus determined, contemplate a few cases in which the quantity of internal motion is artificially changed, and note the effects on the rearrangement of parts.

§ 100. We may fitly begin with a familiar experience, introducing the general principle under a rude but easily comprehensible form. When a vessel has been filled to the brim with loose fragments, shaking the vessel causes them to settle down into less space, so that more may be put in. And when among the fragments there are some of much greater specific gravity than the rest, these, in the course of a prolonged shaking find their way to the bottom. What now is the meaning of such results, when expressed in general terms? We have a group of units acted on by an incident force—the attraction of the Earth. So long as these units are not agitated, this incident force produces no changes in their relative positions; agitate them, and immediately their loose arrangement passes into a more compact arrangement. Again, so long as they are not agitated, the incident force cannot separate the heavier units from the lighter; agitate them, and immediately the heavier units begin to segregate. Mechanical disturbances of more minute kinds, acting on the parts of much denser aggregates, produce analogous effects. A piece of iron which, when it leaves the workshop, is fibrous in structure, becomes crystalline if exposed to a perpetual jar. The polar forces mutually exercised by the atoms, fail to change the disorderly arrangement into an orderly arrangement while the atoms are relatively quiescent; but these forces succeed in rearranging them when the atoms are kept in a state of intestine agitation. Similarly, the fact that a bar of steel suspended in the magnetic meridian and repeatedly struck, becomes magnetized, is ascribed to a rearrangement of particles that is produced by the magnetic force of the Earth when vibrations are propagated through them, but is not otherwise produced. Now imperfectly as these cases parallel the mass of those we are considering, they nevertheless serve roughly to illustrate the effect which adding to the quantity of motion an aggregate contains has in facilitating rearrangement of its parts.

More fully illustrative are the instances in which, by artificially adding to or subtracting from that molecular motion which we call its heat, we give an aggregate increased or diminished facility of rearranging its molecules. The process of tempering steel or annealing glass, shows us that internal redistribution is aided by insensible vibrations, as we have just seen it to be by sensible vibrations. When some molten glass is dropped into water, and when its outside is thus, by sudden solidification, prevented from partaking in that contraction which the subsequent cooling of the inside tends to produce; the units are left in such a state of tension, that the mass flies into fragments if a small portion of it be broken off. But if this mass be kept for a day or two at a considerable heat, though a heat not sufficient to alter its form or produce any sensible diminution of hardness, this extreme brittleness disappears: the component particles being thrown into greater agitation, the tensile forces are enabled to rearrange them into a state of equilibrium. Much more conspicuously do we see the effect of the insensible motion called heat, where the rearrangement of parts taking place is that of visible segregation. An instance is furnished by the subsidence of fine precipitates. These sink down very slowly from solutions that are cold; while warm solutions deposit them with comparative rapidity. That is to say, exalting the molecular oscillation throughout the mass, allows the suspended particles to separate more readily from the particles of fluid. The influence of heat on chemical changes is so familiar, that examples are scarcely needed. Be the substances concerned gaseous, liquid, or solid, it equally holds that their chemical unions and disunions are aided by rise of temperature. Affinities which do not suffice to effect the rearrangement of mixed units that are in a state of feeble agitation, suffice to effect it when the agitation is raised to a certain point. And so long as this molecular motion is not great enough to prevent those chemical cohesions which the affinities tend to produce, increase of it gives increased facility of chemical rearrangement.

Another class of facts may be adduced which, though not apparently, are really illustrative of the same general truth. Other things equal, the liquid form of matter implies a greater quantity of contained motion than the solid form —the liquidity is itself a consequence of such greater quantity. Hence, an aggregate made up partly of liquid matter and partly of solid matter, contains a greater quantity of motion than one which, otherwise like it, is made up wholly of solid matter. It is inferable, then, that a liquid-solid aggregate, or, as we commonly call it, a plastic aggregate, will admit of internal redistribution with comparative facility; and the inference is verified by experience. A magma of unlike substances ground up with water, while it continues thin allows a settlement of its heavier components— a separation of them from the lighter. As the water evaporates this separation is impeded, and ceases when the magma becomes very thick. But even when it has reached the semi-solid state in which gravitation fails to cause further segregation of its mixed components, other forces may still continue to produce segregation: witness the fact to which attention was first drawn by Mr. Babbage, that when the pasty mixture of ground flints and kaolin, prepared for the manufacture of porcelain, is kept some time, it becomes gritty and unfit for use, in consequence of the particles of silica separating themselves from the rest, and uniting together in grains; or witness the fact known to every house-wife, that in long-kept currant-jelly the sugar takes the shape of imbedded crystals.

No matter then under what form the motion contained by an aggregate exists—be it mere mechanical agitation, or the mechanical vibrations such as produce sound, be it molecular motion absorbed from without, or the constitutional molecular motion of some component liquid, the same truth holds throughout. Incident forces work secondary redistributions easily when the contained motion is large in quantity; and work them with increasing difficulty as the contained motion diminishes.

§ 101. Yet another class of facts that fall within the same generalization, little as they seem related to it, must be indicated before proceeding. They are those presented by certain contrasts in chemical stability. Speaking generally, stable compounds contain comparatively little molecular motion; and in proportion as the contained molecular motion is great the instability is great.

The common and marked illustration of this to be first named, is that chemical stability decreases as temperature increases. Compounds of which the elements are strongly united and compounds of which the elements are feebly united, are alike in this, that raising their heats or increasing the quantities of their contained molecular motion, diminishes the strengths of the unions of their elements;

and by continually adding to the quantity of contained molecular motion, a point is in each case reached at which the chemical union is destroyed. That is to say, the redistribution of matter which constitutes simple chemical decomposition, is easy in proportion as the quantity of contained motion is great. The like holds with double decompositions. Two compounds, A B and C D, mingled together and kept at a low temperature, may severally remain unchanged—the cross affinities between their components may fail to cause redistribution. Increase the heat of the mixture, or add to the molecular motion throughout it, and redistribution takes place; ending in the formation of the compounds, A C and B D.

Another chemical truth having a like implication, is that chemical elements which, as they ordinarily exist, contain much motion, have combinations less stable than those of which the elements, as they ordinarily exist, contain little motion. The gaseous form of matter implies a relatively large amount of molecular motion; while the solid form implies a relatively small amount of molecular motion. What are the characters of their respective compounds? The compounds which the permanent gases form with one another, cannot resist high temperatures: most of them are easily decomposed by heat; and at a red heat, even the stronger ones yield up their components. On the other hand, the chemical unions between elements that are solid except at very high temperatures, are extremely stable. In many, if not indeed in most, cases, such combined elements are not separable by any heat we can produce.

There is, again, the relation, which appears to have a kindred meaning, between instability and amount of composition. "In general, the molecular heat of a compound increases with the degree of complexity." With increase of complexity there also goes increased facility of decomposition. Whence it follows that molecules which contain much motion in virtue of their complexity, are those of which the components are most readily redistributed. This holds not only of the complexity resulting from the union of several unlike elements; but it holds also of the complexity resulting from the union of the same elements in higher multiples. Matter has two solid states, distinguished as crystalloid and colloid; of which the first is due to union of the individual atoms or molecules, and the second to the union of groups of such individual atoms or molecules; and of which the first is stable and the second unstable.

But the most striking and conclusive illustration is furnished by the combinations into which nitrogen enters. These have the two characters of being specially unstable and of containing specially great quantities of motion. A recently-ascertained peculiarity of nitrogen, is, that instead of giving out heat when it combines with other elements, it absorbs heat. That is to say, besides carrying with it into the liquid or solid compound it forms, the motion which previously constituted it a gas, it takes up additional motion; and where the other element with which it unites is gaseous, the molecular motion proper to this, also, is locked up in the compound. Now these nitrogen-compounds are unusually prone to decomposition; and the decompositions of many of them take place with extreme violence. All our explosive substances are nitrogenous— the most terribly destructive of them all, chloride of nitrogen, being one which contains the immense quantity of motion proper to its component gases, plus a certain further quantity of motion.

Clearly these general chemical truths, are parts of the more general physical truth we are tracing out. We see in them that what holds of sensible aggregates, holds also of the insensible aggregates we call molecules. Like the aggregates formed of them, these ultimate aggregates become more or less integrated according as they lose or gain motion; and like them also, according as they contain much or little motion, they are liable to undergo secondary redistributions of parts along with the primary redistribution.

§ 102. And now having got this general principle clearly into view, let us go on to observe how, in conformity with it, Evolution becomes, according to the conditions, either simple or compound.

If a little sal-ammoniac, or other volatile solid, be heated, it is disintegrated by the absorbed molecular motion, and rises in gas. When the gas so produced, coming in contact with a cold surface, loses its excess of molecular motion, integration takes place—the substance assumes the form of crystals. This is a case of simple evolution. The process of concentration of matter and dissipation of motion does not here proceed in a gradual manner—does not pass through stages occupying considerable periods; but the molecular motion which reduced it to the gaseous state being dissipated, the matter passes suddenly to a completely solid state. The result is that along with this primary redistribution there go on no appreciable secondary redistributions. Substantially the same thing holds with crystals deposited from solutions. Loss of that molecular motion which, down to a certain point, keeps the molecules from uniting, and sudden solidification when the loss goes below that point, occur here as before; and here as before, the absence of a period during which the molecules are partially free and gradually losing their freedom, is accompanied by the absence of supplementary rearrangements.

Mark, conversely, what happens when the concentration is slow. A gaseous mass losing its heat, and undergoing a consequent decrease of bulk, is not subject only to this change which brings its parts nearer to their common centre, but also to many simultaneous changes. The great quantity of molecular motion contained in it, giving, as we have seen that it must, great molecular mobility, renders every part sensitive to every incident force; and, as a result, its parts have various motions besides that implied by their progressing integration. Indeed these secondary motions, which we know as currents, are so important and conspicuous as quite to subordinate the primary motion.

Suppose that presently, the loss of molecular motion has reached that point at which the gaseous state can no longer be maintained, and condensation follows. Under their more closely-united form, the parts of the aggregate display, to a considerable degree, the same phenomena as before. The molecular motion and accompanying molecular mobility implied by the liquid state, permit easy rearrangement; and hence, along with further contraction of volume, consequent on further loss of motion, there go on rapid and marked changes in the relative positions of parts—local streams produced by slight disturbing forces. But now, assuming the substance to be formed of molecules that have not those peculiarities leading to the sudden integration which we call crystallization, what happens as the molecular motion further decreases? The liquid thickens—its parts cease to be relatively movable among one another with ease; and the transpositions caused by feeble incident forces become comparatively slow. Little by little the currents are stopped, but the mass still continues modifiable by stronger incident forces. Gravitation makes it bend or spread out when not supported on all sides; and it may easily be indented. As it cools, however, it continues to grow stiffer as we say—less capable of having its parts changed in their relative positions. And eventually further loss of heat rendering it quite hard, its parts are no longer appreciably rearrangeable by any save violent actions.

Among inorganic aggregates, then, secondary redistributions accompany the primary redistribution, throughout the whole process of concentration, where this is gradual. During the gaseous and liquid stages, the secondary redistributions, rapid and extensive as they are, leave no traces—the molecular mobility being such as to negative the fixed arrangement of parts we call structure. On approaching solidity we arrive at a condition called plastic, in which redistributions can still be made, though much less easily; and in which, being changeable less easily, they have a certain persistence—a persistence which can, however, become decided, only where further solidification stops further redistribution.

Here we see, in the first place, what are the conditions under which Evolution instead of being simple becomes compound, while we see, in the second place, how the compounding of it can be carried far only under conditions more special than any hitherto contemplated; since, on the one hand, a large amount of secondary redistribution is possible only where there is a great quantity of contained motion, and, on the other hand, these redistributions can have permanence only where the contained motion has become small —opposing conditions which seem to negative any large amount of permanent secondary redistribution.

§ 103. And now we are in a position to observe how these apparently contradictory conditions are reconciled; and how, by the reconciliation of them, permanent secondary redistributions immense in extent are made possible. We shall appreciate the distinctive peculiarity of the aggregates classed as organic, in which Evolution becomes so highly compounded; and shall see that this peculiarity consists in the combination of matter into a form embodying an enormous amount of motion at the same time that it has a great degree of concentration.

For notwithstanding its semi-solid consistence, organic matter contains molecular motion locked up in each of the ways above contemplated separately. Let us note its several constitutional traits. Three out of its four chief components are gaseous; and in their uncombined states the gases united in it have so much molecular motion that they are incondensable. Hence as the characters of elements, though disguised, cannot be absolutely lost in combinations, it is to be inferred that the protein-molecule concentrates a comparatively large amount of motion in a small space. And since many equivalents of these gaseous elements unite in one of these protein-molecules, there must be in it a large quantity of relative motion in addition to that which the ultimate atoms possess. Moreover, organic matter has the peculiarity that its molecules are aggregated into the colloid and not into the crystalloid arrangement; forming, as is supposed, clusters of clusters which have movements in relation to one another. Here, then, is a further mode in which molecular motion is included. Yet again, these compounds of which the essential parts of organisms are built, are nitrogenous; and we have lately seen it to be a peculiarity of nitrogenous compounds, that instead of giving out heat during their formation they absorb heat. To all the molecular motion possessed by gaseous nitrogen, is added more motion; and the whole is concentrated in solid protein. Organic aggregates are very generally distinguished, too, by having much insensible motion in a free state—the motion we call heat. Though in many cases the quantity of this contained insensible motion is inconsiderable, in other cases a temperature greatly above that of the environment is constantly maintained. Once more, there is the still larger quantity of motion embodied by the water that permeates organic matter. It is this which, giving to the water its high molecular mobility, gives mobility to the organic molecules partially suspended in it; and preserves that plastic condition which so greatly facilitates redistribution.

From these several statements, no adequate idea can be formed of the extent to which living organic substance is thus distinguished from other substances having like sensible forms of aggregation. But some approximation to such an idea may be obtained by contrasting the bulk occupied by this substance, with the bulk which its constituents would occupy if uncombined. An accurate comparison cannot be made in the present state of science. What expansion would occur if the constituents of the nitrogenous compounds could be divorced without the addition of motion from without, is too complex a question to be answered. But respecting the constituents of that which forms some four-fifths of the total weight of an ordinary animal—its water—a tolerably definite answer can be given. Were the oxygen and hydrogen of water to lose their affinities, and were no molecular motion supplied to them beyond that contained in water at blood-heat, they would assume a volume twenty times that of the water.[1] Whether protein under like conditions would expand in a greater or a less degree, must remain an open question; but remembering the gaseous nature of three out of its four chief components, remembering the above-named peculiarity of nitrogenous compounds, remembering the high multiples and the colloidal form, we may conclude that the expansion would be great. We shall not be far wrong, therefore, in saying that the elements of the human body, if suddenly disengaged from one another, would occupy a score times the space they do: the movements of their atoms would compel this wide diffusion. Thus the essential characteristic of living organic matter, is that it unites this large quantity of contained motion with a degree of cohesion that permits temporary fixity of arrangement.

§ 104. Further proofs that the secondary redistributions which make Evolution compound, depend for their possibility on the reconciliation of these conflicting conditions, are yielded by comparisons of organic aggregates with one another. Besides seeing that organic aggregates differ from other aggregates, alike in the quantity of motion they contain and the amount of rearrangement of parts that accompanies their progressive integration; we shall see that among organic aggregates themselves, differences in the quantities of contained motion are accompanied by differences in the amounts of redistribution.

The contrasts among organisms in chemical composition yield us the first illustration. Animals are distinguished from plants by their far greater amounts of structure, as well as by the far greater rapidity with which changes of structure go on in them; and in comparison with plants, animals

---

[1] I am indebted for this result to Dr. Frankland, who has been good enough to have the calculation made for me.

are at the same time conspicuous for containing immensely larger proportions of those highly-compounded nitrogenous molecules in which so much motion is locked up. So, too, is it with the contrasts between the different parts of each animal. Though certain nitrogenous parts, as cartilage, are inert, yet the parts in which the secondary redistributions have gone on, and are ever going on, most actively, are those in which the most highly-compounded molecules predominate; and parts which, like the deposits of fat, consist of relatively-simple molecules, are seats of but little structure and but little change.

We find clear proof, too, that the continuance of the secondary redistributions by which organic aggregates are so remarkably distinguished, depends on the presence of that motion contained in the water diffused through them; and that, other things equal, there is a direct relation between the amount of redistribution and the amount of contained water. The evidences may be put in three groups. There is the familiar fact that a plant has its formative changes arrested by cutting off the supply of water: the primary redistribution continues—it withers and shrinks or becomes more integrated—but the secondary redistributions cease. There is the less familiar, but no less certain, fact, that the like result occurs in animals—occurs, indeed, as might be expected, after a relatively smaller diminution of water. Certain of the lower animals furnish additional proofs. The *Rotifera* may be rendered apparently lifeless by dessication, and will yet revive if wetted. When the African rivers which it inhabits are dried up, the *Lepidosiren* remains torpid in the hardened mud, until the return of the rainy season brings water. Humboldt states that during the summer drought, the alligators of the Pampas lie buried in a state of suspended animation beneath the parched surface, and struggle up out of the earth as soon as it becomes humid. The history of each organism teaches us the same thing. The young plant, just putting its head above the soil, is far more succulent than the adult plant; and the amount of transformation going on in it is relatively much greater. In that portion of an egg which displays the formative processes during the early stages of incubation, the changes of arrangement are more rapid than those which an equal portion of the body of a hatched chick undergoes. As may be inferred from their respective powers to acquire habits and aptitudes, the structural modifiability of a child is greater than that of an adult man; and the structural modifiability of an adult man is greater than that of an old man: contrasts which are accompanied by corresponding contrasts in the densities of the tissues; since the ratio of water to solid matter diminishes with advancing age. And then we have this relation repeated in the contrasts between parts of the same organism. In a tree, rapid structural changes go on at the ends of shoots, where the ratio of water to solid matter is very great; while the changes are very slow in the dense and almost dry substance of the trunk. Similarly in animals, we have the contrast between the high rate of change going on in a soft tissue like the brain, and the low rate of change going on in dry non-vascular tissues, such as those which form hairs, nails, horns, etc.

Other groups of facts prove, in an equally unmistakable way, that the quantity of secondary redistribution in an organism varies, *cæteris paribus*, according to the contained quantity of the motion we call heat. The contrasts between different organisms, and different states of the same organism, unite in showing this. Speaking generally, the amounts of structure and rates of structural change, are smaller throughout the vegetal kingdom than throughout the animal kingdom; and, speaking generally, the heat of plants is less than the heat of animals. A comparison of the several divisions of the animal kingdom with one another, discloses among them parallel relations. Regarded as a whole, vertebrate animals are higher in temperature than invertebrate ones; and they are as a whole higher in organic activity and complexity. Between subdivisions of the vertebrata themselves, like differences in the state of molecular vibration accompany like differences in the degree of evolution. The least compounded of the *Vertebrata* are the fishes; and in most cases, the heat of fishes is nearly the same as that of the water in which they swim: only some of them being decidedly warmer. Though we habitually speak of reptiles as cold-blooded; and though they have not much more power than fishes of maintaining a temperature above that of their medium; yet since their medium (which is, in the majority of cases, the air of warm climates) is on the average warmer than the medium inhabited by fishes, the temperature of the class of reptiles is higher than that of the class of fishes; and we see in them a correspondingly higher complexity. The much more active molecular agitation in mammals and birds, is associated with a considerably greater multiformity of structure and a very far greater vivacity. The most instructive contrasts, however, are those occurring in the same organic aggregates at different temperatures. Plants exhibit structural changes that vary in rate as the temperature varies. Though light is the agent which effects those molecular changes causing vegetal growth, yet we see that in the absence of heat, such changes are not effected: in winter there is enough light, but the heat being insufficient, plant-life is suspended. That this is the sole cause of the suspension, is proved by the fact that at the same season, plants contained in hothouses, where they receive even a smaller amount of light, go on producing leaves and flowers. We see, too, that their seeds, to which light is not simply needless but detrimental, begin to germinate only when the return of a warm season raises the rate of molecular agitation. In like manner the ova of animals, undergoing those changes by which structure is produced in them, must be kept more or less warm: in the absence of a certain amount of motion among their molecules, the rearrangement of parts does not go on. Hibernating animals also supply proof that loss of heat carried far, retards extremely the processes of transformation. In animals which do not hibernate, as in man, prolonged exposure to intense cold produces an irresistible tendency to sleep (which implies a lowered rate of structural and functional changes); and if the abstraction of heat continues, this sleep ends in death, or stoppage of these changes.

Here, then, is an accumulation of proofs, general and special. Living aggregates are distinguished by the connected facts, that during integration they undergo very remarkable secondary changes which other aggregates do not undergo to any considerable extent; and that they contain (bulks being supposed equal) immensely greater quantities of motion, locked up in various ways.

§ 105. The last chapter closed with the remark that while Evolution is always an integration of Matter and dissipation of Motion, it is in most cases much more. And this chapter opened by briefly specifying the conditions under which Evolution is integrative only, or remains simple, and the conditions under which it is something further than integrative, or becomes compound. In illustrating this contrast between simple and compound Evolution, and in explaining how the contrast arises, a vague idea of Evolution in general has been conveyed. Unavoidably, we have to some extent forestalled the full discussion of Evolution about to be commenced.

There is nothing in this to regret. A preliminary conception, indefinite but comprehensive, is always useful as an introduction to a complete conception—cannot, indeed, be dispensed with. A complex idea is not communicable directly, by giving one after another its component parts in their finished forms; since if no outline pre-exists in the mind of the recipient, these component parts will not be rightly combined. The intended combination can be made only when the recipient has discovered for himself how the components are to be arranged. Much labor has to be gone through which would have been saved had a general notion, however cloudy, been conveyed before the distinct and detailed delineation was commenced.

That which the reader has incidentally gathered respecting the nature of Evolution from the foregoing sections, he may thus advantageously use as a rude sketch, enabling him to seize the relations among the several parts of the enlarged picture as they are worked out before him. He will constantly bear in mind that the total history of every sensible existence is included in its Evolution and Dissolution; which last process we leave for the present out of consideration. He will remember that whatever aspect of it we are for the moment considering, Evolution is always to be regarded as fundamentally an integration of Matter and dissipation of Motion, which may be, and usually is, accompanied incidentally by other transformations of Matter and Motion. And he will everywhere expect to find that the primary redistribution ends in forming aggregates which are simple where it is rapid, but which become compound in proportion as its slowness allows the effects of secondary redistributions to accumulate.

§ 106. There is much difficulty in tracing out transformations so vast, so varied, and so intricate as those now to be entered upon. Besides having to deal with concrete phenomena of all orders, we have to deal with each group of phenomena under several aspects, no one of which can be fully understood apart from the rest and no one of which can be studied simultaneously with the rest. Already we have seen that during Evolution two great classes of changes are going on together; and we shall presently see that the second of these great classes is redivisible. Entangled with one another as all these changes are, explanation of any one class or order involves direct or indirect reference to others not yet explained. We have nothing for it but to make the best practicable compromise.

It will be most convenient to devote the next chapter to a detailed account of Evolution under its primary aspect; tacitly recognizing its secondary aspects only so far as the exposition necessitates.

The succeeding two chapters, occupied exclusively with the secondary redistributions, will make no reference to the primary redistribution beyond that which is unavoidable: each being also limited to one particular trait of the secondary redistributions.

In a further chapter will be treated a third, and still more distinct, character of the secondary redistributions.

————

CHAPTER XIV

THE LAW OF EVOLUTION

§ 107. DEDUCTION has now to be verified by induction. Thus far the argument has been that all sensible existences *must*, in some way or other and at some time or other, reach their concrete shapes through processes of concentration; and such facts as have been named have been named merely to clarify the perception of this necessity. But we cannot be said to have arrived at that unified knowledge constituting Philosophy, until we have seen how existences of all orders *do* exhibit a progressive integration of Matter and concomitant loss of Motion. Tracing, so far as we may by observation and inference, the objects dealt with by the Astronomer and the Geologist, as well as those which Biology, Psychology and Sociology treat of, we have to consider what direct proof there is that the Cosmos, in general and in detail, conforms to this law.

In doing this, manifestations of the law more involved than those hitherto indicated, will chiefly occupy us. Throughout the classes of facts successively contemplated, our attention will be directed not so much to the truth that every aggregate has undergone, or is undergoing, integration, as to the further truth that in every more or less separate part of every aggregate, integration has been, or is, in progress. Instead of simple wholes and wholes of which the complexity has been ignored, we have here to deal with wholes as they actually exist—mostly made up of many members combined in many ways. And in them we shall have to trace the transformation as displayed under several forms—a passage of the total mass from a more diffused to a more consolidated state; a concurrent similar passage in every portion of it that comes to have a distinguishable individuality; and a simultaneous increase of combination among such individuated portions.

§ 108. Our Sidereal System by its general form, by its clusters of stars of all degrees of closeness, and by its nebulæ in all stages of condensation, gives us grounds to suspect that, generally and locally, concentration is going on. Assume that its matter has been, and still is being, drawn together by gravitation, and we have an explanation of all its leading traits of structure; from its solidified masses up to its collections of attenuated flocculi barely discernible by the most powerful telescopes, from its double stars up to such complex aggregates as the nubeculæ. Without dwelling on this evidence, however, let us pass to the case of the Solar System.

The belief, for which there are so many reasons, that this has had a nebular genesis, is the belief that it has arisen by the integration of matter and concomitant loss of motion. Evolution, under its primary aspect, is illustrated most simply and clearly by this passage of the Solar System from a widely diffused incoherent state to a consolidated coherent state. While, according to the nebular hypothesis, there has been going on this gradual concentration of the Solar System as an aggregate, there has been a simultaneous concentration of each partially-independent member. The substance of every planet in passing through its stages of nebulous ring, gaseous spheroid, liquid spheroid, and spheroid externally solidified, has in essentials paralleled the changes gone through by the general mass; and every satellite has done the like. Moreover, at the same time that the matter of the whole, as well as the matter of each

partially-independent part, has been thus integrating, there
has been the further integration implied by increasing combination among the parts. The satellites of each planet are
linked with their primary into a balanced cluster; while the
planets and their satellites form with the Sun a compound
group of which the members are more strongly bound up
with one another than were the far-spread portions of the
nebulous medium out of which they arose.

Even apart from the nebular hypothesis, the Solar System
furnishes evidence having a like general meaning. Not to
make much of the meteoric matter perpetually being added
to the mass of the Earth, and probably to the masses of
other planets, as well as, in larger quantities, to the mass
of the Sun, it will suffice to name two generally-admitted
instances. The one is the appreciable retardation of comets
by the ethereal medium, and the inferred retardation of
planets—a process which, in time, must bring comets, and
eventually planets, into the Sun. The other is the Sun's
still-continued loss of motion in the shape of radiated heat;
accompanying the still-continued integration of his mass.

§ 109. To geologic evolution we pass without break from
the evolution which, for convenience, we separate as astronomic. The history of the Earth, as traced out from the
structure of its crust, carries us back to that molten state
which the nebular hypothesis implies; and, as before
pointed out (§ 69), the changes classed as igneous are the
accompaniments of the progressing consolidation of the
Earth's substance and accompanying loss of its contained
motion. Both the general and the local effects may be
briefly exemplified.

Leaving behind the period when the more volatile elements now existing as solids were kept by the high temperature in a gaseous form, we may begin with the fact
that until the Earth's surface had cooled down below 212°,
the vast mass of water at present covering three-fifths of it
must have existed as vapor. This enormous volume of dis-

integrated liquid became integrated as fast as the dissipation of the Earth's contained motion allowed; leaving, at length, a comparatively small portion unintegrated, which would be far smaller but for the unceasing absorption of molecular motion from the Sun. In the formation of the Earth's crust we have a similar change similarly caused. The passage from a thin solid film, everywhere fissured and movable on the subjacent molten matter, to a crust so thick and strong as to be but now and then very slightly dislocated by disturbing forces, illustrates the process. And while, in this superficial solidification, we see under one form how concentration accompanies loss of contained motion, we see it under another form in that diminution of the Earth's bulk implied by superficial corrugation.

Local or secondary integrations have advanced along with this general integration. A molten spheroid merely skinned over with solid matter could have presented nothing beyond small patches of land and water. Differences of elevation great enough to form islands of considerable size, imply a crust of some rigidity; and only as the crust grew thick could the land be united into continents divided by oceans. So, too, with the more striking elevations. The collapse of a thin crust round its cooling and contracting contents, would throw it into low ridges: it must have acquired a relatively great depth and strength before extensive mountain systems of vast elevation became possible. In sedimentary changes, also, a like progress is inferable. Denudation acting on the small surfaces exposed during early stages, would produce but small local deposits. The collection of detritus into strata of great extent, and the union of such strata into extensive "systems," imply wide surfaces of land and water, as well as subsidences great, in both area and depth; whence it follows that integrations of this order must have grown more pronounced as the Earth's crust thickened.

§ 110. Already we have recognized the fact that organic evolution is primarily the formation of an aggregate, by the continued incorporation of matter previously spread through a wider space. Merely reminding the reader that every plant grows by concentrating in itself elements that were before diffused as gases, and that every animal grows by reconcentrating these elements previously dispersed in surrounding plants and animals; it will be here proper to complete the conception by pointing out that the early history of a plant or animal, still more clearly than its later history, shows us this fundamental process. For the microscopic germ of each organism undergoes, for a long time, no other change than that implied by absorption of nutriment. Cells imbedded in the stroma of an ovarium, become ova by little else than continued growth at the expense of adjacent materials. And when, after fertilization, a more active evolution commences, its most conspicuous trait is the drawing-in, to a germinal centre, of the substance which the ovum contains.

Here, however, our attention must be directed mainly to the secondary integrations which habitually accompany the primary integration. We have to observe how, along with the formation of a larger mass of matter, there goes on a drawing together and consolidation of the matter into parts, as well as an increasingly-intimate combination of parts. In the mammalian embryo, the heart, at first a long pulsating blood-vessel, by and by twists upon itself and integrates. The bile-cells constituting the rudimentary liver, do not simply become different from the wall of the intestine in which they at first lie; but, as they accumulate, they simultaneously diverge from it and consolidate into an organ. The anterior segments of the cerebro-spinal axis, which are at first continuous with the rest, and distinguished only by their larger size, undergo a gradual union; and at the same time the resulting head folds into a mass clearly marked off from the rest of the vertebral column. The like process, variously exemplified in other organs, is meanwhile exhibited by the body as a whole; which becomes integrated somewhat in the same way that an outspread handkerchief and its contents become integrated when its edges are drawn in and fastened to make a bundle. Analogous changes go on long after birth, and continue even up to old age. In man, that solidification of the bony framework which, during childhood, is seen in the coalescence of portions of the same bone ossified from different centres, is afterward seen in the coalescence of bones that were originally distinct. The appendages of the vertebræ unite with the vertebral centres to which they belong—a change not completed until toward thirty. At the same time the epiphyses, formed separately from the main bodies of their respective bones, have their cartilaginous connections turned into osseous ones—are fused to the masses beneath them. The component vertebræ of the sacrum, which remain separate till about the sixteenth year, then begin to unite; and in ten or a dozen years more their union is complete. Still later occurs the coalescence of the coccygeal vertebræ; and there are some other bony unions which remain unfinished unless advanced age is reached. To which add that the increase of density and toughness, going on throughout the tissues in general during life, is the formation of a more highly integrated substance.

The species of change thus illustrated under several aspects in the unfolding human body, may be traced in all animals. That mode of it which consists in the union of similar parts originally separate, has been described by Milne-Edwards and others, as exhibited in various of the *Invertebrata;* though it does not seem to have been included by them as an essential peculiarity in the process of organic development. We shall, however, see clearly that local integration is an all-important part of this process, when we find it displayed not only in the successive stages passed through by every embryo, but also in ascending from the lower creatures to the higher. As manifested in either way, it goes on both longitudinally and transversely: under which different forms we may, indeed, most conveniently consider it. Of *longitudinal integration,* the sub-kingdom *Annulosa* supplies abundant examples. Its lower members, such as

worms and myriapods, are mostly characterized by the great
number of segments composing them; reaching in some
cases to several hundreds. But in the higher divisions—
crustaceans, insects, and spiders—we find this number reduced down to twenty-two, thirteen, or even fewer; while,
accompanying the reduction, there is a shortening or integration of the whole body, reaching its extreme in the crab
and the spider. The significance of these contrasts, as bearing on the general doctrine of Evolution, will be seen when
it is pointed out that they are parallel to those which arise
during the development of individual annulose animals.
In the lobster, the head and thorax form one compact box,
made by the union of a number of segments which in the
embryo were separable. Similarly, the butterfly shows us
segments so much more closely united than they were in the
caterpillar, as to be, some of them, no longer distinguishable
from one another. The *Vertebrata* again, throughout their
successively higher classes, furnish like instances of longitudinal union. In most fishes, and in reptiles that have no
limbs, none of the vertebræ coalesce. In most mammals
and in birds, a variable number of vertebræ become fused
together to form the sacrum; and in the higher apes and in
man, the caudal vertebræ also lose their separate individualities in a single *os coccygis*. That which we may distinguish
as *transverse integration,* is well illustrated among the *Annulosa* in the development of the nervous system. Leaving
out those most degraded forms which do not present distinct
ganglia, it is to be observed that the lower annulose animals,
in common with the larvæ of the higher, are severally characterized by a double chain of ganglia running from end to
end of the body; while in the more perfectly-formed annulose animals, this double chain becomes united into a single
chain. Mr. Newport has described the course of this concentration as exhibited in insects; and by Rathke it has
been traced in crustaceans. During the early stages of the
Astacus fluviatilis, or common crayfish, there is a pair of
separate ganglia to each ring. Of the fourteen pairs belong-

ing to the head and thorax, the three pairs in advance of the mouth consolidate into one mass to form the brain or cephalic ganglion. Meanwhile, out of the remainder, the first six pairs severally unite in the median line, while the rest remain more or less separate. Of these six double ganglia thus formed, the anterior four coalesce into one mass; the remaining two coalesce into another mass; and then these two masses coalesce into one. Here we see longitudinal and transverse integration going on simultaneously; and in the highest crustaceans they are both carried still further. The *Vertebrata* clearly exhibit transverse integration in the development of the generative system. The lowest mammals —the *Monotremata*—in common with birds, to which they are in many respects allied, have oviducts which toward their lower extremities are dilated into cavities, severally performing in an imperfect way the function of a uterus. "In the *Marsupialia* there is a closer approximation of the two lateral sets of organs on the median line; for the oviducts converge toward one another and meet (without coalescing) on the median line; so that their uterine dilatations are in contact with each other, forming a true 'double uterus.' . . . As we ascend the series of 'placental' mammals, we find the lateral coalescence becoming more and more complete. . . . In many of the *Rodentia* the uterus still remains completely divided into two lateral halves; while in others these coalesce at their lower portions, forming a rudiment of the true 'body' of the uterus in the human subject. This part increases at the expense of the lateral 'cornua' in the higher herbivora and carnivora; but even in the lower quadrumana the uterus is somewhat cleft at its summit."[1]

Under the head of organic integrations, there remain to be noted some which do not occur within the limits of one organism, and which only in an indirect way involve concentration of matter and dissipation of motion. These are the integrations by which organisms are made dependent on one another. We may set down two kinds of them—those

[1] Carpenter's Prin. of Comp. Phys., p. 617.

which occur within the same species, and those which occur
among different species. More or less of the gregarious tendency is general in animals; and when it is marked, there
is, in addition to simple aggregation, a certain degree of
combination. Creatures that hunt in packs, or that have
sentinels, or that are governed by leaders, form bodies partially united by co-operation. Among polygamous mammals and birds this mutual dependence is closer; and the
social insects show us assemblages of individuals of a still
more consolidated character: some of them having carried
the consolidation so far that the individuals cannot exist if
separated. How organisms in general are mutually dependent, and in that sense integrated, we shall see on remembering—first, that while all animals live directly or indirectly
on plants, plants live on the carbonic acid excreted by animals; second, that among animals the flesh-eaters cannot
exist without the plant-eaters; third, that a large proportion
of plants can continue their respective races only by the help
of insects, and that in many cases particular plants need particular insects. Without detailing the more complex connections, which Mr. Darwin has so beautifully illustrated, it
will suffice to say that the Flora and Fauna in each habitat,
constitute an aggregate so far integrated that many of its
species die out if placed amid the plants and animals of another habitat. And it is to be remarked that this integration, too, increases as organic evolution progresses.

§ 111. The phenomena set down in the foregoing paragraph are introductory to others of a higher order, with
which they ought, perhaps, in strictness, to be grouped—
phenomena which, for want of a better word, we may term
super-organic. Inorganic bodies present us with certain
facts. Certain other facts, mostly of a more involved kind,
are presented by organic bodies. There remain yet further
facts, not presented by any organic body taken singly; but
which result from the actions of aggregated organic bodies
on one another and on inorganic bodies. Though phenom-

ena of this order are, as we see, foreshadowed among inferior organisms, they become so extremely conspicuous in mankind as socially united, that practically we may consider them to commence here.

In the social organism integrative changes are clearly and abundantly exemplified. Uncivilized societies display them when wandering families, such as we see among Bushmen, join into tribes of considerable numbers. A further progress of like nature is everywhere manifested in the subjugation of weaker tribes by stronger ones; and in the subordination of their respective chiefs to the conquering chief. The combinations thus resulting, which, among aboriginal races, are being continually formed and continually broken up, become, among superior races, relatively permanent. If we trace the stages through which our own society, or any adjacent one, has passed, we see this unification from time to time repeated on a larger scale and gaining in stability. The aggregation of juniors and the children of juniors under elders and the children of elders; the consequent establishment of groups of vassals bound to their respective nobles; the subsequent subordination of groups of inferior nobles to dukes or earls; and the still later growth of the kingly power over dukes and earls; are so many instances of increasing consolidation. This process through which petty tenures are aggregated in feuds, feuds into provinces, provinces into kingdoms, and finally contiguous kingdoms into a single one, slowly completes itself by destroying the original lines of demarcation. And it may be further remarked of the European nations as a whole, that in the tendency to form alliances more or less lasting, in the restraining influences exercised by the several governments over one another, in the system, now becoming customary, of settling international disputes by Congresses, as well as in the breaking down of commercial barriers and the increasing facilities of communication, we may trace the beginnings of a European federation—a still larger integration than any now established.

But it is not only in these external unions of groups with groups, and of the compound groups with one another, that the general law is exemplified. It is exemplified also in unions that take place internally, as the groups become more highly organized. There are two orders of these, which may be broadly distinguished as regulative and operative. A civilized society is made unlike a barbarous one by the establishment of regulative classes—governmental, administrative, military, ecclesiastical, legal, etc., which, while they have their several special bonds of union, constituting them sub-classes, are also held together as a general class by a certain community of privileges, of blood, of education, of intercourse. In some societies, fully developed after their particular types, this consolidation into castes, and this union among the upper castes by separation from the lower, eventually grow very decided: to be afterward rendered less decided, only in cases of social metamorphosis caused by the industrial regime. The integrations that accompany the operative or industrial organization, later in origin, are not merely of this indirect kind, but they are also direct—they show us physical approach. We have integrations consequent on the simple growth of adjacent parts performing like functions; as, for instance, the junction of Manchester with its calico-weaving suburbs. We have other integrations that arise when, out of several places producing a particular commodity, one monopolizing more and more of the business, draws to it masters and workers, and leaves the other places to dwindle; as witness the growth of the Yorkshire cloth-districts at the expense of those in the West of England; or the absorption by Staffordshire of the pottery-manufacture, and the consequent decay of the establishments that once flourished at Derby and elsewhere. We have those more special integrations that arise within the same city; whence result the concentration of publishers in Paternoster Row, of corn-merchants about Mark Lane, of civil engineers in Great George Street, of bankers in the centre of the City. Industrial combinations that consist [sic] not in the approximation or fusion of parts, but in the establishment of common centres of connection, are exhibited in the Bank clearing-house and the Railway clearing-house. While of yet another species are those unions which bring into relation the more or less dispersed citizens who are occupied in like ways; as traders are brought by the Exchange, and as are professional men by institutes like those of Civil Engineers, Architects, etc.

At first sight these seem to be the last of our instances. Having followed up the general law to social aggregates, there apparently remain no other aggregates to which it can apply. This however is not true. Among what we have above distinguished as super-organic phenomena, we shall find sundry groups of very remarkable and interesting illustrations. Though evolution of the various products of human activities cannot be said directly to exemplify the integration of matter and dissipation of motion, yet they exemplify it indirectly. For the progress of Language, of Science, and of the Arts, industrial and æsthetic, is an objective register of subjective changes. Alterations of structure in human beings, and concomitant alterations of structure in aggregates of human beings, jointly produce corresponding alterations of structure in all those things which humanity creates. As in the changed impress on the wax, we read a change in the seal; so in the integrations of advancing Language, Science, and Art, we see reflected certain integrations of advancing human structure, individual and social. A section must be devoted to each group.

§ 112. Among uncivilized races, the many-syllabled names used for not uncommon objects, as well as the descriptive character of proper names, show us that the words used for the less-familiar things are formed by compounding the words used for the more familiar things. This process of composition is sometimes found in its incipient stage—a stage in which the component words are temporarily united to signify some un-named object, and, from lack of frequent use, do not permanently cohere. But in the majority of inferior languages, the process of "agglutination," as it is called, has gone far enough to produce considerable stability in the compound words: there is a manifest integration. How small is the degree of this integration, however, when compared with that reached in well-developed languages, is shown both by the great length of the compound words used for things and acts of constant occurrence, and by the separableness of their elements. Certain North-American tongues illustrate this very well. In a Ricaree vocabulary extending to fifty names of common objects, which in English are nearly all expressed by single syllables, there is not one monosyllabic word; and in the nearly-allied vocabulary of the Pawnees, the names for these same common objects are monosyllabic in but two instances. Things so familiar to these hunting tribes as *dog* and *bow,* are, in the Pawnee language, *ashakish* and *teeragish;* the *hand* and the *eyes* are respectively *iksheeree* and *keereekoo;* for *day* the term is *shakorooeeshairet,* and for *devil* it is *tsaheekshkakooraiwah;* while the numerals are composed of from two syllables up to five, and in Ricaree up to seven. That the great length of these familiar words implies a low degree of development, and that in the formation of higher languages out of lower there is a progressive integration, which reduces the polysyllables to dissyllables and monosyllables, is an inference confirmed by the history of our own language. Anglo-Saxon *steorra* has been in course of time consolidated into English *star, mona* into *moon,* and *nama* into *name.* The transition through the intermediate semi-Saxon is clearly traceable. *Sunu* became in semi-Saxon *sune,* and in English *son:* the final *e* of *sune* being an evanescent form of the original *u.* The change from the Anglo-Saxon plural, formed by the distinct syllable *as,* to our plural formed by the appended consonant *s,* shows us the same thing: *smithas* in becoming *smiths,* and *endas* in becoming *ends,* illustrate progressive coalescence. So, too, does the disappearance of the terminal *an* in the infinitive mood of verbs; as shown in the transition from the Anglo-Saxon *cuman* to the semi-Saxon *cumme,* and to the English *come.* Moreover the process has been slowly going on, even since what we distinguish as English was formed. In Elizabeth's time, verbs were still very frequently pluralized by the addition of *en*—we *tell* was we *tellen;* and in some rural districts this form of speech may even now be heard. In like manner the terminal *ed* of the past tense has united with the word it modifies. *Burn-ed* has in pronunciation become *burnt;* and even in writing the terminal *t* has in some cases taken the place of the *ed.* Only where antique forms in general are adhered to, as in the Church service, is the distinctness of this inflection still maintained. Further, we see that the compound vowels have been in many cases fused into single vowels. That in *bread* the *e* and *a* were originally both sounded, is proved by the fact that they are still so sounded in parts where old habits linger. We, however, have contracted the pronunciation into *bred;* and we have made like changes in many other common words. Lastly, let it be noted that where the frequency of repetition is greatest, the process is carried furthest; as instance the contraction of *lord* (originally *laford*) into *lud* in the mouths of barristers; and, still better, the coalescence of *God be with you* into *Good bye.*

Besides exhibiting in this way the integrative process, Language equally exhibits it throughout all grammatical development. The lowest kinds of human speech, having merely nouns and verbs without inflections to them, manifestly permit no such close union of the elements of a proposition as results when the relations are marked either by inflections or by connective words. Such speech is necessarily what we significantly call "incoherent." To a considerable extent, incoherence is seen in the Chinese language. "If, instead of saying *I go* to *London, figs come* from *Turkey, the sun shines* through *the air,* we said, *I go* end *London, figs come* origin *Turkey, the sun shines* passage *air,* we should discourse after the manner of the Chinese." From this "aptotic" form, there is clear evidence of a transition, by coalescence, to a form in which the connections of words are expressed by the addition to them of certain inflectional words. "In Languages like the Chinese," remarks Dr. Latham, "the separate words most in use to express relation may become adjuncts or annexes." To this he adds the fact that "the numerous inflectional languages fall into two classes. In one, the inflections have no appearance of having been separate words. In the other, their origin as separate words is demonstrable." From which the inference drawn is, that the "aptotic" languages, by the more and more constant use of adjuncts, gave rise to the "agglutinate" languages, or those in which the original separateness of the inflectional parts can be traced; and that out of these, by further use, arose the "amalgamate" languages, or those in which the original separateness of the inflectional parts can no longer be traced. Strongly corroborative of this inference is the unquestionable fact, that by such a process there have grown out of the amalgamate languages, the "anaptotic" languages; of which our own is the most perfect example—languages in which, by further consolidation, inflections have almost disappeared, while, to express the verbal relations, certain new kinds of words have been developed. When we see the Anglo-Saxon inflections gradually lost by contraction during the development of English, and, though to a less degree, the Latin inflections dwindling away during the development of French, we cannot deny that grammatical structure is modified by integration; and seeing how clearly the earlier stages of grammatical structure are explained by it, we can scarcely doubt that it has been going on from the first.

In proportion to the degree of this integration, is the extent to which integration of another order is carried. Aptotic languages are, as already pointed out, necessarily incoherent—the elements of a proposition cannot be completely tied into a whole. But as fast as coalescence produces inflected words, it becomes possible to unite them into sentences of which the parts are so mutually dependent that no considerable change can be made without destroying the meaning. Yet a further stage in this process may be noted. After the development of those grammatical forms which make definite statements possible, we do not at first find them used to express anything beyond statements of a simple kind. A single subject with a single predicate, accompanied by but few qualifying terms, are usually all. If we compare, for instance, the Hebrew Scriptures with writings of modern times, a marked difference of aggregation among the groups of words, is visible. In the number of subordinate propositions which accompany the principal one; in the various complements to subjects and predicates; and in the numerous qualifying clauses—all of them united into one complex whole—many sentences in modern compositions exhibit a degree of integration not to be found in ancient ones.

§ 113. The history of Science presents facts of the same meaning at every step. Indeed the integration of groups of like entities and like relations, may be said to constitute the most conspicuous part of scientific progress. A glance at the classificatory sciences, shows us that the confused incoherent aggregations which the vulgar make of natural objects, are gradually rendered complete and compact, and bound up into groups within groups. While, instead of considering all marine creatures as fish, shell-fish, and jelly-fish, Zoology establishes divisions and subdivisions under the heads *Vertebrata, Annulosa, Mollusca,* etc.; and while, in place of the wide and vague assemblage popularly described as "creeping things," it makes the specific classes *Annelida, Myriopoda, Insecta, Arachnida;* it simultaneously gives to these an increasing consolidation. The several orders and genera of which each consists, are arranged according to their affinities and tied together under common definitions; at the same time that, by extended observation and rigorous criticism, the previously unknown and undetermined forms are integrated with their respective con-geners. Nor is the process less clearly manifested in those sciences which have for their subject-matter, not classified objects but classified relations. Under one of its chief aspects, scientific advance is the advance of generalization; and generalizing is uniting into groups all like co-existences and sequences among phenomena. The colligation of many concrete relations into a generalization of the lowest order, exemplifies this principle in its simplest form; and it is again exemplified in a more complex form by the colligation of these lowest generalizations into higher ones, and these into still higher ones. Year by year are established certain connections among orders of phenomena that appear unallied; and those connections, multiplying and strengthening, gradually bring the seemingly unallied orders under a common bond. When, for example, Humboldt quotes the saying of the Swiss—"it is going to rain because we hear the murmur of the torrents nearer"—when he remarks the relation between this and an observation of his own, that the cataracts of the Orinoco are heard at a greater distance by night than by day—when he notes the essential parallelism existing between these facts and the fact that the unusual visibility of remote objects is also an indication of coming rain—and when he points out that the common cause of these variations is the smaller hindrance offered to the passage of both light and sound, by media which are comparatively homogenous, either in temperature or hydrometric state; he helps in bringing under one generalization the phenomena of light and those of sound. Experiment having shown that these conform to like laws of reflection and refraction, the conclusion that they are both produced by undulations gains probability: there is an incipient integration of two great orders of phenomena, between which no connection was suspected in times past. A still more decided integration has been of late taking place between the once independent sub-sciences of Electricity, Magnetism, and Light.

The process will manifestly be carried much further. Such propositions as those set forth in preceding chapters, on "The Persistence of Force," "The Transformation and Equivalence of Forces," "The Direction of Motion," and "The Rhythm of Motion," unite within single bonds phenomena belonging to all orders of existences. And if there is such a thing as that which we here understand by Philosophy, there must eventually be reached a universal integration.

§ 114. Nor do the industrial and æsthetic Arts fail to supply us with equally conclusive evidence. The progress from rude, small, and simple tools, to perfect, complex, and large machines, is a progress in integration. Among what are classed as the mechanical powers, the advance from the lever to the wheel-and-axle is an advance from a simple agent to an agent made up of several simple ones. On comparing the wheel-and-axle or any of the machines used in early times with those used now, we see that in each of our machines several of the primitive machines are united into one. A modern apparatus for spinning or weaving, for making stockings or lace, contains not simply a lever, an inclined plane, a screw, a wheel-and-axle, joined together; but several of each integrated into one whole. Again, in early ages, when horse-power and man-power were alone employed, the motive agent was not bound up with the tool moved; but the two have now become in many cases fused together. The fire-box and boiler of a locomotive are combined with the machinery which the steam works. A still more extensive integration is exhibited in every factory. Here we find a large number of complicated machines, all connected by driving shafts with the same steam-engine— all united with it into one vast apparatus.

Contrast the mural decorations of the Egyptians and Assyrians with modern historical paintings, and there becomes manifest a great advance in unity of composition—in the subordination of the parts to the whole. One of these ancient frescoes is, in truth, made up of a number of pictures that have little mutual dependence. The several figures of which each group consists, show very imperfectly by their attitudes, and not at all by their expressions, the relations in which they stand to each other: the respective groups might be separated with but little loss of meaning; and the centre of chief interest, which should link all parts together, is often inconspicuous. The same trait may be noted in the tapestries of medieval days. Representing perhaps a hunting scene, one of these contains men, horses, dogs, beasts, birds, trees, and flowers, miscellaneously dispersed: the living objects being variously occupied, and mostly with no apparent consciousness of each other's proximity. But in the paintings since produced, faulty as many of them are in this respect, there is always a more or less distinct coordination of parts—an arrangement of attitudes, expressions, lights, and colors, such as to combine the picture into an organic whole; and the success with which unity of effect is educed from variety of components, is a chief test of merit.

In music, progressive integration is displayed in still more numerous ways. The simple cadence embracing but a few notes, which in the chants of savages is monotonously repeated, becomes, among civilized races, a long series of different musical phrases combined into one whole; and so complete is the integration, that the melody cannot be broken off in the middle, nor shorn of its final note, without giving us a painful sense of incompleteness. When to the air, a bass, a tenor, and an alto are added; and when to the harmony of different voice-parts there is added an accompaniment; we see exemplified integrations of another order, which grow gradually more elaborate. And the process is carried a stage higher when these complex solos, concerted pieces, choruses, and orchestral effects, are combined into the vast ensemble of a musical drama; of which, be it remembered, the artistic perfection largely consists in the subordination of the particular effects to the total effect.

Once more the Arts of literary delineation, narrative and dramatic, furnish us with parallel illustrations. The tales of primitive times, like those with which the story-tellers of the East still daily amuse their listeners, are made up of successive occurrences that are not only in themselves unnatural, but have no natural connection: they are but so many separate adventures put together without necessary sequence. But in a good modern work of imagination, the events are the proper products of the characters working under given conditions; and cannot at will be changed in their order or kind, without injuring or destroying the general effect. Further, the characters themselves, which in early fictions play their respective parts without showing how their minds are modified by one another or by the events, are now presented to us as held together by complex moral relations, and as acting and reacting upon one another's natures.

§ 115. Evolution then, under its primary aspect, is a change from a less coherent form to a more coherent form, consequent on the dissipation of motion and integration of matter. This is the universal process through which sensible existences, individually and as a whole, pass during the ascending halves of their histories. This proves to be a character displayed equally in those earliest changes which the universe at large is supposed to have undergone, and in those latest changes which we trace in society and the products of social life. And throughout, the unification proceeds in several ways simultaneously.

Alike during the evolution of the Solar System, of a planet, of an organism, of a nation, there is progressive aggregation of the entire mass, This may be shown by the increasing density of the matter already contained in it; or by the drawing into it of matter that was before separate; or by both. But in any case it implies a loss of relative motion. At the same time, the parts into which the mass has divided, severally consolidate in like manner. We see this in that formation of planets and satellites which has

gone on along with the concentration of the nebula out of
which the Solar System originated; we see in it the growth
of separate organs that advances, *pari passu*, with the growth
of each organism; we see it in that rise of special industrial
centres and special masses of population, which is associated
with the rise of each society. Always more or less of local
integration accompanies the general integration. And then,
beyond the increased closeness of juxtaposition among the
components of the whole, and among the components of
each part, there is increased closeness of combination among
the parts, producing mutual dependence of them. Dimly
foreshadowed as this mutual dependence is in inorganic
existences, both celestial and terrestrial, it becomes distinct
in organic and super-organic existences. From the lowest
living forms upward, the degree of development is marked
by the degree in which the several parts constitute a co-
operative assemblage. The advance from those creatures
which live on in each part when cut to pieces, up to those
creatures which cannot lose any considerable part without
death, nor any inconsiderable part without great constitutional disturbance, is an advance to creatures which, while
more integrated in respect to their solidification, are also
more integrated as consisting of organs that live for and by
each other. The like contrast between undeveloped and
developed societies, need not be shown in detail: the ever-
increasing co-ordination of parts, is conspicuous to all. And
it must suffice just to indicate that the same thing holds true
of social products: as, for instance, of Science; which has
become highly integrated not only in the sense that each
division is made up of mutually-dependent propositions, but
in the sense that the several divisions are mutually dependent—cannot carry on their respective investigations without
aid from one another.

CHAPTER XV

THE LAW OF EVOLUTION CONTINUED

§ 116. CHANGES great in their amounts and various in their kinds, which accompany those dealt with in the last chapter, have thus far been wholly ignored—or, if tacitly recognized, have not been avowedly recognized. Integration of each whole has been described as taking place simultaneously with integration of each of the parts into which the whole divides itself. But how comes each whole to divide itself into parts? This is a transformation more remarkable than the passage of the whole from an incoherent to a coherent state; and a formula which says nothing about it omits more than half the phenomena to be formulated.

This larger half of the phenomena we have now to treat. In this chapter we are concerned with those secondary redistributions of matter and motion that go on along with the primary redistribution. We saw that while in very incoherent aggregates, secondary redistributions produce but evanescent results, in aggregates that reach and maintain a certain medium state, neither very incoherent nor very coherent, results of a relatively persistent character are produced—structural modifications. And our next inquiry must be—What is the universal expression for these structural modifications?

Already an implied answer has been given by the title—Compound Evolution. Already in distinguishing as simple Evolution, that integration of matter and dissipation of motion which is unaccompanied by secondary redistributions, it has been tacitly asserted that where secondary redistributions occur, complexity arises. Obviously if, while there has gone on a transformation of the incoherent into the coherent, there have gone on other transformations, the mass, instead of remaining uniform, must have become multiform. The proposition is an identical one. To say that the primary redistribution is accompanied by secondary redistributions, is to say that along with the change from a diffused to a concentrated state, there goes on a change from a homogeneous state to a heterogeneous state. The components of the mass while they become integrated also become differentiated.[1]

This, then, is the second aspect under which we have to study Evolution. As, in the last chapter, we contemplated existences of all orders as displaying progressive integration; so, in this chapter, we have to contemplate them as displaying progressive differentiation.

§ 117. A growing variety of structure throughout our Sidereal System, is implied by the contrasts that indicate an aggregative process throughout it. We have nebulæ that are diffused and irregular, and others that are spiral, annular, spherical, etc. We have groups of stars the members of which are scattered, and groups concentrated in all degrees down to closely-packed globular clusters. We have these groups differing in the numbers of their members, from those containing several thousand stars to those containing but two. Among individual stars there are great contrasts, real as well as apparent, of size; and from their unlike colors, as well as from their unlike spectra, numerous contrasts among their physical states are inferable. Beyond which heterogeneities in detail there are general heterogeneities. Nebulæ are abundant in some regions of the heavens, while

---

[1] The terms here used must be understood in relative senses. Since we know of no such thing as absolute diffusion or absolute concentration, the change can never be anything but a change from a more diffused to a less diffused state—from smaller coherence to greater coherence; and, similarly, as no concrete existences present us with absolute simplicity—as nothing is perfectly uniform—as we nowhere find complete homogeneity—the transformation is literally always toward greater complexity, or increased multiformity, or further heterogeneity. This qualification the reader must habitually bear in mind.

in others there are only stars. Here the celestial spaces are almost void of objects; and there we see dense aggregations, nebular and stellar together.

The matter of our Solar System during its concentration has become more multiform. The aggregating gaseous spheroid, dissipating its motion, acquiring more marked unlikenesses of density and temperature between interior and exterior, and leaving behind from time to time annular portions of its mass, underwent differentiations that increased in number and degree, until there was evolved the existing organized group of sun, planets, and satellites. The heterogeneity of this is variously displayed. There are the immense contrasts between the sun and the planets, in bulk and in weight; as well as the subordinate contrasts of like kind between one planet and another, and between the planets and their satellites. There is the further contrast between the sun and the planets in respect of temperature; and there is reason to suppose that the planets and satellites differ from one another in their proper heats, as well as in the heats which they receive from the sun. Bearing in mind that they also differ in the inclinations of their orbits, the inclinations of their axes, in their specific gravities and in their physical constitutions, we see how decided is the complexity wrought in the Solar System by those secondary redistributions that have accompanied the primary redistribution.

§ 118. Passing from this hypothetical illustration, which must be taken for what it is worth, without prejudice to the general argument, let us descend to an order of evidence less open to objection.

It is now generally agreed among geologists that the Earth was once a mass of molten matter, and that its inner parts are still fluid and incandescent. Originally, then, it was comparatively homogeneous in consistence; and, because of the circulation that takes place in heated fluids, must have been comparatively homogeneous in temperature.

It must, too, have been surrounded by an atmosphere consisting partly of the elements of air and water, and partly of those various other elements which assume gaseous forms at high temperatures. That cooling by radiation which, though originally far more rapid than now, necessarily required an immense time to produce decided change, must at length have resulted in differentiating the portion most able to part with its heat; namely, the surface. A further cooling, leading to deposition of all solidifiable elements contained in the atmosphere, and finally to precipitation of the water and separation of it from the air, must thus have caused a second marked differentiation; and as the condensation must have commenced on the coolest parts of the surface—namely, about the poles—there must so have resulted the first geographical distinctions.

To these illustrations of growing heterogeneity, which, though deduced from the known laws of matter, may be regarded as hypothetical, Geology adds an extensive series that have been inductively established. The Earth's structure has been age after age further involved by the multiplication of the strata which form its crust; and it has been age after age further involved by the increasing composition of these strata, the more recent of which, formed from the detritus of the more ancient, are many of them rendered highly complex by the mixtures of materials they contain. This heterogeneity has been vastly increased by the action of the Earth's still molten nucleus on its envelope; whence have resulted not only a great variety of igneous rocks, but the tilting up of sedimentary strata at all angles, the formation of faults and metallic veins, the production of endless dislocations and irregularities. Again, geologists teach us that the Earth's surface has been growing more varied in elevation—that the most ancient mountain systems are the smallest, and the Andes and Himalayas the most modern; while, in all probability, there have been corresponding changes in the bed of the ocean. As a consequence of this ceaseless multiplication of differences, we now find that no considerable portion of the Earths' exposed surface, is like any other portion, either in contour, in geologic structure, or in chemical composition; and that, in most parts, the surface changes from mile to mile in all these characteristics.

There has been simultaneously going on a gradual differentiation of climates. As fast as the Earth cooled and its crust solidified, inequalities of temperature arose between those parts of its surface most exposed to the sun and those less exposed; and thus in time there came to be the marked contrasts between regions of perpetual ice and snow, regions where winter and summer alternately reign for periods varying according to the latitude, and regions where summer follows summer with scarcely an appreciable variation. Meanwhile, elevations and subsidences, recurring here and there over the Earth's crust, tending as they have done to produce irregular distribution of land and sea, have entailed various modifications of climate beyond those dependent on latitude; while a yet further series of such modifications has been produced by increasing differences of height in the lands, which have in sundry places brought arctic, temperate, and tropical climates to within a few miles of one another. The general results of these changes are, that every extensive region has its own meteorologic conditions, and that every locality in each region differs more or less from others in those conditions: as in its structure, its contour, its soil.

Thus, between our existing Earth, the phenomena of whose varied crust neither geographers, geologists, mineralogists nor meteorologists have yet enumerated, and the molten globe out of which it was evolved, the contrast in heterogeneity is sufficiently striking.

§ 119. The clearest, most numerous, and most varied illustrations of the advance in multiformity that accompanies the advance in integration, are furnished by living organic bodies. Distinguished as we found these to be by the great quantity of their contained motion, they exhibit in an extreme degree the secondary redistributions which contained motion facilitates.　The history of every plant and every animal, while it is a history of increasing bulk, is also a history of simultaneously-increasing differences among the parts.　This transformation has several aspects.

The chemical composition which is almost uniform throughout the substance of a germ, vegetal or animal, gradually ceases to be uniform.　The several compounds, nitrogenous and non-nitrogenous, which were homogeneously mixed, segregate by degrees, become diversely proportioned in diverse places, and produce new compounds by transformation or modification.　In plants the albuminous and amylaceous matters which form the substance of the embryo, give origin here to a preponderance of chlorophyll and there to a preponderance of cellulose.　Over the parts that are becoming leaf-surfaces, certain of the materials are metamorphosed into wax.　In this place starch passes into one of its isomeric equivalents, sugar; and in that place into another of its isomeric equivalents, gum.　By secondary change some of the cellulose is modified into wood; while some of it is modified into the allied substance which, in large masses, we distinguish as cork.　And the more numerous compounds thus gradually arising, initiate further unlikenesses by mingling in unlike ratios.　An animal-ovum, the components of which are at first evenly diffused among one another, chemically transforms itself in like manner. Its protein, its fats, its salts, become dissimilarly proportioned in different localities; and multiplication of isomeric forms leads to further mixtures and combinations that constitute many minor distinctions of parts.　Here a mass darkening by accumulation of hematine, presently dissolves into blood.　There fatty and albuminous matters uniting, compose nerve-tissues.　At this spot the nitrogenous substance takes on the character of cartilage; and at that, calcareous salts, gathering together in the cartilage, lay the foundation of bone.　All these chemical differentiations slowly and insensibly become more marked and more multiplied.

Simultaneously there arise contrasts of minute structure. Distinct tissues take the place of matter that had previously no recognizable unlikenesses of parts; and each of the tissues first produced undergoes secondary modifications, causing sub-species of tissues. The granular protoplasm of the vegetable germ, equally with that which forms the unfolding point of every shoot, gives origin to cells that are at first alike. Some of these, as they grow, flatten and unite by their edges to form the outer layer. Others elongate greatly, and at the same time join together in bundles to lay the foundation of woody-fibre. Before they begin to elongate, certain of these cells show a breaking-up of the lining deposit, which, during elongation, becomes a spiral thread, or a reticulated framework, or a series of rings; and by the longitudinal union of cells so lined, vessels are formed. Meanwhile each of these differentiated tissues is redifferentiated: instance that which constitutes the essential part of the leaf, the upper stratum of which is composed of chlorophyll-cells that remain closely packed, while the lower stratum becomes spongy. Of the same general character are the transformations undergone by the fertilized ovum, which, at first a cluster of similar cells, quickly reaches a stage in which these cells have become dissimilar. More frequently recurring fission of the superficial cells, a resulting smaller size of them, and subsequent union of them into an outer layer, constitute the first differentiation; and the middle area of this layer is rendered unlike the rest by still more active processes of like kind. By such modifications upon modifications, too multitudinous to enumerate here, arise the classes and sub-classes of tissues which, variously involved one with another, compose organs.

Equally conforming to the law are the changes of general shape and of the shapes of organs. All germs are at first spheres and all organs are at first buds or mere rounded lumps. From this primordial uniformity and simplicity, there takes place divergence, both of the wholes and the leading parts, toward multiformity of contour and toward complexity of contour. Cut away the compactly-folded young leaves that terminate every shoot, and the nucleus is found to be a central knob bearing lateral knobs, one of which may grow into either a leaf, a sepal, a petal, a stamen, a carpel: all these eventually-unlike parts being at first alike. The shoots themselves also depart from their primitive unity of form; and while each branch becomes more or less different from the rest, the whole exposed part of the plant becomes different from the imbedded part. So, too, is it with the organs of animals. One of the *Articulata*, for instance, has limbs that are originally indistinguishable from one another—compose a homogeneous series; but by continuous divergences there arise among them unlikenesses of size and form, such as we see in the crab and the lobster. Vertebrate creatures equally exemplify this truth. The wings and legs of a bird are of similar shapes when they bud out from the sides of the embryo.

Thus in every plant and animal, conspicuous secondary redistributions accompany the primary redistribution. A first difference between two parts; in each of these parts other differences that presently become as marked as the first; and a like multiplication of differences in geometrical progression, until there is reached that complex combination constituting the adult. This is the history of all living things whatever. Pursuing an idea which Harvey set afloat, it has been shown by Wolff and Von Baer, that during its evolution each organism passes from a state of homogeneity to a state of heterogeneity. For a generation this truth has been accepted by biologists.[1]

---

[1] It was in 1852 that I became acquainted with Von Baer's expression of this general principle. The universality of law had ever been with me a postulate, carrying with it a correlative belief, tacit if not avowed, in unity of method throughout Nature. This statement that every plant and animal, originally homogeneous becomes gradually heterogeneous, set up a process of co-ordina-

7

§ 120. When we pass from individual forms of life to life in general, and ask whether the same law is seen in the *ensemble* of its manifestations—whether modern plants and animals have more heterogeneous structures than ancient ones, and whether the Earth's present Flora and Fauna are more heterogeneous than the Flora and Fauna of the past—we find the evidence so fragmentary that every conclusion is open to dispute. Two-thirds of the Earth's surface being covered by water; a great part of the exposed land being inaccessible to, or untravelled by, the geologist; the greater part of the remainder having been scarcely more than glanced at; and even the most familiar portions, as England, having been so imperfectly explored, that a new series of strata has been added within these few years—it is manifestly impossible for us to say with any certainty what creatures have, and what have not, existed at any particular period. Considering the perishable nature of many of the lower organic forms, the metamorphosis of many sedimentary strata, and the gaps that occur among the rest, we shall see further reason for distrusting our deductions. On the

---

tion among accumulated thoughts that were previously unorganized, or but partially organized. It is true that in "Social Statics" (Part IV., §§ 12–16), written before meeting with Von Baer's formula, the development of an individual organism and the development of the social organism, are described as alike consisting in advance from simplicity to complexity, and from independent like parts to mutually-dependent unlike parts—a parallelism implied by Milne-Edwards' doctrine of "the physiological division of labor." But though admitting of extension to other super-organic phenomena, this statement was too special to admit of extension to inorganic phenomena. The great aid rendered by Von Baer's formula arose from its higher generality; since, only when organic transformations had been expressed in the most general terms, was the way opened for seeing what they had in common with inorganic transformations. The conviction that this process of change gone through by each evolving organism is a process gone through by all things, found its first coherent statement in an essay on "Progress: its Law and Cause," which I published in the "Westminister Review" for April, 1857—an essay with the first half of which this chapter coincides in substance, and partly in form. In that essay, however, as also in the first edition of this work, I fell into the error of supposing that the transformation of the homogeneous into the heterogeneous constitutes Evolution; whereas, as we have seen, it constitutes the secondary redistribution accompanying the primary redistribution in that Evolution which we distinguish as compound—or rather, as we shall presently see, it constitutes the most conspicuous part of this secondary redistribution.

SPENCER—Vol. X—15

one hand, the repeated discovery of vertebrate remains in strata previously supposed to contain none—of reptiles where only fish were thought to exist—of mammals where it was believed there were no creatures higher than reptiles; renders it daily more manifest how small is the value of negative evidence. On the other hand, the worthlessness of the assumption that we have discovered the earliest, or anything like the earliest, organic remains, is becoming equally clear. That the oldest known aqueous formations have been greatly changed by igneous action, and that still older ones have been totally transformed by it, is becoming undeniable. And the fact that sedimentary strata earlier than any we know, have been melted up, being admitted, it must also be admitted that we cannot say how far back in time this destruction of sedimentary strata has been going on. Thus it is manifest that the title *Palæozoic*, as applied to the earliest known fossiliferous strata, involves a *petitio principii;* and that for aught we know to the contrary, only the last few chapters of the Earth's biological history may have come down to us.

All inferences drawn from such scattered facts as we find must thus be extremely questionable. If, looking at the general aspect of evidence, a progressionist argues that the earliest known vertebrate remains are those of Fishes, which are the most homogeneous of the vertebrata; that Reptiles, which are more heterogeneous, are later; and that later still, and more heterogeneous still, are Mammals and Birds; it may be replied that the Palæozoic deposits, not being estuary deposits, are not likely to contain the remains of terrestrial vertebrata, which may nevertheless have existed at that era. The same answer may be made to the argument that the vertebrate fauna of the Palæozoic period, consisting, so far as we know, entirely of Fishes, was less heterogeneous than the modern vertebrate fauna, which includes Reptiles, Birds and Mammals, of multitudinous genera; or the uniformitarian may contend with great show of truth, that this appearance of higher and more varied forms in later geologic eras was

due to progressive immigration—that a continent slowly
upheaved from the ocean at a point remote from pre-existing
continents, would necessarily be peopled from them in a
succession like that which our strata display. At the same
time the counter-arguments may be proved equally incon-
clusive. When, to show that there cannot have been a continuous evolution of the more homogeneous organic forms
into the more heterogeneous ones, the uniformitarian points
to the breaks that occur in the succession of these forms;
there is the sufficient answer that current geological changes
show us why such breaks must occur, and why, by subsidences and elevations of large area, there must be produced
such marked breaks as those which divide the three great
geologic epochs. Or again, if the opponent of the development hypothesis cites the facts set forth by Professor Huxley in his lecture on "Persistent Types"—if he points out
that "of some two hundred known orders of plants, not one
is exclusively fossil," while "among animals, there is not a
single totally extinct class; and of the orders, at the outside
not more than seven per cent are unrepresented in the existing creation"—if he urges that among these some have continued from the Silurian epoch to our own day with scarcely
any change—and if he infers that there is evidently a much
greater average resemblance between the living forms of the
past and those of the present, than consists with this hypothesis; there is still a satisfactory reply, on which in fact Professor Huxley insists; namely, that we have evidence of a
"pre-geologic era" of unknown duration. And indeed,
when it is remembered, that the enormous subsidences of
the Silurian period show the Earth's crust to have been
approximately as thick then as it is now—when it is concluded that the time taken to form so thick a crust, must
have been immense as compared with the time which has
since elapsed—when it is assumed, as it must be, that during
this comparatively immense time the geologic and biologic
changes went on at their usual rates; it becomes manifest,
not only that the paleontological records which we find, do

not negative the theory of evolution, but that they are such as might rationally be looked for.

Moreover, it must not be forgotten that though the evidence suffices neither for proof nor disproof, yet some of its most conspicuous facts support the belief, that the more heterogeneous organisms and groups of organisms, have been evolved from the less heterogeneous ones. The average community of type between the fossils of adjacent strata, and still more the community that is found between the latest tertiary fossils and creatures now existing, is one of these facts. The discovery in some modern deposits of such forms as the Palæotherium and Anaplotherium, which, if we may rely on Professor Owen, had a type of structure intermediate between some of the types now existing, is another of these facts. And the comparatively recent appearance of Man, is a third fact of this kind, which possesses still greater significance. Hence we may say, that though our knowledge of past life upon the Earth is too scanty to justify us in asserting an evolution of the simple into the complex, either in individual forms or in the aggregate of forms; yet the knowledge we have, not only consists with the belief that there has been such an evolution, but rather supports it than otherwise.

§ 121. Whether an advance from the homogeneous to the heterogeneous is or is not displayed in the biological history of the globe, it is clearly enough displayed in the progress of the latest and most heterogeneous creature—Man. It is alike true that, during the period in which the Earth has been peopled, the human organism has grown more heterogeneous among the civilized divisions of the species; and that the species, as a whole, has been made more heterogeneous by the multiplication of races and the differentiation of these races from each other. In proof of the first of these positions, we may cite the fact that, in the relative development of the limbs, the civilized man departs more widely from the general type of the placental mammalia, than do the lower human races. Though often possessing well-developed body and arms, the Papuan has extremely small legs: thus reminding us of the quadrumana, in which there is no great contrast in size between the hind and fore limbs. But in the European, the greater length and massiveness of the legs has become very marked—the fore and hind limbs are relatively more heterogeneous. Again, the greater ratio which the cranial bones bear to the facial bones, illustrates the same truth. Among the vertebrata in general, evolution is marked by an increasing heterogeneity in the vertebral column, and more especially in the segments constituting the skull: the higher forms being distinguished by the relatively larger size of the bones which cover the brain, and the relatively smaller size of those which form the jaws, etc. Now, this characteristic, which is stronger in Man than in any other creature, is stronger in the European than in the savage. Moreover, judging from the greater extent and variety of faculty he exhibits, we may infer that the civilized man has also a more complex or heterogeneous nervous system than the uncivilized man; and indeed the fact is in part visible in the increased ratio which his cerebrum bears to the subjacent ganglia. If further elucidation be needed, we may find it in every nursery. The infant European has sundry marked points of resemblance to the lower human races; as in the flatness of the alæ of the nose, the depression of its bridge, the divergence and forward opening of the nostrils, the form of the lips, the absence of a frontal sinus, the width between the eyes, the smallness of the legs. Now, as the developmental process by which these traits are turned into those of the adult European, is a continuation of that change from the homogeneous to the heterogeneous displayed during the previous evolution of the embryo, which every physiologist will admit; it follows that the parallel developmental process by which the like traits of the barbarous races have been turned into those of the civilized races, has also been a continuation of the change from the homogeneous to the heterogeneous. The truth of the second position—that Mankind, as a whole, have become more heterogeneous—is so obvious as scarcely to need illustration. Every work on Ethnology, by its divisions and subdivisions of races, bears testimony to it. Even were we to admit the hypothesis that Mankind originated from several separate stocks, it would still remain true that as, from each of these stocks, there have sprung many now widely different tribes, which are proved by philological evidence to have had a common origin, the race as a whole is far less homogeneous than it once was. Add to which, that we have, in the Anglo-Americans, an example of a new variety arising within these few generations; and that, if we may trust to the descriptions of observers, we are likely soon to have another such example in Australia.

§ 122. On passing from Humanity under its individual form, to Humanity as socially embodied, we find the general law still more variously exemplified. The change from the homogeneous to the heterogeneous, is displayed equally in the progress of civilization as a whole, and in the progress of every tribe or nation; and is still going on with increasing rapidity.

As we see in existing barbarous tribes, society in its first and lowest form is a homogeneous aggregation of individuals having like powers and like functions: the only marked difference of function being that which accompanies difference of sex. Every man is warrior, hunter, fisherman, toolmaker, builder; every woman performs the same drudgeries; every family is self-sufficing, and, save for purposes of aggression and defence, might as well live apart from the rest. Very early, however, in the process of social evolution, we find an incipient differentiation between the governing and the governed. Some kind of chieftainship seems coeval with the first advance from the state of separate wandering families to that of a nomadic tribe. The authority of the strongest makes itself felt among a body of savages, as in a herd of animals, or a posse of schoolboys. At first, however, it is indefinite, uncertain; is shared by others of scarcely inferior power; and is unaccompanied by any difference in occupation or style of living: the first ruler kills his own game, makes his own weapons, builds his own hut, and, economically considered, does not differ from others of his tribe. Gradually, as the tribe progresses, the contrast between the governing and the governed grows more decided. Supreme power becomes hereditary in one family; the head of that family, ceasing to provide for his own wants, is served by others; and he begins to assume the sole office of ruling. At the same time there has been arising a co-ordinate species of government—that of Religion. As all ancient records and traditions prove, the earliest rulers are regarded as divine personages. The maxims and commands they uttered during their lives are held sacred after their deaths, and are enforced by their divinely-descended successors; who in their turns are promoted to the pantheon of the race, there to be worshipped and propitiated along with their predecessors; the most ancient of whom is the supreme god, and the rest subordinate gods. For a long time these connate forms of government—civil and religious—continue closely associated. For many generations the king continues to be the chief priest, and the priesthood to be members of the royal race. For many ages religious law continues to contain more or less of civil regulation, and civil law to possess more or less of religious sanction; and even among the most advanced nations these two controlling agencies are by no means completely differentiated from each other. Having a common root with these, and gradually diverging from them, we find yet another controlling agency—that of Manners or ceremonial usages. All titles of honor are originally the names of the god-king; afterward of God and the king; still later of persons of high rank; and finally come, some of them, to be used between man and man. All forms of complimentary address were at first the expressions of submission from prisoners to their conqueror, or from subjects to their ruler, either human or divine—expressions that were afterward used to propitiate subordinate authorities, and slowly descended into ordinary intercourse. All modes of salutation were once obeisances made before the monarch and used in worship of him after his death. Presently others of the god-descended race were similarly saluted; and by degrees some of the salutations have become the due of all.[1] Thus, no sooner does the originally homogeneous social mass differentiate into the governed and the governing parts, than this last exhibits an incipient differentiation into religious and secular—Church and State; while at the same time there begins to be differentiated from both, that less definite species of government which rules our daily intercourse—a species of government which, as we may see in heralds' colleges, in books of the peerage, in masters of ceremonies, is not without a certain embodiment of its own. Each of these kinds of government is itself subject to successive differentiations. In the course of ages, there arises, as among ourselves, a highly complex political organization of monarch, ministers, lords and commons, with their subordinate administrative departments, courts of justice, revenue offices, etc., supplemented in the provinces by municipal governments, county governments, parish or union governments—all of them more or less elaborated. By its side there grows up a highly complex religious organization, with its various grades of officials from archbishops down to sextons, its colleges, convocations, ecclesiastical courts, etc.; to all which must be added the ever-multiplying independent sects, each with its general and local authorities. And at the same time there is developed a highly complex aggregation of customs, manners, and temporary fashions, enforced by society at large, and serving to control those minor transactions between man and man which are not regulated by civil and religious law. Moreover, it is to be observed that this ever-increasing heterogeneity in the governmental appliances of each nation, has been accompanied by an increasing

[1] For detailed proof of these assertions see essay on "Manners and Fashion."

heterogeneity in the governmental appliances of different nations: all of which are more or less unlike in their political systems and legislation, in their creeds and religious institutions, in their customs and ceremonial usages.

Simultaneously there has been going on a second differentiation of a more familiar kind; that, namely, by which the mass of the community has been segregated into distinct classes and orders of workers. While the governing part has undergone the complex development above detailed, the governed part has undergone an equally complex development; which has resulted in that minute division of labor characterizing advanced nations. It is needless to trace out this progress from its first stages, up through the caste divisions of the East and the incorporated guilds of Europe, to the elaborate producing and distributing organization existing among ourselves. Political economists have long since indicated the evolution which, beginning with a tribe whose members severally perform the same actions, each for himself, ends with a civilized community whose members severally perform different actions for each other; and they have further pointed out the changes through which the solitary producer of any one commodity is transformed into a combination of producers who, united under a master, take separate parts in the manufacture of such commodity. But there are yet other and higher phases of this advance from the homogeneous to the heterogeneous in the industrial organization of society. Long after considerable progress has been made in the division of labor among the different classes of workers, there is still little or no division of labor among the widely separated parts of the community: the nation continues comparatively homogeneous in the respect that in each district the same occupations are pursued. But when roads and other means of transit become numerous and good, the different districts begin to assume different functions, and to become mutually dependent. The calico manufacture locates itself in this county, the woollen manufacture in that; silks are produced here, lace there; stock-

ings in one place, shoes in another; pottery, hardware, cut-
lery, come to have their special towns; and ultimately every
locality grows more or less distinguished from the rest by
the leading occupation carried on in it. Nay, more, this
subdivision of functions shows itself not only among the
different parts of the same nation, but among different nations. That exchange of commodities which free-trade
promises so greatly to increase, will ultimately have the
effect of specializing, in a greater or less degree, the industry of each people. So that beginning with a barbarous
tribe, almost if not quite homogeneous in the functions
of its members, the progress has been, and still is, toward
an economic aggregation of the whole human race; growing
ever more heterogeneous in respect of the separate functions
assumed by separate nations, the separate functions assumed
by the local sections of each nation, the separate functions
assumed by the many kinds of makers and traders in each
town, and the separate functions assumed by the workers
united in producing each commodity.

§ 123. Not only is the law thus clearly exemplified in
the evolution of the social organism, but it is exemplified
with equal clearness in the evolution of all products of
human thought and action; whether concrete or abstract,
real or ideal. Let us take Language as our first illustration.
The lowest form of language is the exclamation, by which
an entire idea is vaguely conveyed through a single sound;
as among the lower animals. That human language ever
consisted solely of exclamations, and so was strictly homogeneous in respect of its parts of speech, we have no evidence. But that language can be traced down to a form
in which nouns and verbs are its only elements, is an established fact. In the gradual multiplication of parts of speech
out of these primary ones—in the differentiation of verbs
into active and passive, of nouns into abstract and concrete—in the rise of distinctions of mood, tense, person, of
number and case—in the formation of auxiliary verbs,

of adjectives, adverbs, pronouns, prepositions, articles—
in the divergence of those orders, genera, species, and
varieties of parts of speech by which civilized races express minute modifications of meaning—we see a change
from the homogeneous to the heterogeneous. And it may
be remarked, in passing, that it is more especially in virtue
of having carried this subdivision of functions to a greater
extent and completeness, that the English language is superior to all others. Another aspect under which we may
trace the development of language, is the differentiation of
words of allied meanings. Philology early disclosed the
truth that in all languages words may be grouped into
families having a common ancestry. An aboriginal name
applied indiscriminately to each of an extensive and ill-
defined class of things or actions, presently undergoes
modifications by which the chief divisions of the class are
expressed. These several names springing from the primitive root, themselves become the parents of other names
still further modified. And by the aid of those systematic
modes which presently arise, of making derivatives and forming compound terms expressing still smaller distinctions,
there is finally developed a tribe of words so heterogeneous
in sound and meaning, that to the uninitiated it seems incredible they should have had a common origin. Meanwhile, from other roots there are being evolved other such
tribes, until there results a language of some sixty thousand
or more unlike words, signifying as many unlike objects,
qualities, acts. Yet another way in which language in general advances from the homogeneous to the heterogeneous,
is in the multiplication of languages. Whether, as Max
Müller and Bunsen think, all languages have grown from
one stock, or whether, as some philologists say, they have
grown from two or more stocks, it is clear that since large
families of languages, as the Indo-European, are of one
parentage, they have become distinct through a process of
continuous divergence. The same diffusion over the Earth's
surface which has led to the differentiation of the race, has

simultaneously led to a differentiation of their speech: a truth which we see further illustrated in each nation by the peculiarities of dialect found in separate districts. Thus the progress of Language conforms to the general law, alike in the evolution of languages, in the evolution of families of words, and in the evolution of parts of speech.

On passing from spoken to written language, we come upon several classes of facts, all having similar implications. Written language is connate with Painting and Sculpture; and at first all three are appendages of Architecture, and have a direct connection with the primary form of all Government—the theocratic. Merely noting by the way the fact that sundry wild races, as for example the Australians and the tribes of South Africa, are given to depicting personages and events upon the walls of caves, which are probably regarded as sacred places, let us pass to the case of the Egyptians. Among them, as also among the Assyrians, we find mural paintings used to decorate the temple of the god and the palace of the king (which were, indeed, originally identical); and as such they were governmental appliances in the same sense that state-pageants and religious feasts were. Further, they were governmental appliances in virtue of representing the worship of the god, the triumphs of the god-king, the submission of his subjects, and the punishment of the rebellious. And yet again they were governmental, as being the products of an art reverenced by the people as a sacred mystery. From the habitual use of this pictorial representation, there naturally grew up the but slightly-modified practice of picture-writing—a practice which was found still extant among the Mexicans at the time they were discovered. By abbreviations analogous to those still going on in our own written and spoken language, the most familiar of these pictured figures were successively simplified; and ultimately there grew up a system of symbols, most of which had but a distant resemblance to the things for which they stood. The inference that the hieroglyphics of the Egyptians were thus produced, is confirmed by the fact that the picture-writing of the Mexicans was found to have given birth to a like family of ideographic forms; and among them, as among the Egyptians, these had been partially differentiated into the *kuriological* or imitative, and the *tropical* or symbolic: which were, however, used together in the same record. In Egypt, written language underwent a further differentiation; whence resulted the *hieratic* and the *epistolographic* or *enchorial:* both of which are derived from the original hieroglyphic. At the same time we find that for the expression of proper names, which could not be otherwise conveyed, phonetic symbols were employed; and though it is alleged that the Egyptians never actually achieved complete alphabetic writing, yet it can scarcely be doubted that these phonetic symbols occasionally used in aid of their ideographic ones, were the germs out of which alphabetic writing grew. Once having become separate from hieroglyphics, alphabetic writing itself underwent numerous differentiations—multiplied alphabets were produced: between most of which, however, more or less connection can still be traced. And in each civilized nation there has now grown up, for the representation of one set of sounds, several sets of written signs, used for distinct purposes. Finally, through a yet more important differentiation came printing; which, uniform in kind as it was at first, has since become multiform.

§ 124. While written language was passing through its earlier stages of development, the mural decoration which formed its root was being differentiated into Painting and Sculpture. The gods, kings, men, and animals represented, were originally marked by indented outlines and colored. In most cases these outlines were of such depth, and the object they circumscribed so far rounded and marked out in its leading parts, as to form a species of work intermediate between intaglio and bass-relief. In other cases we see an advance upon this: the raised spaces between the figures being chiselled off, and the figures themselves appropriately tinted, a painted bass-relief was produced. The restored Assyrian architecture at Sydenham, exhibits this style of art carried to greater perfection—the persons and things represented, though still barbarously colored, are carved out with more truth and in greater detail; and in the winged lions and bulls used for the angles of gateways, we may see a considerable advance toward a completely sculptured figure; which, nevertheless, is still colored, and still forms part of the building. But while in Assyria the production of a statue proper, seems to have been little, if at all, attempted, we may trace in Egyptian art the gradual separation of the sculptured figure from the wall. A walk through the collection in the British Museum will clearly show this; while it will at the same time afford an opportunity of observing the evident traces which the independent statues bear of their derivation from bass-relief: seeing that nearly all of them not only display that union of the limbs with the body which is the characteristic of bass-relief, but have the back of the statue united from head to foot with a block which stands in place of the original wall. Greece repeated the leading stages of this progress. As in Egypt and Assyria, these twin arts were at first united with each other and with their parent, Architecture; and were the aids of Religion and Government. On the friezes of Greek temples, we see colored bass-reliefs representing sacrifices, battles, processions, games—all in some sort religious. On the pediments we see painted sculptures more or less united with the tympanum, and having for subjects the triumphs of gods or heroes. Even when we come to statues that are definitely separated from the buildings to which they pertain, we still find them colored; and only in the later periods of Greek civilization, does the differentiation of sculpture from painting appear to have become complete. In Christian art we may clearly trace a parallel regenesis. All early paintings and sculptures throughout Europe were religious in subject—represented Christs, crucifixions, virgins, holy families, apostles, saints. They formed integral parts of church architecture, and were among the means of exciting worship: as in Roman Catholic countries they still are. Moreover, the early sculptures of Christ on the cross, of virgins, of saints, were colored; and it needs but to call to mind the painted madonnas and crucifixes still abundant in Continental churches and highways, to perceive the significant fact that painting and sculpture continue in closest connection with each other, where they continue in closest connection with their parent. Even when Christian sculpture was pretty clearly differentiated from painting, it was still religious and governmental in its subjects—was used for tombs in churches and statues of kings; while, at the same time, painting, where not purely ecclesiastical, was applied to the decoration of palaces, and besides representing royal personages, was almost wholly devoted to sacred legends. Only in quite recent times have painting and sculpture become entirely secular arts. Only within these few centuries has painting been divided into historical, landscape, marine, architectural, genre, animal, still-life, etc., and sculpture grown heterogenous in respect of the variety of real and ideal subjects with which it occupies itself.

Strange as it seems then, we find it no less true, that all forms of written language, of painting, and of sculpture, have a common root in the politico-religious decorations of ancient temples and palaces. Little resemblance as they now have, the bust that stands on the console, the landscape that hangs against the wall, and the copy of the "Times" lying upon the table, are remotely akin; not only in nature, but by extraction. The brazen face of the knocker which the postman has just lifted, is related not only to the woodcuts of the "Illustrated London News" which he is delivering, but to the characters of the *billet-doux* which accompanies it. Between the painted window, the prayer-book on which its light falls, and the adjacent monument, there is consanguinity. The effigies on our coins, the signs over shops, the figures that fill every ledger, the coat of arms outside the carriage-panel, and the placards inside the omnibus, are, in common with dolls, blue-books and paper-hangings, lineally descended from the rude sculpture-paintings in which the Egyptians represented the triumphs and worship of their god-kings. Perhaps no example can be given which more vividly illustrates the multiplicity and heterogeneity of the products that in course of time may arise by successive differentiations from a common stock.

Before passing to other classes of facts, it should be observed that the evolution of the homogeneous into the heterogeneous is displayed not only in the separation of Painting and Sculpture from Architecture and from each other, and in the greater variety of subjects they embody; but it is further shown in the structure of each work. A modern picture or statue is of far more heterogeneous nature than an ancient one. An Egyptian sculpture-fresco represents all its figures as on one plane—that is, at the same distance from the eye; and so is less heterogeneous than a painting that represents them as at various distances from the eye. It exhibits all objects as exposed to the same degree of light; and so is less heterogeneous than a painting which exhibits different objects, and different parts of each object, as in different degrees of light. It uses scarcely any but the primary colors, and these in their full intensity; and so is less heterogeneous than a painting which, introducing the primary colors but sparingly, employs an endless variety of intermediate tints, each of heterogeneous composition, and differing from the rest not only in quality but in intensity. Moreover, we see in these earliest works a great uniformity of conception. The same arrangement of figures is perpetually reproduced—the same actions, attitudes, faces, dresses. In Egypt the modes of representation were so fixed that it was sacrilege to introduce a novelty; and indeed it could have been only in consequence of a fixed mode of representation that a system of hieroglyphics became possible. The Assyrian bass-reliefs display parallel characters. Deities, kings, attendants, winged-figures and animals, are severally depicted in like positions, holding like implements, doing like things, and with like expression or non-expression of face. If a palm-grove is introduced, all the trees are of the same height, have the same number of leaves, and are equidistant. When water is imitated, each wave is a counterpart of the rest; and the fish, almost always of one kind, are evenly distributed over the surface. The beards of the kings, the gods, and the winged-figures, are everywhere similar; as are the manes of the lions, and equally so those of the horses. Hair is represented throughout by one form of curl. The king's beard is quite architecturally built up of compound tiers of uniform curls, alternating with twisted tiers placed in a transverse direction, and arranged with perfect regularity; and the terminal tufts of the bulls' tails are represented in exactly the same manner. Without tracing out analogous facts in early Christian art, in which, though less striking, they are still visible, the advance in heterogeneity will be sufficiently manifest on remembering that in the pictures of our own day the composition is endlessly varied; the attitudes, faces, expressions, unlike; the subordinate objects different in size, form, position, texture; and more or less of contrast even in the smallest details. Or, if we compare an Egyptian statue, seated bolt upright on a block, with hands on knees, fingers outspread and parallel, eyes looking straight forward, and the two sides perfectly symmetrical in every particular, with a statue of the advanced Greek or the modern school, which is asymmetrical in respect of the position of the head, the body, the limbs, the arrangement of the hair, dress, appendages, and in its relations to neighboring objects, we shall see the change from the homogeneous to the heterogeneous clearly manifested.

§ 125. In the co-ordinate origin and gradual differentiation of Poetry, Music, and Dancing, we have another series of illustrations. Rhythm in speech, rhythm in sound, and rhythm in motion, were, in the beginning, parts of the same thing; and have only in process of time become separate things. Among various existing barbarous tribes we find them still united. The dances of savages are accompanied by some kind of monotonous chant, the clapping of hands, the striking of rude instruments: there are measured movements, measured words, and measured tones; and the whole ceremony, usually having reference to war or sacrifice, is of governmental character. In the early records of the historic races we similarly find these three forms of metrical action united in religious festivals. In the Hebrew writings we read that the triumphal ode composed by Moses on the defeat of the Egyptians, was sung to an accompaniment of dancing and timbrels. The Israelites danced and sung "at the inauguration of the golden calf. And as it is generally agreed that this representation of the Deity was borrowed from the mysteries of Apis, it is probable that the dancing was copied from that of the Egyptians on those occasions." There was an annual dance in Shiloh on the sacred festival; and David danced before the Ark. Again, in Greece the like relation is everywhere seen: the original type being there, as probably in other cases, a simultaneous chanting and mimetic representation of the life and adventures of the god. The Spartan dances were accompanied by hymns and songs; and in general the Greeks had "no festivals or religious assemblies but what were accompanied with songs and dances"—both of them being forms of worship used before altars. Among the Romans, too, there were sacred dances: the Salian and Lupercalian being named as of that kind. And even in Christian countries, as at Limoges in comparatively recent times, the people have danced in the choir in honor of a saint. The incipient separation of these once united arts from each other and from religion, was early visible in Greece. Probably diverging from dances partly religious, partly warlike, as the Corybantian, came the war-dances proper, of which there were various kinds; and from these resulted secular dances. Meanwhile Music and Poetry, though still united, came to have an existence separate from dancing. The aboriginal Greek poems, religious in subject, were not recited but chanted; and though at first the chant of the poet was accompanied by the dance of the chorus, it ultimately grew into independence. Later still, when the poem had been differentiated into epic and lyric—when it became the custom to sing the lyric and recite the epic—poetry proper was born. As during the same period musical instruments were being multiplied, we may presume that music came to have an existence apart from words. And both of them were beginning to assume other forms besides the religious. Facts having like implications might be cited from the histories of later times and peoples; as the practices of our own early minstrels, who sang to the harp heroic narratives versified by themselves to music of their own composition: thus uniting the now separate offices of poet, composer, vocalist and instrumentalist. But without further illustration the common origin and gradual differentiation of Dancing, Poetry, and Music will be sufficiently manifest.

The advance from the homogeneous to the heterogeneous is displayed not only in the separation of these arts from each other and from religion, but also in the multiplied differentiations which each of them afterward undergoes. Not to dwell upon the numberless kinds of dancing that have, in course of time, come into use; and not to occupy space in detailing the progress of poetry, as seen in the development of the various forms of metre, of rhyme, and of general organization; let us confine our attention to music as a type of the group. As argued by Dr. Burney, and as implied by the customs of still extant barbarous races, the first musical instruments were, without doubt, percussive—sticks, calabashes, tom-toms—and were used simply to mark the time of the dance; and in this constant repetition of the same sound, we see music in its most homogeneous form. The Egyptians had a lyre with three strings. The early lyre of the Greeks had four, constituting their tetrachord. In course of some centuries lyres of seven and eight strings were employed. And, by the expiration of a thousand years, they had advanced to their "great system" of the double octave. Through all which changes there of course arose a greater heterogeneity of melody. Simultaneously there came into use the different modes—Dorian, Ionian, Phrygian, Æolian, and Lydian—answering to our keys: and of these there were ultimately fifteen. As yet, however, there was but little heterogeneity in the time of their music. Instrumental music during this period being merely the accompaniment of vocal music, and vocal music being completely subordinated to words—the singer being also the poet, chanting his own compositions and making the lengths of his notes agree with the feet of his verses; there unavoidably arose a tiresome uniformity of measure, which, as Dr. Burney says, "no resources of melody could disguise." Lacking the complex rhythm obtained by our equal bars and unequal notes, the only rhythm was that produced by the quantity of the syllables, and was of necessity comparatively monotonous. And further, it may be observed that the chant thus resulting, being like recitative, was much less clearly differentiated from ordinary speech than is our modern song. Nevertheless, considering the extended range of notes in use, the variety of modes, the occasional variations of time consequent on changes of metre, and the multiplication of instruments, we see that music had, toward the close of Greek civilization, attained to considerable heterogeneity: not indeed as compared with our music, but as compared with that which preceded it. As yet, however, there existed nothing but melody: harmony was unknown. It was not until Christian church-music had reached some development, that music in parts was evolved; and then it came into existence through a very unobtrusive differentiation. Difficult as it may be to conceive, *à priori,* how the advance from melody to harmony could take place without a sudden leap, it is none the less true that it did so. The circumstance which prepared the way for it, was the employment of two choirs singing alternately the same air. Afterward it became the practice (very possibly first suggested by a mistake) for the second choir to commence before the first had ceased; thus producing a fugue. With the simple airs then in use, a partially harmonious fugue might not improbably thus result; and a very partially harmonious fugue satisfied the ears of that age, as we know from still preserved examples. The idea having once been given, the composing of airs productive of fugal harmony would naturally grow up; as in some way it *did* grow up out of this alternate choir-singing. And from the fugue to concerted music of two, three, four, and more parts, the transition was easy. Without pointing out in detail the increasing complexity that resulted from introducing notes of various lengths, from the multiplication of keys, from the use of accidentals, from varieties of time, from modulations and so forth, it needs but to contrast music as it is, with music as it was, to see how immense is the increase of heterogeneity. We see this if, looking at music in its *ensemble,* we enumerate its many different genera and species—if we consider the divisions into vocal, instrumental, and mixed; and their subdivisions into music for different voices and different instruments—if we observe the many forms of sacred music, from the simple hymn, the chant, the canon, motet, anthem, etc., up to the oratorio; and the still more numerous forms of secular music, from the ballad up to the serenata, from the instrumental solo up to the symphony. Again, the same truth is seen on comparing any one sample of aboriginal music with a sample of modern music—even an ordinary song for the piano; which we find to be relatively highly heterogeneous, not only in respect of the varieties in the pitch and in the length of the notes, the number of different notes sounding at the same instant in company with the voice, and the variations of strength with which they are sounded and sung, but in respect of the changes of key, the changes of time, the changes of *timbre* of the voice, and the many other modifications of expression. While between the old monotonous dance-chant and a grand opera of our own day, with its endless orchestral complexities and vocal combinations, the contrast in heterogeneity is so extreme that it seems scarcely credible that the one should have been the ancestor of the other.

§ 126. Were they needed, many further illustrations might be cited. Going back to the early time when the deeds of the god-king, chanted and mimetically represented in dances round his altar, were further narrated in picture writings on the walls of temples and palaces, and so constituted a rude literature, we might trace the development of Literature through phases in which, as in the Hebrew Scriptures, it presents in one work, theology, cosmogony, history, biography, civil law, ethics, poetry; through other phases in which, as in the Iliad, the religious, martial, historical, the epic, dramatic, and lyric elements are similarly commingled; down to its present heterogeneous development, in which its divisions and subdivisions are so numerous and varied as to defy complete classification. Or we might track the evolution of Science: beginning with the era in which it was not yet differentiated from Art, and was, in union with Art, the handmaid of Religion; passing through the era in which the sciences were so few and rudimentary, as to be simultaneously cultivated by the same philosophers; and ending with the era in which the genera and species are so numerous that few can enumerate them, and no one can adequately grasp even one genus. Or we might do the like with Architecture, with the Drama, with Dress. But doubtless the reader is already weary of illustrations; and my promise has been amply fulfilled. I believe it has been shown beyond question, that that which the German physiologists have found to be a law of organic development, is a law of all development. The advance from the simple to the complex, through a process of successive differentiations, is seen alike in the earliest changes of the Universe to which we can reason our way back, and in the earliest changes which we can inductively establish; it is seen in the geologic and climatic evolution of the Earth, and of every single organism on its surface; it is seen in the evolution of Humanity, whether contemplated in the civilized individual, or in the aggregations of races; it is seen in the evolution of Society, in respect alike of its political, its religious, and its economical organization; and it is seen in the evolution of all those endless concrete and abstract products of human activity, which constitute the environment of our daily life. From the remotest past which Science can fathom, up to the novelties of yesterday, an essential trait of Evolution has been the transformation of the homogeneous into the heterogeneous.

§127. Hence the general formula arrived at in the last chapter needs supplementing. It is true that Evolution, under its primary aspect, is a change from a less coherent form to a more coherent form, consequent on the dissipation of motion and integration of matter; but this is by no means the whole truth. Along with a passage from the coherent to the incoherent, there goes on a passage from the uniform to the multiform. Such, at least, is the fact wherever Evolution is compound; which it is in the immense majority of cases. While there is a progressing concentration of the aggregate, either by the closer approach of the matter within its limits, or by the drawing in of further matter, or by both; and while the more or less distinct parts into which the aggregate divides and subdivides are severally concentrating; these parts are also becoming unlike—unlike in size, or in form, or in texture, or in composition, or in several or all of these. The same process is exhibited by the whole and by its members. The entire mass is integrating, and simultaneously differentiating from other masses; and each member of it is also integrating and simultaneously differentiating from other members.

Our conception, then, must unite these characters. As we now understand it, Evolution is definable as a change from an incoherent homogeneity to a coherent heterogeneity, accompanying the dissipation of motion and integration of matter.

CHAPTER XVI

THE LAW OF EVOLUTION CONTINUED

§ 128. BUT now, does this generalization express the whole truth? Does it include everything essentially characterizing Evolution and exclude everything else? Does it comprehend all the phenomena of secondary redistribution which Compound Evolution presents, without comprehending any other phenomena? A critical examination of the facts will show that it does neither.

Changes from the less heterogeneous to the more heterogeneous, which do not come within what we call Evolution, occur in every local disease. A portion of the body in which there arises a morbid growth, displays a new differentiation. Whether this morbid growth be, or be not, more heterogeneous than the tissues in which it is seated, is not the question. The question is, whether the organism as a whole is, or is not, rendered more heterogeneous by the addition of a part unlike every pre-existing part, in form, or composition, or both. And to this question there can be none but an affirmative answer. Again, it may be contended that the earlier stages of decomposition in a dead body involve increase of heterogeneity. Supposing the chemical changes to commence in some parts sooner than in other parts, as they commonly do; and to affect different tissues in different ways, as they must; it seems to be a necessary admission that the entire body, made up of undecomposed parts and parts decomposed in various modes and degrees, has become more heterogeneous than it was. Though greater homogeneity will be the eventual result, the immediate result is the opposite. And yet this immediate result is certainly not Evolution. Other instances are furnished by social disorders and disasters. A rebellion, which, while leaving some provinces undisturbed, develops itself here in secret societies, there in public demonstrations, and elsewhere in actual conflicts, necessarily renders the society, as a whole, more heterogeneous. Or when a dearth causes commercial derangement with its entailed bankruptcies, closed factories, discharged operatives, food-riots, incendiarisms; it is manifest that, as a large part of the community retains its ordinary organization displaying the usual phenomena, these new phenomena must be regarded as adding to the complexity previously existing. But such changes, so far from constituting further Evolution, are steps toward Dissolution.

Clearly, then, the definition arrived at in the last chapter is an imperfect one. The changes above instanced as coming within the formula as it now stands, are so obviously unlike the rest, that the inclusion of them implies some distinction hitherto overlooked. Such further distinction we have now to supply.

§ 129. At the same time that Evolution is a change from the homogeneous to the heterogeneous, it is a change from the indefinite to the definite. Along with an advance from simplicity to complexity, there is an advance from confusion to order—from undetermined arrangement to determined arrangement. Development, no matter of what kind, exhibits not only a multiplication of unlike parts, but an increase in the distinctness with which these parts are marked off from one another. And this is the distinction sought. For proof, it needs only to reconsider the instances given above. The changes constituting disease, have no such definiteness, either in locality, extent, or outline, as the changes constituting development: though certain morbid growths are more common in some parts of the body than in others (as warts on the hands, cancer on the breasts, tubercle in the lungs), yet they are not confined to these parts; nor, when found on them, are they anything like so precise in their relative positions as are the normal parts around them. Their sizes are extremely variable: they bear no such constant proportions to the body as organs do. Their forms, too, are far less specific than organic forms. And they are extremely confused in their internal structures. That is, they are in all respects comparatively indefinite. The like peculiarity may be traced in decomposition. That total indefiniteness to which a dead body is finally reduced, is a state toward which the putrefactive changes tend from their commencement. The advancing destruction of the organic compounds, blurs the minute structure—diminishes its distinctness. From the portions that have undergone most decay, there is a gradual transition to the less decayed portions. And step by step the lines of organization, once so precise, disappear. Similarly with social changes of an abnormal kind. The disaffection which initiates a political outbreak, implies a loosening of those ties by which citizens are bound up into distinct classes and subclasses. Agitation, growing into revolutionary meetings, fuses ranks that are usually separated. Acts of insubordination break through the ordained limits to individual conduct; and tend to obliterate the lines previously existing between those in authority and those beneath them. At the same time, by the arrest of trade, artisans and others lose their occupations; and in ceasing to be functionally distinguished, merge into an indefinite mass. And when at last there comes positive insurrection, all magisterial and official powers, all class distinctions, and all industrial differences, cease: organized society lapses into an unorganized aggregation of social units. Similarly, in so far as famines and pestilences cause changes from order toward disorder, they cause changes from definite arrangements to indefinite arrangements.

Thus, then, is that increase of heterogeneity which constitutes Evolution, distinguished from that increase of heterogeneity which does not do so. Though in disease and death, individual or social, the earliest modifications are additions to the pre-existing heterogeneity, they are not additions to the pre-existing definiteness. They begin from the very outset to destroy this definiteness; and gradually produce a heterogeneity that is indeterminate instead of determinate. As a city, already multiform in its variously-arranged structures of various architecture, may be made more multiform by an earthquake, which leaves part of it standing and overthrows other parts in different ways and degrees, but is at the same time reduced from orderly arrangement to disorderly arrangement; so may organized bodies be made for a time more multiform by changes which are nevertheless disorganizing changes. And in the one case as in another, it is the absence of definiteness which distinguishes the multiformity of regression from the multiformity of progression.

If advance from the indefinite to the definite is an essential characteristic of Evolution, we shall of course find it everywhere displayed; as in the last chapter we found the advance from the homogeneous to the heterogeneous. With a view of seeing whether it is so, let us now reconsider the same several classes of facts.

§ 130. Beginning, as before, with a hypothetical illustration, we have to note that each step in the evolution of the Solar System, supposing it to have originated from diffused matter, was an advance toward more definite structure. At first irregular in shape and with indistinct margin, the attenuated substance, as it concentrated and began to rotate, must have assumed the form of an oblate spheroid, which, with every increase of density, became more specific in outline, and had its surface more sharply marked off from the surrounding void. Simultaneously, the constituent portions of nebulous matter, instead of moving independently toward their common centre of gravity from all points, and revolving round it in various planes, as they would at first do, must have had these planes more and more merged into a single plane, that became less variable as the concentration progressed—became gradually defined.

According to the hypothesis, change from indistinct characters to distinct ones, was repeated in the evolution of planets and satellites; and may in them be traced much further. A gaseous spheroid is less definitely limited than a fluid spheroid, since it is subject to larger and more rapid undulations of surface, and to much greater distortions of general form; and, similarly, a liquid spheroid, covered as it must be with waves of various magnitudes, is less definite than a solid spheroid. The decrease of oblateness that goes along with increase of integration, brings relative definiteness of other elements. A planet having an axis inclined to the plane of its orbit, must, while its form is very oblate, have its plane of rotation much disturbed by the attraction of external bodies; whereas its approach to a spherical form, involving a smaller precessional motion, involves less marked variations in the direction of its axis.

With progressing settlement of the space-relations, the force-relations simultaneously become more settled. The exact calculations of physical astronomy, show us how definite these force-relations now are; while their original indefiniteness is implied in the extreme difficulty, if not impossibility, of subjecting the nebular hypothesis to mathematical treatment.

§ 131. From that primitive molten state of the Earth inferable from geological data—a state accounted for by the nebular hypothesis but inexplicable on any other—the transition to its existing state has been through stages in which the characters became more determinate. Besides being comparatively unstable in surface and contour, a liquid spheroid is less specific than a solid spheroid in having no fixed distribution of parts. Currents of molten matter, though kept to certain general circuits by the conditions of equilibrium, cannot, in the absence of solid boundaries, be precise or permanent in their directions: all parts must be in motion with respect to other parts. But a superficial solidification, even though partial, is manifestly a step toward the establishment of definite relations of position. In a thin crust, however, frequently ruptured by disturbing forces, and moved by every tidal undulation, fixity of relative position can be but temporary. Only as the crust thickens, can there arise distinct and settled geographical relations. Observe, too, that when, on a surface that has cooled to the requisite degree, there begins to precipitate the water floating above as vapor, the deposits cannot maintain any definiteness either of state or place. Falling on a solid envelope not thick enough to preserve anything beyond slight variations of level, the water must form shallow pools over areas sufficiently cool to permit condensation; which areas must pass insensibly into others that are too hot for this, and must themselves from time to time be so raised in temperature as to drive off the water lying on them. With progressing refrigeration, however—with a growing thickness of crust, a consequent formation of larger elevations and depressions, and the precipitation of more atmospheric water, there comes an arrangement of parts that is comparatively fixed in both time and space; and the definiteness of state and position increases, until there results such a distribution of continents and oceans as we now see—a distribution that is not only topographically precise, but also in its cliff-marked coast-lines presents divisions of land from water more definite than could have existed when all the uncovered areas were low islands with shelving beaches, over which the tide ebbed and flowed to great distances.

Respecting the characteristics classed as geological, we may draw parallel inferences. While the Earth's crust was thin, mountain-chains were impossibilities: there could not have been long and well-defined axes of elevation, with distinct water-sheds and areas of drainage. Moreover, the denudation of small islands by small rivers, and by tidal streams both feeble and narrow, would produce no clearly-marked sedimentary strata. Confused and varying masses of detritus, such as we now find at the mouths of brooks, must have been the prevailing formations. And these could give place to distinct strata, only as there arose continents and oceans, with their great rivers, long coast-lines, and wide-spreading marine currents.

How there must simultaneously have resulted more definite meteorological characters, need not be pointed out in detail. That differences of climates and seasons grew relatively decided as the heat of the Sun became distinguishable from the proper heat of the Earth; and that the production of more specific conditions in each locality was aided by increasing permanence in the distribution of lands and seas; are conclusions sufficiently obvious.

§ 132. Let us turn now to the evidence furnished by organic bodies. In place of deductive illustrations like the foregoing, we shall here find numerous illustrations which have been inductively established, and are therefore less open to criticism. The process of mammalian development, for example, will supply us with numerous proofs ready-described by embryologists.

The first change which the ovum of a mammal undergoes after continued segmentation has reduced its yelk to a mulberry-like mass, is the appearance of a greater definiteness in the peripheral cells of this mass; each of which acquires a distinct enveloping membrane. These peripheral cells, vaguely distinguished from the internal ones by their minuter sub-division as well as by their greater completeness, coalesce to form the blastoderm or germinal membrane. Presently, one portion of this membrane is rendered unlike the rest by the accumulation of cells still more subdivided, which, together, form an opaque roundish spot. This *area germinativa,* as it is called, shades off gradually into the surrounding parts of the blastoderm; and the *area pellucida,* subsequently formed in the midst of it, is similarly without precise margin. The "primitive trace," which makes its appearance in the centre of the *area pellucida,* and is the rudiment of that vertebrate axis which is to be the fundamental characteristic of the mature animal, is shown by its name to be at first indefinite—a mere trace. Beginning as a shallow groove, it becomes slowly more pronounced: its sides grow higher; their summits overlap, and at last unite; and so the indefinite groove passes into a definite tube, forming the vertebral canal. In this vertebral canal the leading divisions of the brain are at first discernible only as slight bulgings; while the vertebræ commence as indistinct modifications of the tissue bounding the canal. Simultaneously, the outer surface of the blastoderm has been differentiating from the inner surface: there has arisen a division into the serous and mucous layers—a division at the outset indistinct, and traceable only about the germinal area, but which insensibly spreads throughout nearly the whole germinal membrane, and becomes definite. From the mucous layer, the development of the alimentary canal proceeds as that of the vertebral canal does from the serous layer. Originally a simple channel along the under surface of the embryonic mass, the intestine is rendered distinct by the bending down, on each side, of ridges which finally join to form a tube—the permanent absorbing surface is by degrees cut off from that temporary absorbing surface with which it was continuous and uniform. And in an analogous manner the entire embryo, which at first lies outspread on the yelk-sack, gradually rises up from it, and by the infolding of its ventral region, becomes a separate mass, connected with the yelk-sack only by a narrow duct.

These changes through which the general structure is marked out with slowly-increasing precision, are paralleled in the evolution of each organ. The heart begins as a mere aggregation of cells, of which the inner liquefy to form blood, while the outer are transformed into the walls; and when thus sketched out, the heart is indefinite not only as being unlined by limiting membrane, but also as being little more than a dilatation of the central blood-vessel. By and by the receiving portion of the cavity becomes distinct from the propelling portion. Afterward there begins to grow across the ventricle, a septum, which is, however, some time before it shuts off the two halves from each other; while the later-formed septum of the auricle remains incomplete during the whole of fœtal life. Again, the liver commences by multiplication of certain cells in the wall of the intestine. The thickening produced by this multiplication "increases so as to form a projection upon the exterior of the canal"; and at the same time that the organ grows and becomes distinct from the intestine, the channels running through it are transformed into ducts having clearly-marked walls. Similarly, certain cells of the external coat of the alimentary canal at its upper portion, accumulate into lumps or buds from which the lungs are developed; and these, in their general outlines and detailed structure, acquire distinctness step by step.

Changes of this order continue long after birth; and, in the human being, are some of them not completed till middle life. During youth, most of the articular surfaces of the bones remain rough and fissured—the calcareous deposit ending irregularly in the surrounding cartilage. But between puberty and the age of thirty, these articular surfaces are finished off into smooth, hard, sharply-cut "epiphyses." Generally, indeed, we may say that increase of definiteness continues when there has ceased to be any appreciable increase of heterogeneity. And there is reason to think that those modifications which take place after maturity, bringing about old age and death, are modifications of this nature; since they cause rigidity of structure, a consequent restriction of movement and of functional pliability, a gradual narrowing of the limits within which the vital processes go on, ending in an organic adjustment too precise—too narrow in its margin of possible variation to permit the requisite adaptation to changes of external conditions.

§ 133. To prove that the Earth's Flora and Fauna, regarded either as wholes or in their separate species, have progressed in definiteness, is no more possible than it was to prove that they have progressed in heterogeneity: lack of facts being an obstacle to the one conclusion as to the other. If, however, we allow ourselves to reason from the hypothesis, now daily rendered more probable, that every species, up to the most complex, has arisen out of the simplest through the accumulation of modifications upon modifications, just as every individual arises; we shall see that there must have been a progress from the indeterminate to the determinate, both in the particular forms and in the groups of forms.

We may set out with the significant fact that the lowest organisms (which are analogous in structure to the germs of all higher ones) have so little definiteness of character that it is difficult, if not impossible, to decide whether they are plants or animals. Respecting sundry of them there are unsettled disputes between zoologists and botanists; and it is proposed to group them into a separate kingdom, forming a common basis to the animal and vegetal kingdoms. Note next that among the *Protozoa,* extreme indefiniteness of shape is general. In sundry shell-less Rhizopods the form is so irregular as to admit of no description; and it is neither alike in any two individuals nor in the same individual at successive moments. By aggregation of such creatures, are produced, among other indefinite bodies, the Sponges— bodies that are indefinite in size, in contour, in internal arrangement. As further showing how relatively indeterminate are the simplest organisms, it may be mentioned that their structures vary greatly with surrounding conditions: so much so that, among the *Protozoa* and *Protophyta,* many forms which were once classed as distinct species, and even as distinct genera, are found to be merely varieties of one species. If now we call to mind how precise in their attributes are the highest organisms—how sharply cut their outlines, how invariable their proportions, and how comparatively constant their structures under changed conditions, we cannot deny that greater definiteness is one of their characteristics. We must admit that if they have been evolved out of lower organisms, an increase of definiteness has been an accompaniment of their evolution.

That, in course of time, species have become more sharply marked off from other species, genera from genera, and orders from orders, is a conclusion not admitting of a more positive establishment than the foregoing; and must, indeed, stand or fall with it.   If, however, species and genera and orders have arisen by "natural selection," then, as Mr. Darwin shows, there must have been a tendency to divergence, causing the contrasts between groups to become greater. Disappearance of intermediate forms, less fitted for special spheres of existence than the extreme forms they connected, must have made the differences between the extreme forms decided; and so, from indistinct and unstable varieties, must slowly have been produced distinct and stable species—an inference which is in harmony with what we know respecting races of men and races of domestic animals.

§ 134. The successive phases through which societies pass, very obviously display the progress from indeterminate arrangement to determinate arrangement.   A wandering tribe of savages, being fixed neither in its locality nor in its internal distribution, is far less definite in the relative positions of its parts than a nation.   In such a tribe the social relations are similarly confused and unsettled.   Political authority is neither well established nor precise.   Distinctions of rank are neither clearly marked nor impassable. And save in the different occupations of men and women, there are no complete industrial divisions.   Only in tribes of considerable size, which have enslaved other tribes, is the economical differentiation decided.

Any one of these primitive societies, however, that evolves, becomes step by step more specific.   Increasing in size, consequently ceasing to be so nomadic, and restricted in its range by neighboring societies, it acquires, after prolonged border warfare, a settled territorial boundary.   The distinction between the royal race and the people, eventually amounts in the popular apprehension to a difference of nature.   The warrior-class attains a perfect separation from classes devoted to the cultivation of the soil, or other occupations regarded as servile. And there arises a priesthood that is defined in its rank, its functions, its privileges. This sharpness of definition, growing both greater and more variously exemplified as societies advance to maturity, is extremest in those that have reached their full development or are declining. Of ancient Egypt we read that its social divisions were precise and its customs rigid. Recent investigations make it more than ever clear, that among the Assyrians and surrounding peoples, not only were the laws unalterable, but even the minor habits, down to those of domestic routine, possessed a sacredness which insured their permanence. In India at the present day the unchangeable distinctions of caste, not less than the constancy in modes of dress, industrial processes, and religious observances, show us how fixed are the arrangements where the antiquity is great; nor does China, with its long-settled political organization, its elaborate and precise conventions, and its unprogressive literature, fail to exemplify the same truth.

The successive phases of our own and adjacent societies, furnish facts somewhat different in kind but similar in meaning. Originally, monarchical authority was more baronial, and baronial authority more monarchical, than afterward. Between modern priests and the priests of old times, who while officially teachers of religion were also warriors, judges, architects, there is a marked difference in definiteness of function. And among the people engaged in productive occupations, the like contrasts would be found to hold: the industrial class has become more distinct from the military; and its various divisions from one another. A history of our constitution, reminding us how the powers of King, Lords, and Commons, have been gradually settled, would clearly exhibit analogous changes. Countless facts bearing the like construction, would meet us were we to trace the development of legislation; in the successive stages of which we should find statutes gradually rendered more specific in their applications to particular cases. Even now we see that each new law, beginning as a vague proposition, is, in the course of enactment, elaborated into specific clauses; and further that only after its interpretation has been established by judges' decisions in courts of justice, does it reach its final definiteness. From the annals of minor institutions like evidence may be gathered. Religious, charitable, literary, and all other societies, starting with ends and methods roughly sketched out and easily modifiable, show us how, by the accumulation of rules and precedents, the purposes become more distinct and the modes of action more restricted, until at last decay follows a fixity which admits of no adaptation to new conditions. Should it be objected that among civilized nations there are examples of decreasing definiteness (instance the breaking down of limits between ranks), the reply is, that such apparent exceptions are the accompaniments of a social metamorphosis —a change from the military or predatory type of social structure to the industrial or mercantile type, during which the old lines of organization are disappearing and the new ones becoming more marked.

§ 135. All organized results of social action, all superorganic structures, pass through parallel phases. Being, as they are, objective products of subjective processes, they must display corresponding changes; and that they do this the cases of Language, of Science, of Art, clearly prove.

Strike out from our sentences everything but nouns and verbs, and there stands displayed the vagueness characterizing undeveloped tongues. When we note how each inflection of a verb, or addition by which the case of a noun is marked, serves to limit the conditions of action or of existence, we see that these constituents of speech enable men to communicate their thoughts more precisely. That the application of an adjective to a noun or an adverb to a verb narrows the class of things or changes indicated, implies that the additional word serves to make the proposition more distinct. And similarly with other parts of speech.

The like effect results from the multiplication of words of each order. When the names for objects, and acts, and qualities, are but few, the range of each is proportionately wide, and its meaning therefore unspecific. The similes and metaphors so much used by aboriginal races indirectly and imperfectly suggest ideas, which they cannot express directly and perfectly from lack of words. Or, to take a case from ordinary life: if we compare the speech of the peasant, who, out of his limited vocabulary, can describe the contents of the bottle he carries only as "doctor's stuff," which he has got for his "sick" wife, with the speech of the physician, who tells those educated like himself the particular composition of the medicine, and the particular disorder for which he has prescribed it, we have vividly brought home to us the precision which language gains by the multiplication of terms.

Again, in the course of its evolution, each tongue acquires a further accuracy through processes which fix the meaning of each word. Intellectual intercourse slowly diminishes laxity of expression. By and by dictionaries give definitions. And eventually, among the most cultivated, indefiniteness is not tolerated, either in the terms used or in their grammatical combinations.

Once more, languages considered as wholes become gradually more sharply marked off from one another, and from their common parent; as witness, in early times, the divergence from the same root of two languages so unlike as Greek and Latin, and in later times the development of three Latin dialects into Italian, French, and Spanish.

§ 136. In his "History of the Inductive Sciences," Dr. Whewell says that the Greeks failed in physical philosophy because their "ideas were not distinct and appropriate to the facts." I do not quote this remark for its luminousness, since it would be equally proper to ascribe the indistinctness and inappropriateness of their ideas to the imperfection of their physical philosophy; but I quote it because it serves as good evidence of the indefiniteness of primitive science. The same work and its fellow on "The Philosophy of the Inductive Sciences" supply other evidences equally good, because equally independent of any such hypothesis as is here to be established. Respecting mathematics, we have the fact that geometrical theorems grew out of empirical methods; and that these theorems, at first isolated, did not acquire the clearness which complete demonstration gives, until they were arranged by Euclid into a series of dependent propositions. At a later period, the same general truth was exemplified in the progress from the "method of exhaustions" and the "method of indivisibles" to the "method of limits"; which is the central idea of the infinitesimal calculus. In early mechanics, too, may be traced a dim perception that action and reaction are equal and opposite; though, for ages after, this truth remained unformulated. And similarly, the property of inertia, though not distinctly comprehended until Kepler lived, was vaguely recognized long previously. "The conception of statical force," "was never presented in a distinct form till the works of Archimedes appeared"; and "the conception of accelerating force was confused, in the mind of Kepler and his contemporaries, and did not become clear enough for purposes of sound scientific reasoning before the succeeding century." To which specific assertions may be added the general remark, that "terms which originally, and before the laws of motion were fully known, were used in a very vague and fluctuating sense, were afterward limited and rendered precise." When we turn from abstract scientific conceptions to the concrete previsions of science, of which astronomy furnishes numerous examples, a like contrast is visible. The times at which celestial phenomena will occur, have been predicted with every-increasing accuracy. Errors once amounting to days are now diminished to seconds. The correspondence between the real and supposed forms of orbits, has been gradually rendered more precise. Originally thought circular, then epicyclical, then elliptical, orbits are now ascertained to be curves which always deviate from perfect ellipses, and are ever undergoing changes.

But the general advance of Science in definiteness, is best shown by the contrast between its qualitative stage, and its quantitative stage. At first the facts ascertained were, that between such and such phenomena some connection existed—that the appearances a and b always occurred together or in succession; but it was known neither what was the nature of the relation between a and b, nor how much of a accompanied so much of b. The development of Science has in part been the reduction of these vague connections to distinct ones. Most relations have been classed as mechanical, chemical, thermal, electric, magnetic, etc.; and we have learned to infer the amounts of the antecedents and consequents from each other with exactness. Of illustrations, some furnished by physics have been given; and from other sciences plenty may be added. We have positively ascertained the constituents of numerous compounds which our ancestors could not analyze, and of a far greater number which they never even saw; and the combining equivalents of these elements are accurately calculated. Physiology shows advance from qualitative to quantitative prevision in the weighing and measuring of organic products, and of the materials consumed; as well as in measurement of functions by the spirometer and the sphygmograph. By Pathology it is displayed in the use of the statistical method of determining the sources of diseases, and the effects of treatment. In Botany and Zoology, the numerical comparisons of Floras and Faunas, leading to specific conclusions respecting their sources and distributions, illustrate it. And in Sociology, questionable as are the conclusions usually drawn from the classified sum-totals of the census, from Board-of-Trade tables, and from criminal returns, it must be admitted that these imply a progress toward more accurate conceptions of social phenomena.

That an essential characteristic of advancing Science is

increase in definiteness, appears indeed almost a truism, when we remember that Science may be described as definite knowledge, in contradistinction to that indefinite knowledge possessed by the uncultured. And if, as we cannot question, Science has, in the course of ages, been evolved out of this indefinite knowledge of the uncultured, then the gradual acquirement of that great definiteness which now distinguishes it must have been a leading trait in its evolution.

§ 137. The Arts, industrial and æsthetic, supply illustrations perhaps still more striking. Flint implements of the kind recently found in certain of the later geologic deposits show the extreme want of precision in men's first handiworks. Though a great advance on these is seen in the tools and weapons of existing savage tribes, yet an inexactness in forms and fittings distinguishes such tools and weapons from those of civilized races. In a smaller degree, the productions of the less-advanced nations are characterized by like defects. A Chinese junk, with all its contained furniture and appliances, nowhere presents a line that is quite straight, a uniform curve, or a true surface. Nor do the utensils and machines of our ancestors fail to exhibit a similar inferiority to our own. An antique chair, an old fireplace, a lock of the last century, or almost any article of household use that has been preserved for a few generations, proves by contrast how greatly the industrial products of our time excel those of the past in their accuracy. Since planing-machines have been invented it has become possible to produce absolutely straight lines, and surfaces so truly level as to be air-tight when applied to each other. While in the dividing-engine of Troughton, in the micrometer of Whitworth, and in microscopes that show fifty thousand divisions to the inch, we have an exactness as far exceeding that reached in the works of our great grandfathers as theirs exceeded that of the aboriginal celt-makers.

In the Fine Arts there has been a parallel progress.

From the rudely-carved and painted idols of savages, through the early sculptures characterized by limbs without muscular detail, wooden-looking drapery, and faces devoid of individuality, up to the later statues of the Greeks or some of those now produced, the increased accuracy of representation is conspicuous. Compare the mural paintings of the Egyptians with the paintings of medieval Europe, or these with modern paintings, and the more precise rendering of the appearances of objects is manifest. It is the same with fiction and the drama. In the marvellous tales current among Eastern nations, in the romantic legends of feudal Europe, as well as in the mystery-plays and those immediately succeeding them, we see great want of correspondence to the realities of life—alike in the predominance of supernatural events, in the extremely improbable coincidences, and in the vaguely-indicated personages. Along with social advance there has been a progressive diminution of unnaturalness—an approach to truth of representation. And now, novels and plays are applauded in proportion to the fidelity with which they exhibit individual characters; improbabilities, like the impossibilities which preceded them, are disallowed, and there is even an incipient abandonment of those elaborate plots which life rarely if ever furnishes.

§ 138. It would be easy to accumulate evidences of other kinds. The progress from myths and legends, extreme in their misrepresentations, to a history that has slowly become, and is still becoming, more accurate; the establishment of settled systematic methods of doing things, instead of the indeterminate ways at first pursued—these might be enlarged upon in further exemplification of the general law. But the basis of induction is already wide enough. Proof that all Evolution is from the indefinite to the definite, we find to be not less abundant than proof that all Evolution is from the homogeneous to the heterogeneous.

It should, however, be added that this advance in defi-

niteness is not a primary but a secondary phenomenon—
is a result incidental on other changes. The transformation
of a whole that was originally diffused and uniform into
a concentrated combination of multiform parts, implies
progressive separation both of the whole from its environment and of the parts from one another. While this is
going on there must be indistinctness. Only as the whole
gains density, does it become sharply marked off from the
space or matter lying outside of it; and only as each separated division draws into its mass those peripheral portions
which are at first imperfectly disunited from the peripheral
portions of neighboring divisions, can it acquire anything
like a precise outline. That is to say, the increasing definiteness is a concomitant of the increasing consolidation,
general and local. While the secondary redistributions are
ever adding to the heterogeneity, the primary redistribution,
while augmenting the integration, is incidentally giving distinctness to the increasingly-unlike parts as well as to the
aggregate of them.

But though this universal trait of Evolution is a necessary accompaniment of the traits set forth in preceding
chapters, it is not expressed in the words used to describe
them. It is therefore needful further to modify our formula. The more specific idea of Evolution now reached is—
a change from an indefinite, incoherent homogeneity, to a
definite coherent heterogeneity, accompanying the dissipation of motion and integration of matter.

CHAPTER XVII

THE LAW OF EVOLUTION CONCLUDED

§ 139. THE conception of Evolution elaborated in the foregoing chapters, is still incomplete. True though it is, it is not the whole truth. The transformations which all things undergo during the ascending phases of their existence, we have contemplated under three aspects; and by uniting these three aspects as simultaneously presented, we have formed an approximate idea of the transformations. But there are concomitant changes about which nothing has yet been said; and which, though less conspicuous, are no less essential.

For thus far we have attended only to the redistribution of Matter, neglecting the accompanying redistribution of Motion. Distinct or tacit reference has, indeed, repeatedly been made to the dissipation of Motion, that goes on along with the concentration of Matter; and were all Evolution absolutely simple, the total fact would be contained in the proposition that as Motion dissipates Matter concentrates. But while we have recognized the ultimate redistribution of the Motion, we have passed over its proximate redistribution. Though something has from time to time been said about the escaping motion, nothing has been said about the motion that does not escape. In proportion as Evolution becomes compound—in proportion as an aggregate retains, for a considerable time, such a quantity of motion as permits secondary redistributions of its component matter, there necessarily arise secondary redistributions of its retained motion. As fast as the parts are transformed, there goes on a transformation of the sensible or insensible motion possessed by the parts. The parts cannot become progressively integrated, either individually or as a combination, without their motions, individual or combined, becoming more integrated. There cannot arise among the parts heterogeneities of size, of form, of quality, without there also arising heterogeneities in the amounts and directions of their motions, or the motions of their molecules. And increasing definiteness of the parts implies increasing definiteness of their motions. In short, the rhythmical actions going on in each aggregate must differentiate and integrate at the same time that the structure does so.

The general theory of this redistribution of the retained motion must here be briefly stated. Properly to supplement our conception of Evolution under its material aspect by a conception of Evolution under its dynamical aspect, we have to recognize the source for the integrated motions that arise, and to see how their increased multiformity and definiteness are necessitated. If Evolution is a passage of matter from a diffused to an aggregated state—if while the dispersed units are losing part of the insensible motion which kept them dispersed, there arise among coherent masses of them any sensible motions with respect to one another, then this sensible motion must previously have existed in the form of insensible motion among the units. If concrete matter arises by the aggregation of diffused matter, then concrete motion arises by the aggregation of diffused motion. That which comes into existence as the movement of masses implies the cessation of an equivalent molecular movement. While we must leave in the shape of hypothesis the belief that the celestial motions have thus originated, we may see, as a matter of fact, that this is the genesis of all sensible motions on the Earth's surface. As before shown (§ 69), the denudation of lands and deposit of new strata are effected by water in the course of its descent to the sea, or during the arrest of those undulations produced on it by winds; and, as before shown, the elevation of water to the height whence it fell is due to solar heat, as is also the genesis of those aerial currents which drift it about when evaporated and agitate its surface when condensed. That is to say, the molecular motion of the ethereal medium is transformed into the motion of gases, thence into the motion of liquids, and thence into the motion of solids—stages in each of which a certain amount of molecular motion is lost and an equivalent motion of masses gained. It is the same with organic movements. Certain rays issuing from the Sun enable the plant to reduce special elements existing in gaseous combination around it to a solid form—enable the plant, that is, to grow and carry on its functional changes. And since growth, equally with circulation of sap, is a mode of sensible motion, while those rays which have been expended in generating it consist of insensible motions, we have here, too, a transformation of the kind alleged. Animals, derived as their forces are, directly or indirectly, from plants, carry this transformation a step further. The automatic movements of the viscera, together with the voluntary movements of the limbs and body at large, arise at the expense of certain molecular movements throughout the nervous and muscular tissues; and these originally arose at the expense of certain other molecular movements propagated by the Sun to the Earth, so that both the structural and functional motions which organic Evolution displays are motions of aggregates generated by the arrested motions of units. Even with the aggregates of these aggregates the same rule holds. For among associated men, the progress is ever toward a merging of individual actions in the actions of corporate bodies. While, then, during Evolution, the escaping motion becomes, by perpetually widening dispersion, more disintegrated, the motion that is for a time retained becomes more integrated, and so, considered dynamically, Evolution is a decrease in the relative movements of parts and an increase in the relative movements of wholes—using the words parts and wholes in their most general senses. The advance is from the motions of simple molecules to the motions of compound molecules; from molecular motions to the motions of masses; and from the motions of smaller masses to the motions of larger masses. The accompanying change toward greater multiformity among the retained motions takes place under the form of an increased variety of rhythms. We have already seen that all motion is rhythmical, from the infinitesimal vibrations of infinitesimal molecules up to those vast oscillations between perihelion and aphelion performed by vast celestial bodies. And, as the contrast between these extreme cases suggests, a multiplication of rhythms must accompany a multiplication in the degrees and modes of aggregation, and in the relations of the aggregated masses to incident forces. The degree or mode of aggregation will not, indeed, affect the rate or extent of rhythm where the incident force increases as the aggregate increases, which is the case with gravitation; here the only cause of variation in rhythm is difference of relation to the incident forces, as we see in a pendulum, which, though unaffected in its movements by a change in the weight of the bob, alters its rate of oscillation when taken to the equator. But in all cases where the incident forces do not vary as the masses, every new order of aggregation initiates a new order of rhythm: witness the conclusion drawn from the recent researches into radiant heat and light, that the molecules of different gases have different rates of undulation. So that increased multiformity in the arrangement of matter necessarily generates increased multiformity of rhythm, both through increased variety in the sizes and forms of aggregates, and through increased variety in their relations to the forces which move them. That these motions, as they become more integrated and more heterogeneous, must become more definite is a proposition that need not detain us. In proportion as any part of an evolving whole segregates and consolidates, and in so doing loses the relative mobility of its components, its aggregate motion must obviously acquire distinctness.

Here, then, to complete our conception of Evolution we have to contemplate throughout the Cosmos these metamorphoses of retained motion that accompany the metamorphoses of component matter. We may do this with comparative brevity, the reader having now become so far familiar with the mode of looking at the facts that less illustration will suffice. To save space, it will be convenient to deal with the several aspects of the metamorphoses at the same time.

§ 140. Dispersed matter moving, as we see it in a spiral nebula, toward the common centre of gravity, from all points at all distances with all degrees of indirectness, must carry into the nebulous mass eventually formed innumerable momenta contrasted in their amounts and directions. As the integration progresses, such parts of these momenta as conflict are mutually neutralized and dissipated as heat. The outstanding rotatory motion, at first having unlike angular velocities at the periphery and at various distances from the centre, has its differences of angular velocity gradually reduced, advancing toward a final state, now nearly reached by the Sun, in which the angular velocity of the whole mass is the same—in which the motion is integrated. So, too, with each planet and satellite. Progress from the motion of a nebulous ring, incoherent and admitting of much relative motion within its mass, to the motion of a dense spheroid, is progress to a motion that is completely integrated. The rotation and the translation through space severally become one and indivisible. Meanwhile, there goes on that further integration by which the motions of all the parts of the Solar System are rendered mutually dependent. Locally in each planet and its satellites, and generally in the Sun and the planets, we have a system of simple and compound rhythms, with periodic and secular variations, forming together an integrated set of movements.

The matter which, in its original diffused state, had motions that were confused, indeterminate, or without sharply marked distinctions, has, during the evolution of the Solar System, acquired definitely heterogeneous motions. The periods of revolution of all the planets and satellites are unlike, as are also their times of rotation. Out of these definitely heterogeneous motions of a simple kind arise others that are complex, but still definite—as those produced by the revolutions of satellites compounded with the revolutions of their primaries; as those of which precession is the result, and as those which are known as perturbations. Each additional complexity of structure has caused additional complexity of movements, but still a definite complexity, as is shown by having calculable results.

§ 141. While the Earth's surface was molten, the currents in the voluminous atmosphere surrounding it, mainly of ascending heated gases and of descending precipitated liquids, must have been local, numerous, indefinite, and but little distinguished from one another. But as fast as the surface cooled, and solar radiation began to cause appreciable differences of temperature between the equatorial and polar regions, a decided atmospheric circulation from poles to equator and from equator to poles must have slowly established itself; the vast moving masses of air becoming, at last, trade-winds and other such permanent definite currents. These integrated motions, once comparatively homogeneous, were rendered heterogeneous as great islands and continents arose, to complicate them by periodic winds, caused by the varied heating of wide tracts of land at different seasons. Rhythmical motions of a constant and simple kind were, by increasing multiformity of the Earth's surface, differentiated into an involved combination of constant and recurrent rhythmical motions, joined with smaller motions that are irregular.

Parallel changes must have taken place in the motions of water. On a thin crust, admitting of but small elevations and depressions, and therefore of but small lakes and seas, none beyond small local circulations were possible. But along with the formation of continents and oceans came the vast movements of water from warm latitudes to cold and from cold to warm—movements increasing in amount, in definiteness, and in variety of distribution as the features of the Earth's surface became larger and more contrasted. The like holds with drainage-waters. The tricklings of insignificant streams over narrow pieces of land were once the only motions of such waters; but as fast as wide areas came into existence the motions of many tributaries became massed into the motions of great rivers, and instead of motions very much alike there arose motions considerably varied.

Nor can we well doubt that the movements in the Earth's crust itself have presented an analogous progress. Small, numerous, local, and very much like one another, while the crust was thin, the elevations and subsidences must, as the crust thickened, have extended over larger areas, must have continued for longer eras in the same directions, and must have been made more unlike in different regions by local differences of structure in the crust.

§ 142. In organisms, the advance toward a more integrated, heterogeneous, and definite distribution of the retained motion, which accompanies the advance toward a more integrated, heterogeneous, and definite distribution of the component matter, is mainly what we understand as the development of functions. All active functions are either sensible movements, as those produced by contractile organs; or such insensible movements as those propagated through the nerves; or such insensible movements as those by which, in secreting organs, molecular rearrangements are effected, and new combinations of matter produced. And what we have here to observe is, that during evolution, functions, like structures, become more consolidated individually, as well as more combined with one another, at the same time that they become more multiform and more distinct.

The nutritive juices in animals of low types move hither and thither through the tissues quite irregularly, as local strains and pressures determine: in the absence of a distinguishable blood and a developed vascular system, there is no definite circulation. But along with the structural evolution which establishes a finished apparatus for distributing blood, there goes on the functional evolution which establishes large and rapid movements of blood, definite in their courses and definitely distinguished as efferent and afferent, and that are heterogeneous not simply in their directions but in their characters—being here divided into gushes and there continuous.

Instance, again, the way in which, accompanying the structural differentiations and integrations of the alimentary canal, there arise differentiations and integrations both of its mechanical movements and its actions of a non-mechanical kind. Along an alimentary canal of a primitive type, there pass, almost uniformly from end to end, waves of constriction. But in a well-organized alimentary canal, the waves of constriction are widely unlike at different parts, in their kinds, strengths, and rapidities. In the mouth they become movements of prehension and mastication—now occurring in quick succession and now ceasing for hours. In the œsophagus these contractions, propulsive in their office, and travelling with considerable speed, take place at intervals during eating, and then do not take place till the next meal. In the stomach another modification of this originally uniform action occurs: the muscular constrictions are powerful, and continue during the long periods that the stomach contains food. Throughout the upper intestines, again, a further difference shows itself—the waves travel along without cessation but are relatively moderate. Finally, in the rectum this rhythm departs in another way from the common type: quiescence lasting for many hours, is followed by a series of strong contractions. Meanwhile, the essential actions which these movements aid, have been growing more definitely heterogeneous. Secretion and absorption are no longer carried on in much the same way from end to end of the tube; but the general function divides into various subordinate functions. The solvents and ferments furnished by the coats of the canal and the appended glands, become widely unlike at upper, middle, and lower parts of the canal; implying different kinds of molecular changes. Here the process is mainly secretory, there it is mainly absorbent, while in other places, as in the œsophagus, neither secretion nor absorption takes place to any appreciable extent. While these and other internal motions, sensible and insensible, are being rendered more various, and severally more consolidated and distinct, there is advancing the integration by which they are united into local groups of motions and a combined system of motions. While the function of alimentation subdivides, its subdivisions become co-ordinated, so that muscular and secretory actions go on in concert, and so that excitement of one part of the canal sets up excitement of the rest. Moreover, the whole alimentary function, while it supplies matter for the circulatory and respiratory functions, becomes so integrated with them that it cannot for a moment go on without them. And, as evolution advances, all three of these fundamental functions fall into greater subordination to the nervous functions—depend more and more on the due amount of nervous discharge.

When we trace up the functions of external organs the same truth discloses itself. Microscopic creatures are moved through the water by oscillations of the cilia covering their surfaces; and various larger forms, as the *Turbellaria*, progress by ciliary action over solid surfaces. These motions of cilia are, in the first place, severally very minute; in the second place they are homogeneous; and in the third place there is but little definiteness in them individually, or in their joint product, which is mostly a mere random change of place not directed to any selected point. Contrasting this ciliary action with the action of developed locomotive organs of whatever kind, we see that instead of innumerable small or unintegrated movements there are a few comparatively large or integrated movements; that actions all alike are replaced by actions partially unlike; and that instead of being very feebly or almost accidentally co-ordinated, their co-ordination is such as to render the motions of the body, as a whole, precise. A parallel contrast, less extreme but sufficiently decided, is seen when we pass from the lower types of creatures with limbs to the higher types of creatures with limbs. The legs of a Centiped have motions that are numerous, small, and homogeneous; and are so little integrated that when the creature is divided and subdivided, the legs belonging to each part propel that part independently. But in one of the higher *Annulosa,* as a Crab, the relatively few limbs have motions that are comparatively large in their amounts, that are considerably unlike one another, and that are integrated into compound motions of tolerable definiteness.

§ 143. The last illustrations are introductory to illustrations of the kind we class as psychical. They are the physiological aspects of the simpler among those functions which, under a more special and complex aspect, we distinguish as psychological. The phenomena subjectively known as changes in consciousness, are objectively known as nervous excitations and discharges, which science now interprets into modes of motion. Hence, in following up organic evolution, the advance of retained motion in integration, in heterogeneity, and in definiteness, may be expected to show itself alike in the visible nervo-muscular actions and in the correlative mental changes. We may conveniently look at the facts as exhibited during individual evolution, before looking at them as exhibited in general evolution.

The progress of a child in speech, very completely exhibits the transformation. Infantine noises are comparatively homogeneous; alike as being severally long-drawn and nearly uniform from end to end, and as being constantly repeated with but little variation of quality between narrow limits. They are quite uncoördinated—there is no integration of them into compound sounds. They are inarticulate, or without those definite beginnings and endings characterizing the sounds we call words. Progress shows itself first in the multiplication of the inarticulate sounds: the extreme vowels are added to the medium vowels, and the compound to the simple. Presently the movements which form the simpler consonants are achieved, and some of the sounds become sharply cut; but this definiteness is partial, for only initial consonants being used, the sounds end vaguely. While an approach to distinctness thus results, there also results, by combination of different consonants with the same vowels, an increase of heterogeneity; and along with the complete distinctness which terminal consonants give, arises a further great addition to the number of unlike sounds produced. The more difficult consonants and the compound consonants, imperfectly articulated at first, are by and by articulated with precision; and there comes yet another multitude of different and definite words—words that imply many kinds of vocal movements, severally performed with exactness, as well as perfectly integrated into complex groups. The subsequent advance to dissyllables and polysyllables, and to involved combinations of words, shows the still higher degree of integration and heterogeneity eventually reached by these organic motions. The acts of consciousness correlated with these nervo-muscular acts, of course go through parallel phases; and the advance from childhood to maturity yields daily proof that the changes which, on their physical side are nervous processes, and on their mental side are processes of thought, become more various, more defined, more coherent. At first the intellectual functions are very much alike in kind—recognitions and classifications of simple impressions alone go on; but in course of time these functions become multiform. Reasoning grows distinguishable, and eventually we have conscious induction and deduction; deliberate recollection and deliberate imagination are added to simple unguided association of ideas; more special modes of mental action, as those which result in mathematics, music, poetry, arise; and within each of these divisions the mental processes are ever being further differentiated. In definiteness it is the same.

The infant makes its observations so inaccurately that it
fails to distinguish individuals. The child errs continually
in its spelling, its grammar, its arithmetic. The youth forms
incorrect judgments on the affairs of life. Only with maturity comes that precise co-ordination in the nervous processes
that is implied by a good adjustment of thoughts to things.
Lastly, with the integration by which simple mental acts are
combined into complex mental acts, it is so likewise. In
the nursery you cannot obtain continuous attention—there
is inability to form a coherent series of impressions; and
there is a parallel inability to unite many co-existent impressions, even of the same order: witness the way in which
a child's remarks on a picture, show that it attends only to
the individual objects represented, and never to the picture
as a whole. But with advancing years it becomes possible
to understand an involved sentence, to follow long trains of
reasoning, to hold in one mental grasp numerous concurrent
circumstances. The like progressive integration takes place
among the mental changes we distinguish as feelings; which
in a child act singly, producing impulsiveness, but in an
adult act more in concert, producing a comparatively balanced conduct.

After these illustrations supplied by individual evolution, we may deal briefly with those supplied by general
evolution, which are analogous to them. A creature of
very low intelligence, when aware of some large object in
motion near it, makes a spasmodic movement, causing,
it may be, a leap or a dart. The perceptions implied are
relatively simple, homogeneous, and indefinite: the moving
objects are not distinguished in their kinds as injurious or
otherwise, as advancing or receding. The actions of escape
are similarly all of one kind, have no adjustments of direction, and may bring the creature nearer the source of peril
instead of further off. A stage higher, when the dart or the
leap is away from danger, we see the nervous changes so far
specialized that there results distinction of direction; indicating a greater variety among them, a greater co-ordination

or integration of them in each process, and a greater definiteness. In still higher animals that discriminate between enemies and not-enemies, as a bird that flies from a man but not from a cow, the acts of perception have severally become united into more complex wholes, since cognition of certain differential attributes is implied; they have become more multiform, since each additional component impression adds to the number of possible compounds; and they have, by consequence, become more specific in their correspondences with objects—more definite. And then in animals so intelligent that they identify by sight not species only but individuals of a species, the mental changes are yet further distinguished in the same three ways. In the course of human evolution the law is equally manifested. The thoughts of the savage are nothing like so heterogeneous in their kinds as those of the civilized man, whose complex environment presents a multiplicity of new phenomena. His mental acts, too, are much less involved—he has no words for abstract ideas, and is found to be incapable of integrating the elements of such ideas. And in all but simple matters there is none of that precision in his thinking which, among civilized men, leads to the exact conclusions of science. Nor do the emotions fail to exhibit a parallel contrast.

§ 144. How in societies the movements or functions produced by the confluence of individual actions, increase in their amounts, their multiformities, their precision, and their combination, scarcely needs insisting upon after what has been pointed out in foregoing chapters. For the sake of symmetry of statement, however, a typical example or two may be set down.

Take the actions devoted to defence or aggression. At first the military function, undifferentiated from the rest (all men in primitive societies being warriors) is relatively homogeneous, is ill-combined, and is indefinite: savages making a joint attack severally fight independently, in similar ways, and without order. But as societies evolve and the military function becomes separate, we see that while its scale increases, it progresses in multiformity, in definiteness, and in combination. The movements of the thousands of soldiers that replace the tens of warriors, are divided and redivided in their kinds—here are bodies that manœuvre and fire artillery; there are battalions that fight on foot; and elsewhere are troops that charge on horseback. Within each of these differentiated functions there come others: there are distinct duties discharged by privates, sergeants, captains, colonels, generals, as also by those who constitute the commissariat and those who attend to the wounded. The actions that have thus become comparatively heterogeneous in general and in detail, have simultaneously increased in precision. Accuracy of evolutions is given by perpetual drill; so that in battle, men and the regiments formed of them, are made to take definite positions and perform definite acts at definite times. Once more, there has gone on that integration by which the multiform actions of an army are directed to a single end. By a co-ordinating apparatus having the commander-in-chief for its centre, the charges, and halts, and retreats are duly concerted; and a hundred thousand individual actions are united under one will.

The progress here so clearly marked, is a progress traceable throughout social functions at large. Comparing the rule of a savage chief with that of a civilized government, aided by its subordinate local governments and their officers, down to the police in the streets, we see how, as men have advanced from tribes of tens to nations of millions, the regulative process has grown large in amount; how, guided by written laws, it has passed from vagueness and irregularity to comparative precision; and how it has subdivided into processes increasingly multiform. Or observing how the barter that goes on among barbarians, differs from our own commercial processes, by which a million's worth of commodities is distributed daily; by which the relative values of articles immensely varied in kinds and qualities are measured, and the supplies adjusted to the demands; and by which industrial activities of all orders are so combined that each depends on the rest and aids the rest; we see that the kind of action which constitutes trade has become progressively more vast, more varied, more definite, and more integrated.

§ 145. A finished conception of Evolution we thus find to be one which includes the redistribution of the retained motion, as well as that of the component matter. This added element of the conception is scarcely, if at all, less important than the other. The movements of the Solar System have for us a significance equal to that which the sizes, forms, and relative distances of its members possess. And of the phenomena presented by an organism, it must be admitted that the combined sensible and insensible actions we call its life do not yield in interest to its structural traits. Leaving out, however, all implied reference to the way in which these two orders of facts concern us, it is clear that with each redistribution of matter there necessarily goes a redistribution of motion; and that the unified knowledge constituting Philosophy, must comprehend both aspects of the transformation.

While, then, we have to contemplate the matter of an evolving aggregate as undergoing, not progressive integration simply, but as simultaneously undergoing, various secondary redistributions; we have also to contemplate the motion of an evolving aggregate, not only as being gradually dissipated, but as passing through many secondary redistributions on the way toward dissipation. As the structural complexities that arise during compound evolution, are incidental to the progress from the extreme of diffusion to the extreme of concentration; so the functional complexities accompanying them, are incidental to the progress from the greatest quantity of contained motion to the least quantity of contained motion. And we have to state these con-

comitants of both transformations, as well as their begin
nings and ends.

Our formula, therefore, needs an additional clause. T
combine this satisfactorily with the clauses as they stan
in the last chapter, is scarcely practicable; and for con
venience of expression it will be best to change their
order. Doing this, and making the requisite addition, th
formula finally stands thus:—*Evolution is an integration o
matter and concomitant dissipation of motion; during whic
the matter passes from an indefinite, incoherent homogeneit
to a definite, coherent heterogeneity; and during which th
retained motion undergoes a parallel transformation.*

CHAPTER XVIII

THE INTERPRETATION OF EVOLUTION

§ 146. Is this law ultimate or derivative? Must we res
satisfied with the conclusion that throughout all classes o
concrete phenomena such is the course of transformation
Or is it possible for us to ascertain *why* such is the cours
of transformation? May we seek for some all-pervadin
principle which underlies this all-pervading process? Ca
the inductions set forth in the preceding four chapters b
reduced to deductions?

Manifestly this community of result implies communit
of cause. It may be that of such cause no account can b
given, further than that the Unknowable is manifested t
us after this mode. Or, it may be that this mode of mani
festation is reducible to a simpler mode, from which thes
many complex effects follow. Analogy suggests the latte
inference. Just as it was possible to interpret the empirica
generalizations called Kepler's laws as necessary conse
quences of the law of gravitation; so it may be possible t
interpret the foregoing empirical generalizations as neces
sary consequences of some deeper law.

Unless we succeed in finding a *rationale* of this universal metamorphosis, we obviously fall short of that completely unified knowledge constituting Philosophy. As they at present stand, the several conclusions we have lately reached appear to be independent—there is no demonstrated connection between increasing definiteness and increasing heterogeneity, or between both and increasing integration. Still less evidence is there that these laws of the redistribution of matter and motion are necessarily correlated with those laws of the direction of motion and the rhythm of motion, previously set forth. But until we see these now separate truths to be implications of one truth, our knowledge remains imperfectly coherent.

§ 147. The task before us, then, is that of exhibiting the phenomena of Evolution in synthetic order. Setting out from an established ultimate principle, it has to be shown that the course of transformation among all kinds of existences, cannot but be that which we have seen it to be. It has to be shown that the redistribution of matter and motion must everywhere take place in those ways, and produce those traits, which celestial bodies, organisms, societies, alike display. And it has to be shown that this universality of process results from the same necessity which determines each simplest movement around us, down to the accelerated fall of a stone or the recurrent beat of a harp-string.

In other words, the phenomena of Evolution have to be deduced from the Persistence of Force. As before said—"to this an ultimate analysis brings us down; and on this a rational synthesis must build up." This being the ultimate truth which transcends experience by underlying it, so furnishing a common basis on which the widest generalizations stand, these widest generalizations are to be unified by referring them to this common basis. Already the truths manifested throughout concrete phenomena of all orders, that there is equivalence among transformed forces, that motion follows the line of least resistance, and that it is universally rhythmic, we have found to be severally deducible from the persistence of force; and this affiliation of them on the persistence of force has reduced them to a coherent whole. Here we have similarly to affiliate the universal traits of Evolution, by showing that, given the persistence of force, the redistribution of matter and motion necessarily proceeds in such way as to produce them; and by doing this we shall unite them as co-relative aspects of one law, at the same time that we unite this law with the foregoing simpler laws.

§ 148. Before proceeding it will be well to set down some principles that must be borne in mind. In interpreting Evolution we shall have to consider, under their special forms, the various resolutions of force that accompany the redistribution of matter and motion. Let us glance at such resolutions under their most general forms.

Any incident force is primarily divisible into its *effective* and *non-effective* portions. In mechanical impact, the entire momentum of a striking body is never communicated to the body struck: even under those most favorable conditions in which the striking body loses all its sensible motion, there still remains with it some of the original momentum, under the shape of that insensible motion produced among its particles by the collision. Of the light or heat falling on any mass, a part, more or less considerable, is reflected; and only the remaining part works molecular changes in the mass. Next it is to be noted that the effective force is itself divisible into the *temporarily effective* and the *permanently effective*. The units of an aggregate acted on, may undergo those rhythmical changes of relative position which constitute increased vibration, as well as other changes of relative position which are not from instant to instant neutralized by opposite ones. Of these, the first, disappearing in the shape of radiating undulations, leave the molecular arrangement as it originally was; while the second conduce to that rearrangement characterizing compound Evolution. Yet a further distinction has to be made. The permanently effective force works out changes of relative position of two kinds— the *insensible* and the *sensible*. The insensible transpositions among the units are those constituting molecular changes, including what we call chemical composition and decomposition; and it is these which we recognize as the qualitative differences that arise in an aggregate. The sensible transpositions are such as result when certain of the units, instead of being put into different relations with their immediate neighbors, are carried away from them and deposited elsewhere.

Concerning these divisions and subdivisions of any force affecting an aggregate, the fact which it chiefly concerns us to observe is, that they are complementary to each other. Of the whole incident force, the effective must be that which remains after deducting the non-effective. The two parts of the effective force must vary inversely as each other: where much of it is temporarily effective, little of it can be permanently effective; and *vice versâ*. Lastly, the permanently effective force, being expended in working both the insensible rearrangements which constitute molecular modification, and the sensible rearrangements which result in structure, must generate of either kind an amount that is great or small in proportion as it has generated a small or great amount of the other.

CHAPTER XIX

THE INSTABILITY OF THE HOMOGENEOUS[1]

§149. The difficulty of dealing with transformations so many-sided as those which all existences have undergone, or are undergoing, is such as to make a definite or complete deductive interpretation seem almost hopeless. So to grasp the total process of redistribution of matter and motion as to see simultaneously its several necessary results in their actual interdependence, is scarcely possible. There is, however, a mode of rendering the process as a whole tolerably comprehensible. Though the genesis of the rearrangement undergone by every evolving aggregate, is in itself one, it presents to our intelligence several factors; and after interpreting the effects of each separately, we may, by synthesis of the interpretations, form an adequate conception.

On setting out, the proposition which comes first in logical order, is, that some rearrangement must result; and this proposition may be best dealt with under the more specific shape, that the condition of homogeneity is a condition of unstable equilibrium.

First, as to the meaning of the terms; respecting which some readers may need explanation. The phrase *unstable equilibrium* is one used in mechanics to express a balance of forces of such kind that the interference of any further force, however minute, will destroy the arrangement previously subsisting; and bring about a totally different arrangement. Thus, a stick poised on its lower end is in unstable equilibrium: however exactly it may be placed in a perpendicular position, as soon as it is left to itself it

---

[1] The idea developed in this chapter originally formed part of an article on "Transcendental Physiology," published in 1857. See "Essays," pp. 279–290.

begins, at first imperceptibly, to lean on one side, and with increasing rapidity falls into another attitude. Conversely, a stick suspended from its upper end is in stable equilibrium: however much disturbed, it will return to the same position. The proposition is, then, that the state of homogeneity, like the state of the stick poised on its lower end, is one that cannot be maintained. Let us take a few illustrations.

Of mechanical ones the most familiar is that of the scales. If they be accurately made, and not clogged by dirt or rust, it is impossible to keep a pair of scales perfectly balanced: eventually one scale will descend and the other ascend—they will assume a heterogeneous relation. Again, if we sprinkle over the surface of a fluid a number of equal-sized particles, having an attraction for each other, they will, no matter how uniformly distributed, by and by concentrate irregularly into one or more groups. Were it possible to bring a mass of water into a state of perfect homogeneity—a state of complete quiescence, and exactly equal density throughout—yet the radiation of heat from neighboring bodies, by affecting differently its different parts, would inevitably produce inequalities of density and consequent currents; and would so render it to that extent heterogeneous. Take a piece of red-hot matter; and however evenly heated it may at first be, it will quickly cease to be so: the exterior, cooling faster than the interior, will become different in temperature from it. And the lapse into heterogeneity of temperature, so obvious in this extreme case, takes place more or less in all cases. The action of chemical forces supplies other illustrations. Expose a fragment of metal to air or water, and in course of time it will be coated with a film of oxide, carbonate, or other compound: that is—its outer parts will become unlike its inner parts. Usually the heterogeneity produced by the action of chemical forces on the surfaces of masses, is not striking; because the changed portions are soon washed away, or otherwise removed. But if this is prevented, comparatively complex structures result. Quarries of trap-rock contain some striking examples. Not infrequently a piece of trap may be found reduced, by the action of the weather, to a number of loosely-adherent coats, like those of an onion. Where the block has been quite undisturbed, we may trace the whole series of these, from the angular, irregular outer one, through successively included ones in which the shape becomes gradually rounded, ending finally in a spherical nucleus. On comparing the original mass of stone with this group of concentric coats, each of which differs from the rest in form, and probably in the state of decomposition at which it has arrived, we get a marked illustration of the multiformity to which, in lapse of time, a uniform body may be brought by external chemical action. The instability of the homogeneous is equally seen in the changes set up throughout the interior of a mass, when it consists of units that are not rigidly bound together. The atoms of a precipitate never remain separate, and equably distributed through the fluid in which they make their appearance. They aggregate either into crystalline grains, each containing an immense number of atoms, or they aggregate into flocculi, each containing a yet larger number; and where the mass of fluid is great, and the process prolonged, these flocculi do not continue equidistant, but break up into groups. That is to say, there is a destruction of the balance at first subsisting among the diffused particles, and also of the balance at first subsisting among the groups into which these particles unite. Certain solutions of non-crystalline substances in highly volatile liquids, exhibit in the course of half an hour a whole series of changes that are set up in the alleged way. If for example a little shell-lac-varnish (made by dissolving shell-lac in coal-naphtha until it is of the consistence of cream) be poured on a piece of paper, the surface of the varnish will shortly become marked by polygonal divisions, which, first appearing round the edge of the mass, spread toward its centre. Under a lens these irregular polygons of five or more sides, are seen to be severally bounded by dark lines, on each side of which there are light-colored borders. By the addition of matter to their inner edges, the borders slowly broaden, and thus encroach on the areas of the polygons; until at length there remains nothing but a dark spot in the centre of each. At the same time the boundaries of the polygons become curved; and they end by appearing like spherical sacs pressed together; strangely simulating (but only simulating) a group of nucleated cells. Here a rapid loss of homogeneity is exhibited in three ways:—First, in the formation of the film, which is the seat of these changes; second, in the formation of the polygonal sections into which this film divides; and, third, in the contrast that arises between the polygonal sections round the edge, where they are small and early formed, and those in the centre which are larger and formed later.

The instability thus variously illustrated is obviously consequent on the fact, that the several parts of any homogeneous aggregation are necessarily exposed to different forces—forces that differ either in kind or amount; and being exposed to different forces they are of necessity differently modified. The relations of outside and inside, and of comparative nearness to neighboring sources of influence, imply the reception of influences that are unlike in quantity or quality, or both; and it follows that unlike changes will be produced in the parts thus dissimilarly acted upon.

For like reasons it is manifest that the process must repeat itself in each of the subordinate groups of units that are differentiated by the modifying forces. Each of these subordinate groups, like the original group, must gradually, in obedience to the influences acting upon it, lose its balance of parts—must pass from a uniform into a multiform state. And so on continuously. Whence indeed it is clear that not only must the homogeneous lapse into the non-homogeneous, but that the more homogeneous must tend ever to become less homogeneous. If any given whole, instead of being absolutely uniform throughout, consist of parts distinguishable from each other—if each of these parts, while somewhat unlike other parts, is uniform within itself; then, each of them being in unstable equilibrium, it follows that while the changes set up within it must render it multiform, they must at the same time render the whole more multiform than before. The general principle, now to be followed out in its applications, is thus somewhat more comprehensive than the title of the chapter implies. No demurrer to the conclusions drawn, can be based on the ground that perfect homogeneity nowhere exists; since, whether that state with which we commence be or be not one of perfect homogeneity, the process must equally be toward a relative heterogeneity.

§ 150. The stars are distributed with a threefold irregularity. There is first the marked contrast between the plane of the milky way and other parts of the heavens, in respect of the quantities of stars within given visual areas. There are secondary contrasts of like kind in the milky way itself, which has its thick and thin places; as well as throughout the celestial spaces in general, which are much more closely strewn in some regions than in others. And there is a third order of contrasts produced by the aggregation of stars into small clusters. Besides this heterogeneity of distribution of the stars in general, considered without distinction of kinds, a further such heterogeneity is disclosed when they are classified by their differences of color, which doubtless answer to differences of physical constitution. While the yellow stars are found in all parts of the heavens, the red and blue stars are not so: there are wide regions in which both red and blue stars are rare; there are regions in which the blue occur in considerable numbers, and there are other regions in which the red are comparatively abundant. Yet one more irregularity of like significance is presented by the nebulæ—aggregations of matter which, whatever be their nature, most certainly belong to our sidereal system. For the nebulæ are not dispersed with anything like uniformity; but are abundant around the poles of the galactic circle and rare in the neighborhood of its plane. No one will expect that anything like a definite interpretation of this structure can be given on the hypothesis of Evolution, or any other hypothesis. The most that can be looked for is some reason for thinking that irregularities, not improbably of these kinds, would occur in the course of Evolution, supposing it to have taken place. Any one called on to assign such reason might argue, that if the matter of which stars and all other celestial bodies consist, be assumed to have originally existed in a diffused form throughout a space far more vast even than that which our sidereal system now occupies, the instability of the homogeneous would negative its continuance in that state. In default of an absolute balance among the forces with which the dispersed particles acted on each other (which could not exist in any aggregation having limits) he might show that motion and consequent changes of distribution would necessarily result. The next step in the argument would be that in matter of such extreme tenuity and feeble cohesion there would be motion toward local centres of gravity, as well as toward the general centre of gravity; just as, to use a humble illustration, the particles of a precipitate aggregate into flocculi at the same time that they sink toward the earth. He might urge that in the one case as in the other, these smallest and earliest local aggregations must gradually divide into groups, each concentrating to its own centre of gravity—a process which must repeat itself on a larger and larger scale. In conformity with the law that motion once set up in any direction becomes itself a cause of subsequent motion in that direction, he might further infer that the heterogeneities thus set up would tend ever to become more pronounced. Established mechanical principles would justify him in the conclusion that the motions of these irregular masses of slightly aggregated nebular matter toward their common centre of gravity must be severally rendered curvilinear, by the resistance of the medium from which they were precipitated; and that in consequence of the irregularities of distribution already set up, such conflicting curvilinear motions must, by composition of forces, end in a rotation of the incipient sidereal system. He might without difficulty show that the resulting centrifugal force must so far modify the process of general aggregation as to prevent anything like uniform distribution of the stars eventually formed—that there must arise a contrast such as we see between the galactic circle and the rest of the heavens. He might draw the further not unwarrantable inference, that differences in the process of local concentration would probably result from the un-likeness between the physical conditions existing around the general axis of rotation and those existing elsewhere. To which he might add, that after the formation of distinct stars, the ever-increasing irregularities of distribution due to continuance of the same causes would produce that patchiness which distinguishes the heavens in both its larger and smaller areas. We need not here however commit our-selves to such far-reaching speculations. For the purposes of the general argument it is needful only to show, that any finite mass of diffused matter, even though vast enough to form our whole sidereal system, could not be in stable equilibrium; that in default of absolute sphericity, abso-lute uniformity of composition, and absolute symmetry of relation to all forces external to it, its concentration must go on with an ever-increasing irregularity; and that thus the present aspect of the heavens is not, so far as we can judge, incongrous with the hypothesis of a general evolu-tion consequent on the instability of the homogeneous.

Descending to that more limited form of the nebular hypothesis which regards the solar system as having re-sulted by gradual concentration; and assuming this con-centration to have advanced so far as to produce a rotat-ing spheroid of nebulous matter; let us consider what further consequence the instability of the homogeneous necessitates. Having become oblate in figure, unlike in the densities of its centre and surface, unlike in their temperatures, and unlike in the velocities with which its parts move round their common axis, such a mass can no longer be called homogeneous; and therefore any further changes exhibited by it as a whole, can illustrate the general law, only as being changes from a more homogeneous to a less homogeneous state. Changes of this kind are to be found in the transformations of such of its parts as are still homogeneous within themselves. If we accept the conclusion of Laplace, that the equatorial portion of this rotating and contracting spheroid will at successive stages acquire a centrifugal force great enough to prevent any nearer approach to the centre round which it rotates, and will so be left behind by the inner parts of the spheroid in its still-continued contraction; we shall find, in the fate of the detached ring, a fresh exemplification of the principle we are following out. Consisting of gaseous matter, such a ring, even if absolutely uniform at the time of its detachment, cannot continue so. To maintain its equilibrium there must be an almost perfect uniformity in the action of all external forces upon it (almost, we must say, because the cohesion, even of extremely attenuated matter, might suffice to neutralize very minute disturbances); and against this the probabilities are immense. In the absence of equality among the forces, internal and external, acting on such a ring, there must be a point or points at which the cohesion of its parts is less than elsewhere—a point or points at which rupture will therefore take place. Laplace assumed that the ring would rupture at one place only; and would then collapse on itself. But this is a more than questionable assumption —such at least I know to be the opinion of an authority second to none among those now living. So vast a ring, consisting of matter having such feeble cohesion, must break up into many parts. Nevertheless, it is still inferable from the instability of the homogeneous, that the ultimate result which Laplace predicted would take place. For even supposing the masses of nebulous matter into which such a ring separated, were so equal in their sizes and distances as to attract each other with exactly equal forces (which is infinitely improbable); yet the unequal action of external disturbing forces would inevitably destroy their equilibrium—there would be one or more points at which adjacent masses would begin to part company. Separation once commenced, would with ever-accelerating speed lead to a grouping of the masses. And obviously a like result would eventually take place with the groups thus formed; until they at length aggregated into a single mass.

Leaving the region of speculative astronomy, let us consider the Solar System as it at present exists. And here it will be well, in the first place, to note a fact which may be thought at variance with the foregoing argument—namely, the still-continued existence of Saturn's rings; and especially of the internal nebulous ring lately discovered. To the objection that the outer rings maintain their equilibrium, the reply is that the comparatively great cohesion of liquid or solid substance would suffice to prevent any slight tendency to rupture from taking effect. And that a nebulous ring here still preserves its continuity, does not really negative the foregoing conclusion; since it happens under the quite exceptional influence of those symmetrically disposed forces which the external rings exercise on it. Here indeed it deserves to be noted, that though at first sight the Saturnian system appears at variance with the doctrine that a state of homogeneity is one of unstable equilibrium, it does in reality furnish a curious confirmation of this doctrine. For Saturn is not quite concentric with his rings; and it has been proved mathematically that were he and his rings concentrically situated, they could not remain so: the homogeneous relation being unstable, would gravitate into a heterogeneous one. And this fact serves to remind us of the allied one presented throughout the whole Solar System. All orbits, whether of planets or satellites, are more or less eccentric—none of them are perfect circles; and were they perfect circles they would soon become ellipses. Mutual perturbations would inevitably generate eccentricities. That is to say, the homogeneous relations would lapse into heterogeneous ones.

§ 151. Already so many references have been made to the gradual formation of a crust over the originally incandescent Earth, that it may be thought superfluous again to name it. It has not, however, been before considered in connection with the general principle under discussion. Here then it must be noted as a necessary consequence of the instability of the homogeneous. In this cooling down and solidification of the Earth's surface, we have one of the simplest, as well as one of the most important, instances, of that change from a uniform to a multiform state which occurs in any mass through exposure of its different parts to different conditions. To the differentiation of the Earth's exterior from its interior thus brought about, we must add one of the most conspicuous differentiations which the exterior itself afterward undergoes, as being similarly brought about. Were the conditions to which the surface of the Earth is exposed, alike in all directions, there would be no obvious reason why certain of its parts should become permanently unlike the rest. But being unequally exposed to the chief external centre of force—the Sun—its main divisions become unequally modified: as the crust thickens and cools, there arises that contrast, now so decided, between the polar and equatorial regions.

Along with these most marked physical differentiations of the Earth, which are manifestly consequent on the instability of the homogeneous, there have been going on numerous chemical differentiations, admitting of similar interpretation. Without raising the question whether, as some think, the so-called simple substances are themselves compounded of unknown elements (elements which we cannot separate by artificial heat, but which existed separately when the heat of the Earth was greater than any which we can produce)—without raising this question, it will suffice the present purpose to show how, in place of that comparative homogeneity of the Earth's crust, chemically considered, which must have existed when its temperature was high, there has arisen, during its cooling, an increasing chemical heterogeneity: each element or compound, being unable to maintain its homogeneity in presence of various surrounding affinities, having fallen into heterogeneous combinations. Let us contemplate this change somewhat in detail. There is every reason to believe that at an extreme heat, the bodies we call elements cannot combine. Even under such heat as can be generated artificially, some very strong affinities yield; and the great majority of chemical compounds are decomposed at much lower temperatures. Whence it seems not improbable that, when the Earth was in its first state of incandescence, there were no chemical combinations at all. But without drawing this inference, let us set out with the unquestionable fact that the compounds which can exist at the highest temperatures, and which must therefore have been the first formed as the Earth cooled, are those of the simplest constitutions. The protoxides—including under that head the alkalies, earths, etc.—are, as a class, the most fixed compounds known: the majority of them resisting decomposition by any heat we can generate. These, consisting severally of one atom of each component element, are combinations of the simplest order —are but one degree less homogeneous than the elements themselves. More heterogeneous than these, more decomposable by heat, and therefore later in the Earth's history, are the deutoxides, tritoxides, peroxides, etc.; in which two, three, four, or more atoms of oxygen are united with one atom of metal or other base. Still less able to resist heat, are the salts; which present us with compound atoms each made up of five, six, seven, eight, ten, twelve, or more atoms, of three, if not more, kinds. Then there are the hydrated salts, of a yet greater heterogeneity, which undergo partial decomposition at much lower temperatures. After them come the further-complicated supersalts and double salts, having a stability again decreased; and so throughout. After making a few unimportant qualifications demanded by peculiar affinities, I believe no chemist will deny it to be a general law of these inorganic combinations that, other things equal, the stabilty decreases as the complexity increases. And then when we pass to the compounds that make up organic bodies, we find this general law still further exemplified: we find much greater complexity and much less stability. An atom of albumen, for instance, consists of 482 ultimate atoms of five different kinds. Fibrine, still more intricate in constitution, contains in each atom, 298 atoms of carbon, 49 of nitrogen, 2 of sulphur, 228 of hydrogen, and 92 of oxygen—in all, 660 atoms; or, more strictly speaking—equivalents. And these two substances are so unstable as to decompose at quite moderate temperatures; as that to which the outside of a joint of roast meat is exposed. Possibly it will be objected that some inorganic compounds, as phosphuretted hydrogen and chloride of nitrogen, are more decomposable than most organic compounds. This is true. But the admission may be made without damage to the argument. The proposition is not that *all* simple combinations are more fixed than *all* complex ones. To establish our inference it is necessary only to show that, as an *average fact,* the simple combinations can exist at a higher temperature than the complex ones. And this is wholly beyond question. Thus it is manifest that the present chemical heterogeneity of the Earth's surface has arisen by degrees as the decrease of heat has permitted; and that it has shown itself in three forms—first, in the multiplication of chemical compounds; second, in the greater number of different elements contained in the more modern of these compounds; and third, in the higher and more varied multiples in which these more numerous elements combine.

Without specifying them, it will suffice just to name the meteorologic processes eventually set up in the Earth's atmosphere, as further illustrating the alleged law. They equally display that destruction of a homogeneous state which results from unequal exposure to incident forces.

§ 152. Take a mass of unorganized but organizable matter—either the body of one of the lowest living forms, or the germ of one of the higher. Consider its circumstances.

Either it is immersed in water or air, or it is contained within a parent organism. Wherever placed, however, its outer and inner parts stand differently related to surrounding agencies—nutriment, oxygen, and the various stimuli. But this is not all. Whether it lies quiescent at the bottom of the water or on the leaf of a plant; whether it moves through the water preserving some definite attitude; or whether it is in the inside of an adult; it equally results that certain parts of its surface are more exposed to surrounding agencies than other parts—in some cases more exposed to light, heat, or oxygen, and in others to the maternal tissues and their contents. Hence must follow the destruction of its original equilibrium. This may take place in one of two ways. Either the disturbing forces may be such as to overbalance the affinities of the organic elements, in which case there result those changes which are known as decomposition; or, as is ordinarily the case, such changes are induced as do not destroy the organic compounds, but only modify them: the parts most exposed to the modifying forces being most modified. To elucidate this, suppose we take a few cases.

Note first what appear to be exceptions. Certain minute animal forms present us either with no appreciable differentiations or with differentiations so obscure as to be made out with great difficulty. In the Rhizopods, the substance of the jelly-like body remains throughout life unorganized, even to the extent of having no limiting membrane; as is proved by the fact that the thread-like processes protruded by the mass coalesce on touching each other. Whether or not the nearly allied *Amœba,* of which the less numerous and more bulky processes do not coalesce, has, as lately alleged, something like a cell-wall and a nucleus, it is clear that the distinction of parts is very slight; since particles of food pass bodily into the inside through any part of the periphery, and since when the creature is crushed to pieces each piece behaves as the whole did. Now these cases, in which there is either no contrast of structure between ex-

terior and interior or very little, though seemingly opposed
to the above inference, are really very significant evidences
of its truth. For what is the peculiarity of this division of
the *Protozoa?* Its members undergo perpetual and irregular
changes of form—they show no persistent relation of parts.
What lately formed a portion of the interior is now protruded, and, as a temporary limb, is attached to some object
it happens to touch. What is now a part of the surface will
presently be drawn, along with the atom of nutriment stick-
ing to it, into the centre of the mass. Either the relations
of inner and outer have no permanent existence, or they are
very slightly marked. But by the hypothesis, it is only
because of their unlike positions with respect to modifying
forces, that the originally like units of a living mass become
unlike. We must therefore expect no established differentiation of parts in creatures which exhibit no established
differences of position in their parts; and we must expect
extremely little differentiation of parts where the differences
of position are but little determined—which is just what we
find. This negative evidence is borne out by positive evidence. When we turn from these proteiform specks of living jelly to organisms having an unchanging distribution of
substance, we find differences of tissue corresponding to differences of relative position. In all the higher *Protozoa,* as
also in the *Protophyta,* we meet with a fundamental differentiation into cell-membrane and cell-contents; answering to
that fundamental contrast of conditions implied by the terms
outside and inside. On passing from what are roughly
classed as unicellular organisms, to the lowest of those
which consist of aggregated cells, we equally observe the
connection between structural differences and differences of
circumstance. Negatively, we see that in the sponge, per-
meated throughout by currents of sea-water, the indefiniteness of organization corresponds with the absence of definite
unlikeness of conditions: the peripheral and central portions
are as little contrasted in structure as in exposure to surrounding agencies. While positively, we see that in a form

like the *Thalassicolla,* which, though equally humble, maintains its outer and inner parts in permanently unlike circumstances, there is displayed a rude structure obviously subordinated to the primary relations of centre and surface: in all its many and important varieties, the parts exhibit a more or less concentric arrangement.

After this primary modification, by which the outer tissues are differentiated from the inner, the next in order of constancy and importance is that by which some part of the outer tissues is differentiated from the rest; and this corresponds with the almost universal fact that some part of the outer tissues is more exposed to certain environing influences than the rest. Here, as before, the apparent exceptions are extremely significant. Some of the lowest vegetal organisms, as the *Hematococci* and *Protococci,* evenly imbedded in a mass of mucus, or dispersed through the Arctic snow, display no differentiations of surface; the several parts of their surfaces being subjected to no definite contrasts of conditions. Ciliated spheres such as the *Volvox* have no parts of their periphery unlike other parts; and it is not to be expected that they should have; since, as they revolve in all directions, they do not, in traversing the water, permanently expose any part to special conditions. But when we come to organisms that are either fixed, or while moving preserve definite attitudes, we no longer find uniformity of surface. The most general fact which can be asserted with respect to the structures of plants and animals, is, that however much alike in shape and texture the various parts of the exterior may at first be, they acquire unlikenesses corresponding to the unlikenesses of their relations to surrounding agencies. The ciliated germ of a Zoophyte, which, during its locomotive stage, is distinguishable only into outer and inner tissues, no sooner becomes fixed, than its upper end begins to assume a different structure from its lower. The disk-shaped *gemmœ* of the *Marchantia,* originally alike on both surfaces, and falling at random with either side uppermost, immediately begin to develop rootlets on the under side, and *stomata* on the upper side: a fact proving beyond question that this primary differentiation is determined by this fundamental contrast of conditions.

Of course in the germs of higher organisms, the metamorphoses immediately due to the instability of the homogeneous, are soon masked by those due to the assumption of the hereditary type. Such early changes, however, as are common to all classes of organisms, and so cannot be ascribed to heredity, entirely conform to the hypothesis. A germ which has undergone no developmental modifications, consists of a spheroidal group of homogeneous cells. Universally, the first step in its evolution is the establishment of a difference between some of the peripheral cells and the cells which form the interior—some of the peripheral cells, after repeated spontaneous fissions, coalesce into a membrane; and by continuance of the process this membrane spreads until it speedily invests the entire mass, as in mammals, or, as in birds, stops short of that for some time. Here we have two significant facts. The first is, that the primary unlikeness arises between the exterior and the interior. The second is, that the change which thus initiates development, does not take place simultaneously over the whole exterior; but commences at one place, and gradually involves the rest. Now these facts are just those which might be inferred from the instability of the homogeneous. The surface must, more than any other part, become unlike the centre, because it is most dissimilarly conditioned; and all parts of the surface cannot simultaneously exhibit this differentiation, because they cannot be exposed to the incident forces with absolute uniformity. One other general fact of like implication remains. Whatever be the extent of this peripheral layer of cells, or blastoderm as it is called, it presently divides into two layers—the serous and mucous; or, as they have been otherwise called, the ectoderm and the endoderm. The first of these is formed from that portion of the layer which lies in contact with surrounding agents; and the second of them is formed from that portion of the

layer which lies in contact with the contained mass of yelk.
That is to say, after the primary differentiation, more or less
extensive, of surface from centre, the resulting superficial
portion undergoes a secondary differentiation into inner and
outer parts—a differentiation which is clearly of the same
order with the preceding, and answers to the next most
marked contrast of conditions.

But, as already hinted, this principle, understood in the
simple form here presented, supplies no key to the detailed
phenomena of organic development. It fails entirely to
explain generic and specific peculiarities; and indeed leaves
us equally in the dark respecting those more important distinctions by which families and orders are marked out.
Why two ova, similarly exposed in the same pool, should
become the one a fish, and the other a reptile, it cannot tell
us. That from two different eggs placed under the same
hen, should respectively come forth a duckling and a
chicken, is a fact not to be accounted for on the hypothesis
above developed. We have here no alternative but to fall
back upon the unexplained principle of hereditary transmission. The capacity possessed by an unorganized germ of
unfolding into a complex adult, which repeats ancestral
traits in the minutest details, and that even when it has
been placed in conditions unlike those of its ancestors, is a
capacity we cannot at present understand. That a microscopic portion of seemingly structureless matter should embody an influence of such kind that the resulting man will
in fifty years after become gouty or insane, is a truth which
would be incredible were it not daily illustrated. Should
it however turn out, as we shall hereafter find reason for
suspecting, that these complex differentiations which adults
exhibit, are themselves the slowly accumulated and transmitted results of a process like that seen in the first changes
of the germ; it will follow that even those embryonic
changes due to hereditary influence, are remote consequences of the alleged law. Should it be shown that the
slight modifications wrought during life on each adult, and

bequeathed to offspring along with all like preceding modifications, are themselves unlikenesses of parts that are produced by unlikenesses of conditions; then it will follow that the modifications displayed in the course of embryonic development, are partly direct consequences of the instability of the homogeneous, and partly indirect consequences of it. To give reasons for entertaining this hypothesis, however, is not needful for the justification of the position here taken. It is enough that the most conspicuous differentiations which incipient organisms universally display, correspond to the most marked differences of conditions to which their parts are subject. It is enough that the habitual contrast between outside and inside, which we *know* is produced in inorganic masses by unlikeness of exposure to incident forces, is strictly paralleled by the first contrast that makes its appearance in all organic masses.

It remains to point out that in the assemblage of organisms constituting a species, the principle enunciated is equally traceable. We have abundant materials for the induction that each species will not remain uniform, but is ever becoming to some extent multiform; and there is ground for the deduction that this lapse from homogeneity to heterogeneity is caused by the subjection of its members to unlike sets of circumstances. The fact that in every species, animal and vegetal, the individuals are never quite alike; joined with the fact that there is in every species a tendency to the production of differences marked enough to constitute varieties; form a sufficiently wide basis for the induction. While the deduction is confirmed by the familiar experience that varieties are most numerous and decided where, as among cultivated plants and domestic animals, the conditions of life depart from the original ones, most widely and in the most numerous ways. Whether we regard "natural selection" as wholly, or only in part, the agency through which varieties are established, matters not to the general conclusion. For as the survival of any variety proves its constitution to be in harmony with a certain ag-

gregate of surrounding forces—as the multiplication of a
variety and the usurpation by it of an area previously occupied by some other part of the species, implies different
effects produced by such aggregate of forces on the two, is
is clear that this aggregate of forces is the real cause of the
differentiation—it is clear that if the variety supplants the
original species in some localities but not in others, it does
so because the aggregate of forces in the one locality is unlike that in the other—it is clear that the lapse of the species
from a state of homogeneity to a state of heterogeneity arises
from the exposure of its different parts to different aggregates of forces.

§ 153. Among mental phenomena it is difficult to establish the alleged law without an analysis too extensive for
the occasion. To show satisfactorily how states of consciousness, originally homogeneous, become heterogeneous
through differences in the changes wrought by different
forces, would require us carefully to trace out the organization of early experiences. Were this done it would become
manifest that the development of intelligence, is, under one
of its chief aspects, a dividing into separate classes the unlike things previously confounded together in one class—
a formation of sub-classes and sub-sub-classes, until the
once confused aggregate of objects known is resolved into
an aggregate which unites extreme heterogeneity among its
multiplied groups, with complete homogeneity among the
members of each group. If, for example, we followed,
through ascending grades of creatures, the genesis of that
vast structure of knowledge acquired by sight, we should
find that in the first stage, where eyes suffice for nothing
beyond the discrimination of light from darkness, the only
possible classifications of objects seen, must be those based
on the manner in which light is obstructed, and the degree
in which it is obstructed. We should find that by such
undeveloped visual organs, the shadows traversing the
rudimentary retina would be merely distinguished into

those of the stationary objects which the creature passed during its own movements, and those of the moving objects which came near the creature while it was at rest; and that so the extremely general classification of visible things into stationary and moving, would be the earliest formed. We should find that whereas the simplest eyes are not fitted to distinguish between an obstruction of light caused by a small object close to, and an obstruction caused by a large object at some distance, eyes a little more developed must be competent to such a distinction; whence must result a vague differentiation of the class of moving objects into the nearer and the more remote. We should find that such further improvements in vision as those which make possible a better estimation of distances by adjustment of the optic axes, and those which, through enlargement and subdivision of the retina, make possible the discrimination of shapes, must have the effects of giving greater definiteness to the classes already formed, and of subdividing these into smaller classes, consisting of objects less unlike. And we should find that each additional refinement of the perceptive organs, must similarly lead to a multiplication of divisions and a sharpening of the limits of each division. In every infant might be traced the analogous transformation of a confused aggregate of impressions of surrounding objects, not recognized as differing in their distances, sizes, and shapes, into separate classes of objects unlike each other in these and various other respects. And in the one case as in the other, it might be shown that the change from this first indefinite, incoherent and comparatively homogeneous consciousness, to a definite, coherent, and heterogeneous one, is due to differences in the actions of incident forces on the organism. These brief indications of what might be shown, did space permit, must here suffice. Probably they will give adequate clew to an argument by which each reader may satisfy himself that the course of mental evolution offers no exception to the general law. In further aid of such an argument, I will here add an illustration that is comprehensible apart from the process of mental evolution as a whole.

It has been remarked (I am told by Coleridge, though I have been unable to find the passage) that with the advance of language, words which were originally alike in their meanings acquire unlike meanings—a change which he expresses by the formidable word "desynonymization." Among indigenous words this loss of equivalence cannot be clearly shown; because in them the divergences of meaning began before the dawn of literature. But among words that have been coined, or adopted from other languages, since the writing of books commenced, it is demonstrable. In the old divines, *miscreant* is used in its etymological sense of *unbeliever;* but in modern speech it has entirely lost this sense. Similarly with *evil-doer* and *malefactor:* exactly synonymous as these are by derivation, they are no longer synonymous by usage: by a *malefactor* we now understand a convicted criminal, which is far from being the acceptation of *evil-doer.* The verb *produce,* bears in Euclid its primary meaning—to *prolong,* or *draw out;* but the now largely developed meanings of *produce* have little in common with the meaning—to *prolong,* or *draw out.* In the Church of England Liturgy, an odd effect results from the occurrence of *prevent* in its original sense—*to come before,* instead of its modern specialized sense—*to come before with the effect of arresting.* But the most conclusive cases are those in which the contrasted words consist of the same parts differently combined; as in *go under* and *undergo.* We *go under* a tree, and we *undergo* a pain. But though, if analytically considered, the meanings of these expressions would be the same were the words transposed, habit has so far modified their meanings that we could not without absurdity speak of *undergoing* a tree and *going under* a pain. Countless such instances might be brought to show that between two words which are originally of like force, an equilibrium cannot be maintained. Unless they are daily used in exactly equal degrees, in exactly similar relations (against which there are infinite probabilities), there necessarily arises a habit of associating one rather than the other with particular acts, or objects. Such a habit, once commenced, becomes confirmed; and gradually their homogeneity of meaning disappears. In each individual we may see the tendency which inevitably leads to this result. A certain vocabulary and a certain set of phrases distinguish the speech of each person: each person habitually uses certain words in places where other words are habitually used by other persons; and there is a continual recurrence of favorite expressions. This inability to maintain a balance in the use of verbal symbols, which characterizes every man, characterizes, by consequence, aggregates of men; and the desynonymization of words is the ultimate effect.

Should any difficulty be felt in understanding how these mental changes exemplify a law of physical transformations that are wrought by physical forces, it will disappear on contemplating acts of mind as nervous functions. It will be seen that each loss of equilibrium above instanced is a loss of functional equality between some two elements of the nervous system. And it will be seen that, as in other cases, this loss of functional equality is due to differences in the incidence of forces.

§ 154. Masses of men, in common with all other masses, show a like proclivity similarly caused. Small combinations and large societies equally manifest it; and in the one, as in the other, both governmental and industrial differentiations are initiated by it. Let us glance at the facts under these two heads.

A business partnership, balanced as the authorities of its members may theoretically be, practically becomes a union in which the authority of one partner is tacitly recognized as greater than that of the other or others. Though the shareholders have given equal powers to the directors of their company, inequalities of power soon arise among them; and usually the supremacy of some one director grows so marked that his decisions determine the course which the board takes. Nor in associations for political, charitable, literary, or other purposes, do we fail to find a like process of division into dominant and subordinate parties; each having its leader, its members of less influence, and its mass of uninfluential members. These minor instances in which unorganized groups of men, standing in homogeneous relations, may be watched gradually passing into organized groups of men standing in heterogeneous relations, give us the key to social inequalities. Barbarous and civilized communities are alike characterized by separation into classes, as well as by separation of each class into more important and less important units; and this structure is manifestly the gradually-consolidated result of a process like that daily exemplified in trading and other combinations. So long as men are constituted to act on one another, either by physical force or by force of character, the struggles for supremacy must finally be decided in favor of some one; and the difference once commenced must tend to become ever more marked. Its unstable equilibrium being destroyed, the uniform must gravitate with increasing rapidity into the multiform. And so supremacy and subordination must establish themselves, as we see they do, throughout the whole structure of a society, from the great class-divisions pervading its entire body, down to village cliques, and even down to every posse of schoolboys. Probably it will be objected that such changes result, not from the homogeneity of the original aggregations, but from their non-homogeneity—from certain slight differences existing among their units at the outset. This is doubtless the proximate cause. In strictness, such changes must be regarded as transformations of the relatively homogeneous into the relatively heterogeneous. But it is abundantly clear that an aggregation of men, absolutely alike in their endowments, would eventually undergo a similar transformation. For in the absence of perfect uniformity in the lives severally led by them—in their occupations, physical conditions, domestic relations, and trains of thought and feeling—there must arise differences among them; and these must finally initiate social differentiations. Even inequalities of health caused by accidents, must, by entailing inequalities of physical and mental power, disturb the exact balance of mutual influences among the units; and the balance, once disturbed, must inevitably be lost. Whence, indeed, besides seeing that a body of men absolutely homogeneous in their governmental relations, must, like all other homogeneous bodies, become heterogeneous, we also see that it must do this from the same ultimate cause—unequal exposure of its parts to incident forces.

The first industrial divisions of societies are much more obviously due to unlikenesses of external circumstances. Such divisions are absent until such unlikenesses are established. Nomadic tribes do not permanently expose any groups of their members to special local conditions; nor does a stationary tribe, when occupying only a small area, maintain from generation to generation marked contrasts in the local conditions of its members; and in such tribes there are no decided economical differentiations. But a community which, growing populous, has overspread a large tract, and has become so far settled that its members live and die in their respective districts, keeps its several sections in different physical circumstances; and then they no longer remain alike in their occupations. Those who live dispersed continue to hunt or cultivate the earth; those who spread to the sea-shore fall into maritime occupations; while the inhabitants of some spot chosen, perhaps for its centrality, as one of periodical assemblage, become traders, and a town springs up. Each of these classes undergoes a modification of character consequent on its function, and better fitting it to its function. Later in the process of social evolution these local adaptations are greatly multiplied. A result of differences in soil and climate, is that the rural inhabitants in different parts of the kingdom have their occupations partially specialized; and become respectively distinguished as chiefly producing cattle, or sheep, or wheat, or oats, or hops, or cider. People living where coal-fields are discovered are transformed into colliers; Cornishmen take to mining because Cornwall is metalliferous; and the iron-manufacture is the dominant industry where iron-stone is plentiful. Liverpool has assumed the office of importing cotton, in consequence of its proximity to the district where cotton goods are made; and for analogous reasons, Hull has become the chief port at which foreign wools are brought in. Even in the establishment of breweries, of dye-works, of slate-quarries, of brick-yards, we may see the same truth. So that both in general and in detail, the specializations of the social organism which characterize separate districts, primarily depend on local circumstances. Those divisions of labor which under another aspect were interpreted as due to the setting up of motion in the directions of least resistance (§ 80), are here interpreted as due to differences in the incident forces; and the two interpretations are quite consistent with each other. For that which in each case *determines* the direction of least resistance, is the distribution of the forces to be overcome; and hence unlikeness of distribution in separate localities, entails unlikenesses in the course of human action in those localities—entails industrial differentiations.

§ 155. It has still to be shown that this general truth is demonstrable *à priori*. We have to prove specifically that the instability of the homogeneous is a corollary from the persistence of force. Already this has been tacitly implied by assigning unlikeness in the exposure of its parts to surrounding agencies, as the reason why a uniform mass loses its uniformity. But here it will be proper to expand this tacit implication into definite proof.

On striking a mass of matter with such force as either to indent it or make it fly to pieces, we see both that the blow affects differently its different parts, and that the differences are consequent on the unlike relations of its parts to the force impressed. The part with which the striking body comes in contact, receiving the whole of the communicated momentum, is driven in toward the centre of the mass. It thus compresses and tends to displace the more centrally situated portions of the mass. These, however, cannot be compressed or thrust out of their places without pressing on all surrounding portions. And when the blow is violent enough to fracture the mass, we see, in the radial dispersion of its fragments, that the original momentum, in being distributed throughout it, has been divided into numerous minor momenta, unlike in their directions. We see that these directions are determined by the positions of the parts with respect to each other, and with respect to the point of impact. We see that the parts are differently affected by the disruptive force, because they are differently related to it in their directions and attachments—that the effects being the joint products of the cause and the conditions, cannot be alike in parts which are differently conditioned. A body on which radiant heat is falling, exemplifies this truth still more clearly. Taking the simplest case (that of a sphere) we see that while the part nearest to the radiating centre receives the rays at right angles, the rays strike the other parts of the exposed side at all angles from 90° down to 0°. Again, the molecular vibrations propagated through the mass from the surface which receives the heat, must proceed inward at angles differing for each point. Further, the interior parts of the sphere affected by the vibrations proceeding from all points of the heated side, must be dissimilarly affected in proportion as their positions are dissimilar. So that whether they be on the recipient area, in the middle, or at the remote side, the constituent atoms are all thrown into states of vibration more or less unlike each other.

But now, what is the ultimate meaning of the conclusion that a uniform force produces different changes throughout a uniform mass, because the parts of the mass stand in different relations to the force? Fully to understand this, we must contemplate each part as simultaneously subject to other forces—those of gravitation, of cohesion, of molecular motion, etc. The effect wrought by an additional force, must be a resultant of it and the forces already in action. If the forces already in action on two parts of any aggregate, are different in their directions, the effects produced on these two parts by like forces must be different in their directions. Why must they be different? They must be different because such unlikeness as exists between the two sets of factors, is made by the presence in the one of some specially-directed force that is not present in the other; and that this force will produce an effect, rendering the total result in the one case unlike that in the other, is a necessary corollary from the persistence of force. Still more manifest does it become that the dissimilarly-placed parts of any aggregate must be dissimilarly modified by an incident force, when we remember that the *quantities* of the incident force to which they are severally subject, are not equal, as above supposed; but are nearly always very unequal. The outer parts of masses are usually alone exposed to chemical actions; and not only are their inner parts shielded from the affinities of external elements, but such affinities are brought to bear unequally on their surfaces; since chemical action sets up currents through the medium in which it takes place, and so brings to the various parts of the surface unequal quantities of the active agent. Again, the amounts of any external radiant force which the different parts of an aggregate receive, are widely contrasted: we have the contrast between the quantity falling on the side next the radiating centre, and the quantity, or rather no quantity, falling on the opposite side; we have contrasts in the quantities received by differently-placed areas on the exposed side; and we have endless contrasts between the quantities received by the various parts of the interior. Similarly when mechanical force is expended on any aggregate, either by collision, continued pressure, or tension, the amounts of strain distributed throughout the mass are manifestly unlike for unlike positions. But to say the different parts of an aggregate receive different quantities of any incident force, is to say that their states are modified by it in different degrees— is to say that if they were before homogeneous in their relations they must be rendered to a proportionate extent heterogeneous; since, force being persistent, the different quantities of it falling on the different parts, must work in them different quantities of effect—different changes. Yet one more kindred deduction is required to complete the argument. We may, by parallel reasoning, reach the conclusion that, even apart from the action of any external force, the equilibrium of a homogeneous aggregate must be destroyed by the unequal actions of its parts on each other. That mutual influence which produces aggregation (not to mention other mutual influences) must work different effects on the different parts; since they are severally exposed to it in unlike amounts and directions. This will be clearly seen on remembering that the portions of which the whole is made up, may be severally regarded as minor wholes; that on each of these minor wholes, the action of the entire aggregate then becomes an external incident force; that such external incident force must, as above shown, work unlike changes in the parts of any such minor whole; and that if the minor wholes are severally thus rendered heterogeneous, the entire aggregate is rendered heterogeneous.

The instability of the homogeneous is thus deducible from that primordial truth which underlies our intelligence. One stable homogeneity only, is hypothetically possible. If centres of force, absolutely uniform in their powers, were diffused with absolute uniformity through unlimited space, they would remain in equilibrium. This however, though a verbally intelligible supposition, is one that cannot be represented in thought; since unlimited space is inconceivable. But all finite forms of the homogeneous—all forms of it which we can know or conceive, must inevitably lapse into heterogeneity. In three several ways does the persistence of force necessitate this. Setting external agencies aside, each unit of a homogeneous whole must be differently affected from any of the rest by the aggregate action of the rest upon it. The resultant force exercised by the aggregate on each unit, being in no two cases alike in both amount and direction, and usually not in either, any incident force, even if uniform in amount and direction, cannot produce like effects on the units. And the various positions of the parts in relation to any incident force, preventing them from receiving it in uniform amounts and directions, a further difference in the effects wrought on them is inevitably produced.

One further remark is needed. To the conclusion that the changes with which Evolution *commences* are thus necessitated, remains to be added the conclusion that these changes must *continue*. The absolutely homogeneous must lose its equilibrium; and the relatively homogeneous must lapse into the relatively less homogeneous. That which is true of any total mass, is true of the parts into which it segregates. The uniformity of each such part must as inevitably be lost in multiformity, as was that of the original whole; and for like reasons. And thus the continued changes which characterize Evolution, in so far as they are constituted by the lapse of the homogeneous into the heterogeneous, and of the less heterogeneous into the more heterogeneous, are necessary consequences of the persistence of force.

CHAPTER XX

THE MULTIPLICATION OF EFFECTS

§ 156. To the cause of increasing complexity set forth in the last chapter, we have in this chapter to add another. Though secondary in order of time, it is scarcely secondary in order of importance. Even in the absence of the cause already assigned, it would necessitate a change from the homogeneous to the heterogeneous; and joined with it, it makes this change both more rapid and more involved. To come in sight of it, we have but to pursue a step further, that conflict between force and matter already delineated. Let us do this.

When a uniform aggregate is subject to a uniform force, we have seen that its constituents, being differently conditioned, are differently modified. But while we have contemplated the various parts of the aggregate as thus undergoing unlike changes, we have not yet contemplated the unlike changes simultaneously produced on the various parts of the incident force. These must be as numerous and important as the others. Action and reaction being equal and opposite, it follows that in differentiating the parts on which it falls in unlike ways, the incident force must itself be correspondingly differentiated. Instead of being, as before, a uniform force, it must thereafter be a multiform force—a group of dissimilar forces. A few illustrations will make this truth manifest.

A single force is divided by conflict with matter into forces that widely diverge. In the case lately cited, of a body shattered by violent collision, besides the change of the homogeneous mass into a heterogeneous group of scattered fragments, there is a change of the homogeneous momentum into a group of momenta, heterogeneous in both amounts and directions. Similarly with the forces we know as light and heat. After the dispersion of these by a radiating body toward all points, they are redispersed toward all points by the bodies on which they fall. Of the Sun's rays, issuing from him on every side, some few strike the Moon. These being reflected at all angles from the Moon's surface, some few of them strike the Earth. By a like process the few which reach the Earth are again diffused through surrounding space. And on each occasion, such portions of the rays as are absorbed instead of reflected, undergo refractions that equally destroy their parallelism. More than this is true. By conflict with matter, a uniform force is in part changed into forces differing in their directions; and in part it is changed into forces differing in their kinds. When one body is struck against another, that which we usually regard as the effect, is a change of position or motion in one or both bodies. But a moment's thought shows that this is a very incomplete view of the matter. Besides the visible mechanical result, sound is produced; or, to speak accurately, a vibration in one or both bodies, and in the surrounding air: and under some circumstances we call this the effect. Moreover, the air has not simply been made to vibrate, but has had currents raised in it by the transit of the bodies. Further, if there is not that great structural change which we call fracture, there is a disarrangement of the particles of the two bodies around their point of collision; amounting in some cases to a visible condensation. Yet more, this condensation is accompanied by disengagement of heat. In some cases a spark—that is, light—results, from the incandescence of a portion struck off; and occasionally this incandescence is associated with chemical combination. Thus, by the original mechanical force expended in the collision, at least five, and often more, different kinds of forces have been produced. Take, again, the lighting of a candle. Primarily, this is a chemical change consequent on a rise of temperature. The process of combination having once been set going by extraneous heat, there is a continued formation of carbonic acid, water, etc.—in itself a result more complex than the extraneous heat that first caused it. But along with this process of combination there is a production of heat; there is a production of light; there is an ascending column of hot gases generated; there are currents established in the surrounding air. Nor does the decomposition of one force into many forces end here. Each of the several changes worked becomes the parent of further changes. The carbonic acid formed, will by and by combine with some base; or under the influence of sunshine give up its carbon to the leaf of a plant. The water will modify the hygrometric state of the air around; or, if the current of hot gases containing it come against a cold body, will be condensed: altering the temperature, and perhaps the chemical state, of the surface it covers. The heat given out melts the subjacent tallow, and expands whatever it warms. The light, falling on various substances, calls forth from them reactions by which it is modified; and so divers colors are produced. Similarly even with these secondary actions, which may be traced out into ever-multiplying ramifications, until they become too minute to be appreciated. Universally, then, the effect is more complex than the cause. Whether the aggregate on which it falls be homogeneous or otherwise, an incident force is transformed by the conflict into a number of forces that differ in their amounts, or directions, or kinds; or in all these respects. And of this group of variously-modified forces, each ultimately undergoes a like transformation.

Let us now mark how the process of evolution is furthered by this multiplication of effects. An incident force decomposed by the reactions of a body into a group of unlike forces—a uniform force thus reduced to a multiform force—becomes the cause of a secondary increase of multiformity in the body which decomposes it. In the last chapter we saw that the several parts of an aggregate are differently modified by any incident force. It has just been shown that by the reactions of the differently modified parts, the incident force itself must be divided into differently modified parts. Here it remains to point out that each differentiated division of the aggregate, thus becomes a centre from which a differentiated division of the original force is again diffused. And since unlike forces must produce unlike results, each of these differentiated forces must produce, throughout the aggregate, a further series of differentiations. This secondary cause of the change from homogeneity to heterogeneity, obviously becomes more potent in proportion as the heterogeneity increases. When the parts into which any evolving whole has segregated itself, have diverged widely in nature, they will necessarily react very diversely on any incident force—they will divide an incident force into so many strongly contrasted groups of forces. And each of them becoming the centre of a quite distinct set of influences, must add to the number of distinct secondary changes wrought throughout the aggregate. Yet another corollary must be added. The number of unlike parts of which an aggregate consists, as well as the degree of their unlikeness, is an important factor in the process. Every additional specialized division is an additional centre of specialized forces. If a uniform whole, in being itself made multiform by an incident force, makes the incident force multiform; if a whole consisting of two unlike sections, divides an incident force into two unlike groups of multiform forces; it is clear that each new unlike section must be a further source of complication among the forces at work throughout the mass—a further source of heterogeneity. The multiplication of effects must proceed in geometrical progression. Each stage of evolution must initiate a higher stage.

§ 157. The force of aggregation acting on irregular masses of rare matter, diffused through a resisting medium, will not cause such masses to move in straight lines to their common centre of gravity; but, as before said, each will take a curvilinear path, directed to one or other side of the centre of gravity. All of them being differently conditioned, gravitation will impress on each a motion differing in direction, in velocity, and in the degree of its curvature —uniform aggregative force will be differentiated into multiform momenta. The process thus commenced, must go on till it produces a single mass of nebulous matter; and these independent curvilinear motions must result in a movement of this mass round its axis: a simultaneous condensation and rotation in which we see how two effects of the aggregative force, at first but slightly divergent, become at last widely differentiated. A gradual increase of oblateness in this revolving spheroid, must take place through the joint action of these two forces, as the bulk diminishes and the rotation grows more rapid; and this we may set down as a third effect. The genesis of heat, which must accompany augmentation of density, is a consequence of yet another order—a consequence by no means simple; since the various parts of the mass, being variously condensed, must be variously heated. Acting throughout a gaseous spheroid, of which the parts are unlike in their temperatures, the forces of aggregation and rotation must work a further series of changes: they must set up circulating currents, both general and local. At a later stage light as well as heat will be generated. Thus without dwelling on the likelihood of chemical combinations and electric disturbances, it is sufficiently manifest that, supposing matter to have originally existed in a diffused state, the once uniform force which caused its aggregation, must have become gradually divided into different forces; and that each further stage of complication in the resulting aggregate, must have initiated further subdivisions of this force—a further multiplication of effects, increasing the previous heterogeneity.

This section of the argument may however be adequately sustained, without having recourse to any such hypothetical illustrations as the foregoing. The astronomical attributes of the Earth will even alone suffice our purpose. Consider first the effects of its momentum round its axis. There is the oblateness of its form; there is the alternation of day and night; there are certain constant marine currents; and there are certain constant aërial currents. Consider next the secondary series of consequences due to the divergence of the Earth's plane of rotation from the plane of its orbit. The many differences of the seasons, both simultaneous and successive, which pervade its surface, are thus caused. External attraction acting on this rotating oblate spheroid with inclined axis, produces the motion called nutation, and that slower and larger one from which follows the precession of the equinoxes, with its several sequences. And then by this same force are generated the tides, aqueous and atmospheric.

Perhaps, however, the simplest way of showing the multiplication of effects among phenomena of this order will be to set down the influences of any member of the Solar System on the rest. A planet directly produces in neighboring planets certain appreciable perturbations, complicating those otherwise produced in them; and in the remoter planets it directly produces certain less visible perturbations. Here is a first series of effects. But each of the perturbed planets is itself a source of perturbations—each directly affects all the others. Hence, planet A having drawn planet B out of the position it would have occupied in A's absence, the perturbations which B causes are different from what they would else have been; and similarly with C, D, E, etc. Here then is a secondary series of effects: far more numerous though far smaller in their amounts. As these indirect perturbations must to some extent modify the movements of each planet, there results from them a tertiary series; and so on continually. Thus the force exercised by any planet works a different effect on each of the rest; this different effect is from each as a centre partially broken up into minor different effects on the rest; and so on in ever multiplying and diminishing waves throughout the entire system.

§ 158. If the Earth was formed by the concentration of diffused matter, it must at first have been incandescent; and whether the nebular hypothesis be accepted or not, this original incandescence of the Earth must now be regarded as inductively established—or, if not established, at least rendered so probable that it is a generally admitted geological doctrine. Several results of the gradual cooling of the Earth—as the formation of a crust, the solidification of sublimed elements, the precipitation of water, etc., have been already noticed—and I here again refer to them merely to point out that they are simultaneous effects of the one cause, diminishing heat. Let us now, however, observe the multiplied changes afterward arising from the continuance of this one cause. The Earth, falling in temperature, must contract. Hence the solid crust at any time existing, is presently too large for the shrinking nucleus; and being unable to support itself, inevitably follows the nucleus. But a spheroidal envelope cannot sink down into contact with a smaller internal spheroid, without disruption: it will run into wrinkles, as the rind of an apple does when the bulk of its interior decreases from evaporation. As the cooling progresses and the envelope thickens, the ridges consequent on these contractions must become greater; rising ultimately into hills and mountains; and the later systems of mountains thus produced must not only be higher, as we find them to be, but they must be longer, as we also find them to be. Thus, leaving out of view other modifying forces, we see what immense heterogeneity of surface arises from the one cause, loss of heat—a heterogeneity which the telescope shows us to be paralleled on the Moon, where aqueous and atmospheric agencies have been absent. But we have yet to notice another kind of heterogeneity of surface, similarly and simultaneously caused. While the Earth's crust was still thin, the ridges produced by its contraction must not only have been small, but the tracts between them must have rested with comparative smoothness on the subjacent liquid spheroid; and the water in those arctic and antarctic regions where it first condensed, must have been evenly distributed. But as fast as the crust grew thicker and gained corresponding strength, the lines of fracture from time to time caused in it, necessarily occurred at greater distances apart; the intermediate surfaces followed the contracting nucleus with less uniformity; and there consequently resulted larger areas of land and water. If any one, after wrapping an orange in wet tissue paper, and observing both how small are the wrinkles and how evenly the intervening spaces lie on the surface of the orange, will then wrap it in thick cartridge-paper, and note both the greater height of the ridges and the larger spaces throughout which the paper does not touch the orange, he will realize the fact, that as the Earth's solid envelope thickened, the areas of elevation and depression became greater. In place of islands more or less homogeneously scattered over an all-embracing sea, there must have gradually arisen heterogeneous arrangements of continent and ocean, such as we now know. This double change in the extent and in the elevation of the lands, involved yet another species of heterogeneity—that of coast-line. A tolerably even surface raised out of the ocean will have a simple regular sea-margin; but a surface varied by tablelands and intersected by mountain-chains, will, when raised out of the ocean, have an outline extremely irregular, alike in its leading features and in its details. Thus endless is the accumulation of geological and geographical results slowly brought about by this one cause—the escape of the Earth's primitive heat.

When we pass from the agency which geologists term igneous, to aqueous and atmospheric agencies, we see a like ever-growing complication of effects. The denuding actions of air and water have, from the beginning, been modifying every exposed surface: everywhere working many different changes. As already shown (§ 69) the original source of those gaseous and fluid motions which effect denudation, is the solar heat. The transformation of this into various modes of force, according to the nature and condition of the matter on which it falls, is the first stage of complication. The sun's rays, striking at all angles a sphere, that from moment to moment presents and withdraws different parts of its surface, and each of them for a different time daily throughout the year, would produce a considerable variety of changes even were the sphere uniform. But falling as they do on a sphere surrounded by an atmosphere in some parts of which wide areas of cloud are suspended, and which here unveils vast tracts of sea, there of level land, there of mountains, there of snow and ice, they initiate in its several parts countless different movements. Currents of air of all sizes, directions, velocities, and temperatures, are set up; as are also marine currents similarly contrasted in their characters. In this region the surface is giving off water in the state of vapor; in that, dew is being precipitated; and in the other rain is descending—differences that arise from the ever-changing ratio between the absorption and radiation of heat in each place. At one hour, a rapid fall in temperature leads to the formation of ice, with an accompanying expansion throughout the moist bodies frozen; while at another, a thaw unlocks the dislocated fragments of these bodies. And then, passing to a second stage of complication, we see that the many kinds of motion directly or indirectly caused by the sun's rays, severally produce results that vary with the conditions. Oxidation, drought, wind, frost, rain, glaciers, rivers, waves, and other denuding agents effect disintegrations that are determined in their amounts and qualities by local circumstances. Acting upon a tract of granite, such agents here work scarcely an appreciable effect; there cause exfoliations of the surface, and a resulting heap of *debris* and bowlders; and elsewhere, after decomposing the felspar into a white clay, carry away this with the accompanying quartz and mica, and deposit them in separate beds, fluviatile and marine. When the exposed land consists of several unlike formations, sedimentary and igneous, changes proportionably more heterogeneous are wrought. The formations being disintegrable in different degrees, there follows an increased irregularity of surface. The areas drained by different rivers being differently constituted, these rivers carry down to the sea unlike combinations of ingredients; and so sundry new strata of distinct composition arise. And here, indeed, we may see very simply illustrated, the truth, that the heterogeneity of the effects increases in a geometrical progression, with the heterogeneity of the object acted upon. A continent of complex structure, presenting many strata irregularly distributed, raised to various levels, tilted up at all angles, must, under the same denuding agencies, give origin to immensely multiplied results: each district must be peculiarly modified; each river must carry down a distinct kind of detritus; each deposit must be differently distributed by the entangled currents, tidal and other, which wash the contorted shores; and every additional complication of surface must be the cause of more than one additional consequence. But not to dwell on these, let us, for the fuller elucidation of this truth in relation to the inorganic world, consider what would presently follow from some extensive cosmical revolution— say the subsidence of Central America. The immediate results of the disturbance would themselves be sufficiently complex. Besides the numberless dislocations of strata, the ejections of igneous matter, the propagation of earthquake vibrations thousands of miles around, the loud explosions, and the escape of gases, there would be the rush of the Atlantic and Pacific Oceans to supply the vacant space, the subsequent recoil of enormous waves, which would traverse both these oceans and produce myriads of changes along their shores, the corresponding atmospheric waves complicated by the currents surrounding each volcanic vent, and the electrical discharges with which such disturbances are accompanied. But these temporary effects would be insignificant compared with the permanent ones. The complex currents of the Atlantic and Pacific would be altered in directions and amounts. The distribution of heat achieved by these currents would be different from what it is. The arrangement of the isothermal lines, not only on the neighboring continents, but even throughout Europe, would be changed. The tides would flow differently from what they do now. There would be more or less modification of the winds in their periods, strengths, directions, qualities. Rain would fall scarcely anywhere at the same times and in the same quantities as at present. In short, the meterological conditions thousands of miles off, on all sides, would be more or less revolutionized. In these many changes, each of which comprehends countless minor ones, the reader will see the immense heterogeneity of the results wrought out by one force, when that force expends itself on a previously complicated area; and he will readily draw the corollary that from the beginning the complication has advanced at an increasing rate.

§ 159. We have next to trace throughout organic evolution, this same all-pervading principle. And here, where the transformation of the homogeneous into the heterogeneous was first observed, the production of many changes by one cause is least easy to demonstrate. The development of a seed into a plant, or an ovum into an animal, is so gradual; while the forces which determine it are so involved, and at the same time so unobtrusive; that it is difficult to detect the multiplication of effects which is elsewhere so obvious. Nevertheless, by indirect evidence we may establish our proposition; spite of the lack of direct evidence.

Observe, first, how numerous are the changes which any marked stimulus works on an adult organism—a human being, for instance. An alarming sound or sight, besides impressions on the organs of sense and the nerves, may produce a start, a scream, a distortion of the face, a trembling consequent on general muscular relaxation, a burst of perspiration, an excited action of the heart, a rush of blood to the brain, followed possibly by arrest of the heart's action and by syncope; and if the system be feeble, an illness with its long train of complicated symptoms may set in. Similarly in cases of disease. A minute portion of the small-pox virus introduced into the system will, in a severe case, cause, during the first stage, rigors, heat of skin, accelerated pulse, furred tongue, loss of appetite, thirst, epigastric uneasiness, vomiting, headache, pains in the back and limbs, muscular weakness, convulsions, delirium, etc.; in the second stage, cutaneous eruption, itching, tingling, sore throat, swelled fauces, salivation, cough, hoarseness, dyspnœa, etc.; and in the third stage, œdematous inflammations, pneumonia, pleurisy, diarrhœa, inflammation of the brain, ophthalmia, erysipelas, etc.: each of which enumerated symptoms is itself more or less complex. Medicines, special foods, better air, might in like manner be instanced as producing multiplied results. Now it needs only to consider that the many changes thus wrought by one force on an adult organism, must be partially paralleled in an embryo-organism, to understand how here also the production of many effects by one cause is a source of increasing heterogeneity. The external heat and other agencies which determine the first complications of the germ, will, by acting on these, superinduce further complications; on these still higher and more numerous ones; and so on continually: each organ, as it is developed, serving, by its actions and reactions on the rest, to initiate new complexities. The first pulsations of the fœtal heart must simultaneously aid the unfolding of every part. The growth of each tissue, by taking from the blood special proportions of elements, must modify the constitution of the blood; and so must modify the nutrition of all the other tissues. The distributive actions, implying as they do a certain waste, necessitate an addition to the blood of effete matters, which must influence the rest of the system, and perhaps, as some think, initiate the formation of excretory organs. The nervous connections established among the viscera must further multiply their mutual influences. And so with every modification of structure—every additional part and every alteration in the ratios of parts.

Still stronger becomes the proof when we call to mind the fact, that the same germ may be evolved into different forms according to circumstances. Thus, during its earlier stages, every embryo is sexless—becomes either male or female as the balance of forces acting on it determines. Again, it is well-known that the larva of a working-bee will develop into a queen-bee, if, before a certain period, its food be changed to that on which the larvæ of queen-bees are fed. Even more remarkable is the case of certain entozoa. The ovum of a tape-worm, getting into the intestine of one animal, unfolds into the form of its parent; but if carried into other parts of the system, or into the intestine of some unlike animal, it becomes one of the sac-like creatures, called by naturalists *Cysticerci,* or *Cœnuri,* or *Echinococci*—creatures so extremely different from the tape-worm in aspect and structure, that only after careful investigations have they been proved to have the same origin. All which instances imply that each advance in embryonic complication results from the action of incident forces on the complication previously existing. Indeed, the now accepted doctrine of epigenesis necessitates the conclusion that organic evolution proceeds after this manner. For since it is proved that no germ, animal or vegetal, contains the slightest rudiment, trace, or indication of the future organism—since the microscope has shown us that the first process set up in every fertilized germ is a process of repeated spontaneous fissions, ending in the production of a mass of cells, not one of which exhibits any special character; there seems no alternative but to conclude that the partial organization at any moment subsisting in a growing embryo, is transformed by the agencies acting on it into the succeeding phase of organization, and this into the next, until, through ever-increasing complexities, the ultimate form is reached. Thus, though the subtlety of the forces and the slowness of the metamorphosis, prevent us from *directly* tracing the genesis of many changes by one cause, throughout the successive stages which every embryo passes through; yet, *indirectly,* we have strong evidence that this is a source of increasing heterogeneity. We have marked how multitudinous are the effects which a single agency may generate in an adult organism; that a like multiplication of effects must happen in the unfolding organism we have inferred from sundry illustrative cases; further, it has been pointed out that the ability which like germs have to originate unlike forms, implies that the successive transformations result from the new changes superinduced on previous changes; and we have seen that structureless as every germ originally is, the development of an organism out of it is otherwise incomprehensible. Doubtless we are still in the dark respecting those mysterious properties which make the germ, when subject to fit influences, undergo the special changes beginning this series of transformations. All here contended is, that given a germ possessing these mysterious properties, the evolution of an organism from it depends, in part, on that multiplication of effects which we have seen to be a cause of evolution in general, so far as we have yet traced it.

When, leaving the development of single plants and animals, we pass to that of the Earth's flora and fauna the course of the argument again becomes clear and simple. Though, as before admitted, the fragmentary facts Paleontology has accumulated, do not clearly warrant us in saying that, in the lapse of geologic time, there have been evolved more heterogeneous organisms, and more heterogeneous assemblages of organisms; yet we shall now see that there *must* ever have been a tendency toward these results. We shall find that the production of many effects by one cause, which, as already shown, has been all along increasing the physical heterogeneity of the Earth, has further necessitated an increasing heterogeneity in its flora and fauna, individually and collectively. An illustration will make this clear. Suppose that by a series of upheavals, occurring, as they are now known to do, at long intervals, the East Indian Archipelago were to be raised into a continent, and a chain of mountains formed along the axis of elevation. By the first of these upheavals, the plants and animals inhabiting Borneo, Sumatra, New Guinea, and the rest, would be subjected to slightly-modified sets of conditions. The climate in general would be altered in temperature, in humidity, and in its periodical variations; while the local differences would be multiplied. These modifications would affect, perhaps inappreciably, the entire flora and fauna of the region. The change of level would produce additional modifications; varying in different species, and also in different members of the same species, according to their distance from the axis of elevation. Plants, growing only on the sea-shore in special localities, might become extinct. Others, living only in swamps of a certain humidity, would, if they survived at all, probably undergo visible changes of appearance. While more marked alterations would occur in some of the plants that spread over the lands newly raised above the sea. The animals and insects living on these modified plants, would themselves be in some degree modified by change of food, as well as by change of climate; and the modification would be more marked where, from the dwindling or disappearance of one kind of plant, an allied kind was eaten. In the lapse of the many generations arising before the next upheaval, the sensible or insensible alterations thus produced in each species, would become organized—in all the races that survived there would be a more or less complete adaptation to the new conditions. The next upheaval would superinduce further organic changes, implying wider divergences from the primary forms; and so repeatedly. Now however let it be observed that this revolution would not be a substitution of a thousand modified species for the thousand original species; but in place of the thousand original species there would arise several thousand species, or varieties, or changed forms. Each species being distributed over an area of some extent, and tending continually to colonize the new area exposed, its different members would be subject to different sets of changes. Plants and animals migrating toward the equator would not be

affected in the same way with others migrating from it.
Those which spread toward the new shores would undergo
changes unlike the changes undergone by those which spread
into the mountains. Thus, each original race of organisms
would become the root from which diverged several races
differing more or less from it and from each other; and
while some of these might subsequently disappear, probably
more than one would survive in the next geologic period:
the very dispersion itself increasing the chances of survival.
Not only would there be certain modifications thus caused
by changes of physical conditions and food; but also in
some cases other modifications caused by changes of habit.
The fauna of each island, peopling, step by step, the newly-
raised tracts, would eventually come in contact with the
faunas of other islands; and some members of these other
faunas would be unlike any creatures before seen. Her-
bivores, meeting with new beasts of prey, would, in some
cases, be led into modes of defence or escape differing from
those previously used; and simultaneously the beasts of
prey would modify their modes of pursuit and attack. We
know that when circumstances demand it, such changes of
habit *do* take place in animals; and we know that if the new
habits become the dominant ones, they must eventually in
some degree alter the organization. Observe now, however,
a further consequence. There must arise not simply a tendency toward the differentiation of each race of organisms
into several races; but also a tendency to the occasional production of a somewhat higher organism. Taken in the mass,
these divergent varieties, which have been caused by fresh
physical conditions and habits of life, will exhibit alterations quite indefinite in kind and degree; and alterations
that do not necessarily constitute an advance. Probably in
most cases the modified type will be not appreciably more
heterogeneous than the original one. But it *must* now and
then occur, that some division of a species, falling into circumstances which give it rather more complex experiences,
and demand actions somewhat more involved, will have cer-

ain of its organs further differentiated in proportionately
small degrees—will become slightly more heterogeneous.
Hence, there will from time to time arise an increased
heterogeneity both of the Earth's flora and fauna, and of
individual races included in them. Omitting detailed explanations, and allowing for the qualifications which cannot
here be specified, it is sufficiently clear that geological muta-
tions have all along tended to complicate the forms of life,
whether regarded separately or collectively. That multiplication of effects which has been a part-cause of the transformation of the Earth's crust from the simple into the complex, has simultaneously led to a parallel transformation of
the Life upon its surface.[1]

The deduction here drawn from the established truths of
geology and the general laws of life, gains immensely in
weight on finding it to be in harmony with an induction
drawn from direct experience. Just that divergence of
many races from one race, which we inferred must have
been continually occurring during geologic time, we know
to have occurred during the prehistoric and historic periods,
in man and domestic animals. And just that multiplication
of effects which we concluded must have been instrumental to the first, we see has in a great measure wrought the
last. Single causes, as famine, pressure of population, war,
have periodically led to further dispersions of mankind and
of dependent creatures: each such dispersion initiating

---

[1] Had this paragraph, first published in the "Westminster Review" in 1857,
been written after the appearance of Mr. Darwin's work on "The Origin of
Species," it would doubtless have been otherwise expressed. Reference would
have been made to the process of "natural selection," as greatly facilitating
the differentiations described. As it is, however, I prefer to let the passage
stand in its original shape: partly because it seems to me that these successive
changes of conditions would produce divergent varieties or species, apart from
the influence of "natural selection" (though in less numerous ways as well as
less rapidly) ; and partly because I conceive that in the absence of these successive changes of conditions, "natural selection" would effect comparatively
little. Let me add that though these positions are not enunciated in "The
Origin of Species," yet a common friend gives me reason to think that Mr.
Darwin would coincide in them; if he did not indeed consider them as tacitly
implied in his work.

new modifications, new varieties of type. Whether all the human races be or be not derived from one stock, philology makes it clear that whole groups of races, now easily distinguishable from each other, were originally one race—that the diffusion of one race into different climates and conditions of existence has produced many altered forms of it. Similarly with domestic animals. Though in some cases (as that of dogs) community of origin will perhaps be disputed, yet in other cases (as that of the sheep or the cattle of our own country) it will not be questioned that local differences of climate, food, and treatment, have transformed one original breed into numerous breeds, now become so far distinct as to produce unstable hybrids. Moreover, through the complication of effects flowing from single causes, we here find, what we before inferred, not only an increase of general heterogeneity, but also of special heterogeneity. While of the divergent divisions and subdivisions of the human race, many have undergone changes not constituting an advance; others have become decidedly more heterogeneous. The civilized European departs more widely from the vertebrate archetype than does the savage.

§ 160. A sensation does not expend itself in arousing some single state of consciousness; but the state of consciousness aroused is made up of various represented sensations connected by co-existence, or sequence with the presented sensation. And that, in proportion as the grade of intelligence is high, the number of ideas suggested is great, may be readily inferred. Let us, however, look at the proof that here, too, each change is the parent of many changes; and that the multiplication increases in proportion as the area affected is complex.

Were some hitherto unknown bird, driven say by stress of weather from the remote north, to make its appearance on our shores, it would excite no speculation in the sheep or cattle amid which it alighted: a perception of it as a creature like those constantly flying about, would be the sole interruption of that dull current of consciousness which accompanies grazing and rumination. The cow-herd, by whom we may suppose the exhausted bird to be presently caught, would probably gaze at it with some slight curiosity, as being unlike any he had before seen—would note its most conspicuous markings, and vaguely ponder on the questions, where it came from, and how it came. The village bird-stuffer would have suggested to him by the sight of it sundry forms to which it bore a little resemblance; would receive from it more numerous and more specific impressions respecting structure and plumage; would be reminded of various instances of birds brought by storms from foreign parts—would tell who found them, who stuffed them, who bought them. Supposing the unknown bird taken to a naturalist of the old school, interested only in externals (one of those described by the late Edward Forbes, as examining animals as though they were merely skins filled with straw), it would excite in him a more involved series of mental changes: there would be an elaborate examination of the feathers, a noting of all their technical distinctions, with a reduction of these perceptions to certain equivalent written symbols; reasons for referring the new form to a particular family, order, and genus would be sought out and written down; communications with the secretary of some society, or editor of some journal, would follow; and porbably there would be not a few thoughts about the addition of the *ii* to the describer's name, to form the name of the species. Lastly, in the mind of a comparative anatomist, such a new species, should it happen to have any marked internal peculiarity, might produce additional sets of changes —might very possibly suggest modified views respecting the relationships of the division to which it belonged; or, perhaps, alter his conceptions of the homologies and developments of certain organs; and the conclusions drawn might not improbably enter as elements into still wider inquiries concerning the origin of organic forms.

From ideas let us turn to emotions. In a young child, a

father's anger produces little else than vague fear—a disagreeable sense of impending evil, taking various shapes of
physical suffering or deprivation of pleasures. In elder children, the same harsh words will arouse additional feelings:
sometimes a sense of shame, of penitence, or of sorrow for
having offended; at other times, a sense of injustice, and a
consequent anger. In the wife, yet a further range of feelings may come into existence—perhaps wounded affection,
perhaps self-pity for ill-usage, perhaps contempt for groundless irritability, perhaps sympathy for some suffering which
the irritability indicates, perhaps anxiety about an unknown
misfortune which she thinks has produced it. Nor are we
without evidence that among adults, the like differences of
development are accompanied by like differences in the
number of emotions that are aroused, in combination or
rapid succession—the lower natures being characterized by
that impulsiveness which results from the uncontrolled action of a few feelings; and the higher natures being characterized by the simultaneous action of many secondary feelings, modifying those first awakened.

Possibly it will be objected that the illustrations here
given are drawn from the functional changes of the nervous
system, not from its structural changes; and that what is
proved among the first, does not necessarily hold among the
last. This must be admitted. Those, however, who recognize the truth that the structural changes are the slowly accumulated results of the functional changes, will readily
draw the corollary, that a part-cause of the evolution of the
nervous system, as of other evolution, is this multiplication
of effects which becomes ever greater as the development
becomes higher.

§ 161. If the advance of Man toward greater heterogeneity in both body and mind, is in part traceable to the
production of many effects by one cause, still more clearly
may the advance of Society toward greater heterogeneity be
so explained. Consider the growth of an industrial organization. When, as must occasionally happen, some indi-

vidual of a tribe displays unusual aptitude for making an article of general use (a weapon, for instance) which was before made by each man for himself, there arises a tendency toward the differentiation of that individual into a maker of weapons. His companions (warriors and hunters all of them) severally wish to have the best weapons that can be made; and are therefore certain to offer strong inducements to this skilled individual to make weapons for them. He, on the other hand, having both an unusual faculty, and an unusual liking, for making weapons (the capacity and the desire for any occupation being commonly associated), is predisposed to fulfil these commissions on the offer of adequate rewards: especially as his love of distinction is also gratified. This first specialization of function, once commenced, tends ever to become more decided. On the side of the weapon-maker, continued practice gives increased skill—increased superiority to his products. On the side of his clients, cessation of practice entails decreased skill. Thus the influences that determine this division of labor grow stronger in both ways: this social movement tends ever to become more decided in the direction in which it was first set up; and the incipient heterogeneity is, on the average of cases, likely to become permanent for that generation, if no longer. Such a process, besides differentiating the social mass into two parts, the one monopolizing, or almost monopolizing, the performance of a certain function, and the other having lost the habit, and in some measure the power, of performing that function, has a tendency to initiate other differentiations. The advance described implies the introduction of barter: the maker of weapons has, on each occasion, to be paid in such other articles as he agrees to take in exchange. Now he will not habitually take in exchange one kind of article, but many kinds. He does not want mats only, or skins, or fishing-gear; but he wants all these; and on each occasion will bargain for the particular things he most needs. What follows? If among the members of the tribe there exist any slight differences of

skill in the manufacture of these various things, as there
are almost sure to do, the weapon-maker will take from
each one the thing which that one excels in making: he will
exchange for mats with him whose mats are superior, and
will bargain for the fishing-gear of whoever has the best
But he who has bartered away his mats or his fishing-gear
must make other mats or fishing-gear for himself; and in so
doing must, in some degree, further develop his aptitude
Thus it results that the small specialties of faculty possessed by various members of the tribe will tend to grow
more decided. If such transactions are from time to time
repeated, these specializations may become appreciable
And whether or not there ensue distinct differentiations
of other individuals into makers of particular articles, it
is clear that incipient differentiations take place throughout
the tribe: the one original cause produces not only the first
dual effect, but a number of secondary dual effects, like in
kind but minor in degree. This process, of which trace
may be seen among groups of schoolboys, cannot well produce a lasting distribution of functions in an unsettled tribe
but where there grows up a fixed and multiplying community, such differentiations become permanent, and increase with each generation. An addition to the number
of citizens, involving a greater demand for every commodity, intensifies the functional activity of each specialized
person or class; and this renders the specialization more
definite where it already exists, and establishes it where it
is but nascent. By increasing the pressure on the means
of subsistence, a larger population again augments these
results; since every individual is forced more and more to
confine himself to that which he can do best, and by which
he can gain most. And this industrial progress, by aiding
future production, opens the way for further growth of population, which reacts as before. Presently, under the same
stimuli, new occupations arise. Competing workers, severally aiming to produce improved articles, occasionally discover better processes or better materials. In weapons and

cutting-tools, the substitution of bronze for stone entails on him who first makes it a great increase of demand—so great an increase that he presently finds all his time occupied in making the bronze for the articles he sells, and is obliged to depute the fashioning of these articles to others; and eventually the making of bronze, thus gradually differentiated from a pre-existing occupation, becomes an occupation by itself. But now mark the ramified changes which follow this change. Bronze soon replaces stone, not only in the articles it was first used for, but in many others; and so affects the manufacture of them. Further, it affects the processes which such improved utensils subserve, and the resulting products—modifies buildings, carvings, dress, personal decorations. Yet again, it sets going sundry manufactures which were before impossible, from lack of a material fit for the requisite tools. And all these changes react on the people—increase their manipulative skill, their intelligence, their comfort—refine their habits and tastes.

It is out of the question here to follow through its successive complications, this increasing social heterogeneity that results from the production of many effects by one cause. But leaving the intermediate phases of social development, let us take an illustration from its passing phase. To trace the effects of steam-power, in its manifold applications to mining, navigation, and manufactures, would carry us into unmanageable detail. Let us confine ourselves to the latest embodiment of steam-power—the locomotive engine. This, as the proximate cause of our railway-system, has changed the face of the country, the course of trade, and the habits of the people. Consider, first, the complicated sets of changes that precede the making of every railway—the provisional arrangements, the meetings, the registration, the trial-section, the parliamentary survey, the lithographed plans, the books of reference, the local deposits and notices, the application to Parliament, the passing Standing-Orders Committee, the first, second, and third readings: each of which brief heads indicates a multiplicity of transactions, and the further development of sundry occupations (as those of engineers, surveyors, lithographers, parliamentary agents, share brokers) and the creation of sundry others (as those of traffic takers, reference takers). Consider, next, the yet more marked changes implied in railway construction—the cuttings, embankings, tunnellings, diversions of roads; the building of bridges and stations; the laying down of ballast, sleepers, and rails; the making of engines, tenders, carriages, and wagons: which processes, acting upon numerous trades, increase the importation of timber, the quarrying of stone, the manufacture of iron, the mining of coal, the burning of bricks; institute a variety of special manufactures weekly advertised in the "Railway Times"; and call into being some new classes of workers—drivers, stokers, cleaners, plate-layers, etc., etc. Then come the changes, more numerous and involved still, which railways in action produce on the community at large. The organization of every business is more or less modified; ease of communication makes it better to do directly what was before done by proxy; agencies are established where previously they would not have paid; goods are obtained from remote wholesale houses instead of near retail ones; and commodities are used which distance once rendered inaccessible. The rapidity and small cost of carriage tend to specialize more than ever the industries of different districts—to confine each manufacture to the parts in which, from local advantages, it can be best carried on. Economical distribution equalizes prices, and also, on the average, lowers prices; thus bringing divers articles within the means of those before unable to buy them, and so increasing their comforts and improving their habits. At the same time the practice of travelling is immensely extended. Classes who before could not afford it, take annual trips to the sea; visit their distant relations; make tours; and so we are benefited in body, feelings, and intellect. The more prompt transmission of letters and of news produces further changes—makes the pulse of the nation faster. Yet more, there arises a wide dissemination of cheap literature through railway book-stalls, and of advertisements in railway carriages: both of them aiding ulterior progress. And the innumerable changes here briefly indicated are consequent on the invention of the locomotive engine. The social organism has been rendered more heterogeneous, in virtue of the many new occupations introduced, and the many old ones further specialized; prices in all places have been altered; each trader has, more or less, modified his way of doing business; and every person has been affected in his actions, thoughts, emotions.

The only further fact demanding notice, is, that we here see more clearly than ever, that in proportion as the area over which any influence extends, becomes hetergeneous, the results are in a yet higher degree multiplied in number and kind. While among the primitive tribes to whom it was first known, caoutchouc caused but few changes, among ourselves the changes have been so many and varied that the history of them occupies a volume. Upon the small, homogeneous community inhabiting one of the Hebrides, the electric telegraph would produce, were it used, scarcely any results; but in England the results it produces are multitudinous.

Space permitting, the synthesis might here be pursued in relation to all the subtler products of social life. It might be shown how, in Science, an advance of one division presently advances other divisions—how Astronomy has been immensely forwarded by discoveries in Optics, while other optical discoveries have initiated Microscopic Anatomy, and greatly aided the growth of Physiology—how Chemistry has indirectly increased our knowledge of Electricity, Magnetism, Biology, Geology—how Electricity has reacted on Chemistry and Magnetism, developed our views of Light and Heat, and disclosed sundry laws of nervous action. In Literature the same truth might be exhibited in the still-multiplying forms of periodical publications that have descended from the first newspaper, and which have severally acted and reacted on other forms of literature and on each other; or in the bias given by each book of power to various subsequent books. The influence which a new school of Painting (as that of the pre-Raphaelites) exercises on other schools; the hints which all kinds of pictorial art are deriving from Photography; the complex results of new critical doctrines; might severally be dwelt on as displaying the like multiplication of effects. But it would needlessly tax the reader's patience to detail, in their many ramifications, these various changes; here become so involved and subtle as to be followed with some difficulty.

§ 162. After the argument which closed the last chapter, a parallel one seems here scarcely required. For symmetry's sake, however, it will be proper briefly to point out how the multiplication of effects, like the instability of the homogeneous, is a corollary from the persistence of force.

Things which we call different are things which react in different ways; and we can know them as different only by the differences in their reactions. When we distinguish bodies as hard and soft, rough and smooth, we simply mean that certain like muscular forces expended on them are followed by unlike sets of sensations—unlike reactive forces. Objects that are classed as red, blue, yellow, etc., are objects that decompose light in strongly-contrasted ways; that is, we know contrasts of color as contrasts in the changes produced in a uniform incident force. Manifestly, any two things which do not work unequal effects on consciousness, either by unequally opposing our own energies, or by impressing our senses with unequally modified forms of certain external energies, cannot be distinguished by us. Hence the proposition that the different parts of any whole must react differently on a uniform incident force, and must so reduce it to a group of multiform forces, is in essence a truism. A further step will reduce this truism to its lowest terms.

When, from unlikeness between the effects they produce on consciousness, we predicate unlikeness between two objects, what is our warrant? and what do we mean by the unlikeness, objectively considered? Our warrant is the persistence of force. Some kind or amount of change has been wrought in us by the one, which has not been wrought by the other. This change we ascribe to some force exercised by the one which the other has not exercised. And we have no alternative but to do this, or to assert that the change had no antecedent; which is to deny the persistence of force. Whence it is further manifest that what we regard as the objective unlikeness is the presence in the one of some force, or set of forces, not present in the other—something in the kinds or amounts or directions of the constituent forces of the one, which those of the other do not parallel. But now if things or parts of things which we call different, are those of which the constituent forces differ in one or more respects; what must happen to any like forces, or any uniform force, falling on them? Such like forces, or parts of a uniform force, must be differently modified. The force which is present in the one and not in the other, must be an element in the conflict—must produce its equivalent reaction; and must so affect the total reaction. To say otherwise is to say that this differential force will produce no effect; which is to say that force is not persistent.

I need not develop this corollary further. It manifestly follows that a uniform force, falling on a uniform aggregate, must undergo dispersion; that falling on an aggregate made up of unlike parts, it must undergo dispersion from each part, as well as qualitative differentiations; that in proportion as the parts are unlike, these qualitative differentiations must be marked; that in proportion to the number of the parts, they must be numerous; that the secondary forces so produced, must undergo further transformations while working equivalent transformations in the parts that change them; and similarly with the forces they generate. Thus the conclusions that a part-cause of Evolution is the multiplication of effects; and that this increases in geometrical progression as the heterogeneity becomes greater; are not only to be established inductively, but are deducible from the deepest of all truths.

CHAPTER XXI

SEGREGATION

§ 163. THE general interpretation of Evolution is far from being completed in the preceding chapters. We must contemplate its changes under yet another aspect, before we can form a definite conception of the process constituted by them. Though the laws already set forth, furnish a key to the rearrangement of parts which Evolution exhibits, in so far as it is an advance from the uniform to the multiform; they furnish no key to this rearrangement in so far as it is an advance from the indefinite to the definite. On studying the actions and reactions everywhere going on, we have found it to follow inevitably from a certain primordial truth, that the homogeneous must lapse into the heterogeneous, and that the heterogeneous must become more heterogeneous; but we have not discovered why the differently-affected parts of any simple whole become clearly marked off from each other, at the same time that they become unlike. Thus far no reason has been assigned why there should not ordinarily arise a vague chaotic heterogeneity, in place of that orderly heterogeneity displayed in Evolution. It still remains to find out the cause of that local integration which accompanies local differentiation—that gradually-completed segregation of like units into a group, distinctly separated from neighboring groups which are severally made up of other kinds of units. The rationale will be conveniently introduced by a few instances in which we may watch this segregative process taking place.

When, toward the end of September, the trees are gaining their autumn colors, and we are hoping shortly to see a further change increasing still more the beauty of the landscape, we are not uncommonly disappointed by the occurrence of an equinoctial gale. Out of the mixed mass of foliage on each branch, the strong current of air carries away the decaying and brightly-tinted leaves, but fails to detach those which are still green. And while these last, frayed and seared by long-continued beatings against each other, and the twigs around them, give a sombre color to the woods, the red and yellow and orange leaves are collected together in ditches and behind walls and in corners where eddies allow them to settle. That is to say, by the action of that uniform force which the wind exerts on both kinds, the dying leaves are picked out from among their still living companions and gathered in places by themselves. Again, the separation of particles of different sizes, as dust and sand from pebbles, may be similarly effected; as we see on every road in March. And from the days of Homer downward, the power of currents of air, natural and artificial, to part from one another units of unlike specific gravities, has been habitually utilized in the winnowing of chaff from wheat. In every river we see how the mixed materials carried down are separately deposited—how in rapids the bottom gives rest to nothing but bowlders and pebbles; how where the current is not so strong, sand is let fall; and how, in still places, there is a sediment of mud. This selective action of moving water, is commonly applied in the arts to obtain masses of particles of different degrees of fineness. Emery, for example, after being ground, is carried by a slow current through successive compartments; in the first of which the largest grains subside; in the second of which the grains that reach the bottom before the water has escaped, are somewhat smaller; in the third smaller still; until in the last there are deposited only those finest particles which fall so slowly through the water that they have not previously been able to reach the bottom. And in a way that is different though equally significant, this segregative effect of water in motion, is exemplified in the carrying away of soluble from insoluble matters—an application of it hourly made in every laboratory. The effects of the uniform forces which aerial and aqueous currents exercise, are paralleled by those of uniform forces of other orders. Electric attraction will separate small bodies from large, or light bodies from heavy. By magnetism, grains of iron may be selected from among other grains; as by the Sheffield grinder, whose magnetized gauze mask filters out the steel-dust which his wheel gives off, from the stone-dust that accompanies it. And how the affinity of any agent acting differently on the components of a given body, enables us to take away some component and leave the rest behind, is shown in almost every chemical experiment.

What now is the general truth here variously presented? How are these several facts and countless similar ones to be expressed in terms that embrace them all? In each case we see in action a force which may be regarded as simple or uniform—fluid motion in a certain direction at a certain velocity; electric or magnetic attraction of a given amount; chemical affinity of a particular kind: or rather, in strictness, the acting force is compounded of one of these and certain other uniform forces, as gravitation, etc. In each case we have an aggregate made up of unlike units—either atoms of different substances combined or intimately mingled, or fragments of the same substance of different sizes, or other constituent parts that are unlike in their specific gravities, shapes, or other attributes. And in each case these unlike units, or groups of units, of which the aggregate consists, are, under the influence of some resultant force acting indiscriminately on them all, separated from each other—segregated into minor aggregates, each consisting of units that are severally like each other and unlike those of the other minor aggregates. Such being the common aspect of these changes, let us look for the common interpretation of them.

In the chapter on "The Instability of the Homogeneous," it was shown that a uniform force falling on any aggregate, produces unlike modifications in its different parts—turns the uniform into the multiform and the multiform into the more multiform. The transformation thus wrought, consists of either insensible or sensible changes of relative position among the units, or of both—either of those molecular rearrangements which we call chemical, or of those larger transpositions which are distinguished as mechanical, or of the two united. Such portion of the permanently effective force as reaches each different part, or differently-conditioned part, may be expended in modifying the mutual relations of its constituents; or it may be expended in moving the part to another place; or it may be expended partially in the first and partially in the second. Hence, so much of the permanently effective force as does not work the one kind of effect, must work the other kind. It is manifest that if of the permanently effective force which falls on some compound unit of an aggregate, little if any is absorbed in rearranging the ultimate components of such compound unit, much or the whole, must show itself in motion of such compound unit to some other place in the aggregate; and conversely, if little or none of this force is absorbed in generating mechanical transposition, much or the whole must go to produce molecular alterations. What now must follow from this? In cases where none or only part of the force generates chemical redistributions, what physical redistributions must be generated? Parts that are similar to each other will be similarly acted on by the force; and will similarly react on it. Parts that are dissimilar will be dissimilarly acted on by the force; and will dissimilarly react on it. Hence the permanently effective incident force, when wholly or partially transformed into mechanical motion of the units, will produce like motions in units that are alike, and unlike motions in units that are unlike. If then, in an aggregate containing two or more orders of mixed units, those of the same order will be moved in the same way, and in a way that differs from that in which units of other orders are moved, the respective orders must segregate. A group of

like things on which are impressed motions that are alike
in amount and direction, must be transferred as a group to
another place, and if they are mingled with some group
of other things, on which the motions impressed are like
each other, but unlike those of the first group in amount or
direction or both, these other things must be transferred as a
group to some other place—the mixed units must undergo
a simultaneous selection and separation.

In further elucidation of this process, it will be well here
to set down a few instances in which we may see that, other
things equal, the definiteness of the separation is in proportion to the definiteness of the difference between the units.
Take a handful of any pounded substance, containing fragments of all sizes; and let it fall to the ground while a gentle breeze is blowing. The large fragments will be collected
together on the ground almost immediately under the hand;
somewhat smaller fragments will be carried a little to the
leeward; still smaller ones a little further; and those minute
particles which we call dust will be drifted a long way before they reach the earth: that is, the integration is indefinite where the difference among the fragments is indefinite,
though the divergence is greatest where the difference is
greatest. If, again, the handful be made up of quite distinct orders of units—as pebbles, coarse sand, and dust—
these will, under like conditions, be segregated with comparative definiteness: the pebbles will drop almost vertically; the sand will fall in an inclined direction, and deposit
itself within a tolerably circumscrbed space beyond the pebbles; while the dust will be blown almost horizontally to a
great distance. A case in which another kind of force comes
into play will still better illustrate this truth. Through a
mixed aggregate of soluble and insoluble substances, let
water slowly percolate. There will in the first place be a
distinct parting of the substances that are the most widely
contrasted in their relations to the acting forces: the soluble
will be carried away; the insoluble will remain behind.
Further, some separation, though a less definite one, will be

effected among the soluble substances; since the first part of the current will remove the most soluble substances in the largest amounts, and after these have been all dissolved, the current will still continue to bring out the remaining less soluble substances. Even the undissolved matters will have simultaneously undergone a certain segregation; for the percolating fluid will carry down the minute fragments from among the large ones, and will deposit those of small specific gravity in one place, and those of great specific gravity in another. To complete the elucidation we must glance at the obverse fact; namely, that mixed units which differ but slightly, are moved in but slightly-different ways by incident forces, and can therefore be separated only by such adjustments of the incident forces as allow slight differences to become appreciable factors in the result. This truth is made manifest by antithesis in the instances just given; but it may be made much more manifest by a few such instances as those which chemical analysis supplies in abundance. The parting of alcohol from water by distillation is a good one. Here we have atoms consisting of oxygen and hydrogen, mingled with atoms consisting of oxygen, hydrogen, and carbon. The two orders of atoms have a considerable similarity of nature: they similarly maintain a fluid form at ordinary temperatures; they similarly become gaseous more and more rapidly as the temperature is raised; and they boil at points not very far apart. Now this comparative likeness of the atoms is accompanied by difficulty in segregating them. If the mixed fluid is unduly heated, much water distils over with the alcohol: it is only within a narrow range of temperature that the one set of atoms are driven off rather than the others; and even then not a few of the others accompany them. The most interesting and instructive example, however, is furnished by certain phenomena of crystallization. When several salts that have little analogy of constitution are dissolved in the same body of water, they are separated without much trouble, by crystallization: their respective units moved toward each other, as physicists

suppose, by polar forces, segregate into crystals of their respective kinds. The crystals of each salt do, indeed, usually
contain certain small amounts of the other salts present in
the solution—especially when the crystallization has been
rapid; but from these other salts they are severally freed by
repeated re-solutions and crystallizations. Mark now, however, that the reverse is the case when the salts contained in
the same body of water are chemically homologous. The
nitrates of baryta and lead, or the sulphates of zinc, soda,
and magnesia, unite in the same crystals; nor will they crys-
tallize separately if these crystals be dissolved afresh, and
afresh crystallized, even with great care. On seeking the
cause of this anomaly, chemists found that such salts were
isomorphous—that their atoms, though not chemically identical, were identical in the proportions of acid, base, and
water, composing them, and in their crystalline forms:
whence it was inferred that their atoms are nearly alike in
structure. Thus is clearly illustrated the truth, that units
of unlike kinds are selected out and separated with a readiness proportionate to the degree of their unlikeness. In the
first case we see that being dissimilar in their forms, but
similar in so far as they are soluble in water of a certain temperature, the atoms segregate, though imperfectly. In the
second case we see that the atoms, having not only the likeness implied by solubility in the same menstruum, but also
a great likeness of structure, do not segregate—are sorted
and parted from each other only under quite special conditions, and then very incompletely. That is, the incident
force of mutual polarity impresses unlike motions on the
mixed units in proportion as they are unlike; and therefore, in proportion as they are unlike, tends to deposit them
in separate places.

There is a converse cause of segregation, which it is
needless here to treat of with equal fulness. If different
units acted on by the same force must be differently moved;
so, too, must units of the same kind be differently moved by
different forces. Supposing some group of units forming

part of a homogeneous aggregate, are unitedly exposed to a force that is unlike in amount or direction to the force acting on the rest of the aggregate; then this group of units will separate from the rest, provided that, of the force so acting on it, there remains any portion not dissipated in molecular vibrations, nor absorbed in producing molecular rearrangements. After all that has been said above, this proposition needs no defence.

Before ending our preliminary exposition, a complementary truth must be specified; namely, that mixed forces are segregated by the reaction of uniform matters, just as mixed matters are segregated by the action of uniform forces. Of this truth a complete and sufficient illustration is furnished by the dispersion of refracted light. A beam of light, made up of ethereal undulations of different orders, is not uniformly deflected by a homogeneous refracting body; but the different orders of undulations it contains are deflected at different angles: the result being that these different orders of undulations are separated and integrated, and so produce what we know as the colors of the spectrum. A segregation of another kind occurs when rays of light traverse an obstructing medium. Those rays which consist of comparatively short undulations, are absorbed before those which consist of comparatively long ones; and the red rays, which consist of the longest undulations, alone penetrate when the obstruction is very great. How, conversely, there is produced a separation of like forces by the reaction of unlike matters, is also made manifest by the phenomena of refraction: since adjacent and parallel beams of light, falling on, and passing through, unlike substances, are made to diverge.

§ 164. On the assumption of their nebular origin, stars and planets exemplify that cause of material segregation last assigned—the action of unlike forces on like units.

In a preceding chapter (§ 150) we saw that if matter ever existed in a diffused form, it could not continue uniformly distributed, but must break up into masses. It was shown that in the absence of a perfect balance of mutual attractions among atoms dispersed through unlimited space, there must arise breaches of continuity throughout the aggregate formed by them, and a concentration of it toward centres of dominant attraction. Where any such breach of continuity occurs, and the atoms that were before adjacent separate from each other; they do so in consequence of a difference in the forces to which they are respectively subject. The atoms on the one side of the breach are exposed to a certain surplus attraction in the direction in which they begin to move; and those on the other to a surplus attraction in the opposite direction. That is, the adjacent groups of like units are exposed to unlike resultant forces; and accordingly separate and integrate.

The formation and detachment of a nebulous ring, illustrates the same general principle. To conclude, as Laplace did, that the equatorial portion of a rotating nebulous spheroid, will, during concentration, acquire a centrifugal force sufficient to prevent it from following the rest of the contracting mass, is to conclude that such portions will remain behind as are in common subject to a certain differential force. The line of division between the ring and the spheroid, must be a line inside of which the aggregative force is greater than the force resisting aggregation; and outside of which the force resisting aggregation is greater than the aggregative force. Hence the alleged process conforms to the law that among like units, exposed to unlike forces, the similarly conditioned part from the dissimilarly conditioned.

§ 165. Those geologic changes usually classed as aqueous, display under numerous forms the segregation of unlike units by a uniform incident force. On sea-shores, the waves are ever sorting-out and separating the mixed materials against which they break. From each mass of fallen cliff, the rising and ebbing tide carries away all those particles which are so small as to remain long suspended in the water; and, at some distance from shore, deposits them in the shape of fine sediment. Large particles, sinking with comparative rapidity, are accumulated into beds of sand near low water-mark. The coarse grit and small pebbles collect together on the incline up which the breakers rush. And on the top lie the larger stones and bowlders. Still more specific segregations may occasionally be observed. Flat pebbles, produced by the breaking down of laminated rock, are sometimes separately collected in one part of a shingle bank. On this shore the deposit is wholly of mud; on that it is wholly of sand. Here we find a sheltered cove filled with small pebbles almost of one size; and there, in a curved bay one end of which is more exposed than the other, we see a progressive increase in the massiveness of the stones as we walk from the less exposed to the more exposed end. Trace the history of each geologic deposit, and we are quickly led down to the fact, that mixed fragments of matter, differing in their sizes or weights, are, when exposed to the momentum and friction of water, joined with the attraction of the Earth, selected from each other, and united into groups of comparatively like fragments. And we see that, other things equal, the separation is definite in proportion as the differences of the units are marked. After they have been formed, sedimentary strata exhibit segregations of another kind. The flints and the nodules of iron pyrites that are found in chalk, as well as the siliceous concretions which occasionally occur in limestone, can be interpreted only as aggregations of atoms of silex or sulphuret of iron, originally diffused almost uniformly through the deposit, but gradually collected round certain centres, notwithstanding the solid or semi-solid state of the surrounding matter. What is called bog iron-ore supplies the conditions and the result in still more obvious correlation.

Among igneous changes we do not find so many examples of the process described. When distinguishing simple and compound evolution, it was pointed out (§ 102) that an excessive quantity of contained molecular motion, prevents permanence in those secondary redistributions which make evolution compound. Nevertheless, geological phenomena of this order are not barren of illustrations. Where the mixed matters composing the Earth's crust have been raised to a very high temperature, segregation habitually takes place as the temperature diminishes. Sundry of the substances that escape in a gaseous form from volcanoes, sublime into crystals on coming against cool surfaces; and solidifying as these substances do, at different temperatures, they are deposited at different parts of the crevices through which they are emitted together. The best illustration, however, is furnished by the changes that occur during the slow cooling of igneous rock. When, through one of the fractures from time to time made in the solid shell which forms the Earth's crust, a portion of the molten nucleus is extruded; and when this is cooled with comparative rapidity, through free radiation and contact with cold masses; it forms a substance known as trap or basalt—a substance that is uniform in texture, though made up of various ingredients. But when, not escaping through the superficial strata, such a portion of the molten nucleus is slowly cooled, it becomes what we know as granite: the mingled particles of quartz, felspar, and mica, being kept for a long time in a fluid and semi-fluid state—a state of comparative mobility—undergo those changes of position which the forces impressed on them by their fellow units necessitate. Having time in which to generate the requisite motions of the atoms, the differential forces arising from mutual polarity, segregate the quartz, felspar, and mica, into crystals. How completely this is dependent on the long-continued agitation of the mixed particles, and consequent long-continued mobility by small differential forces, is proved by the fact that in granite dikes, the crystals in the centre of the mass, where the fluidity or semi-fluidity continued for a longer time, are much larger than those at the sides, where contact with the neighboring rock caused more rapid cooling and solidification.

§ 166. The actions going on throughout an organism are so involved and subtle, that we cannot expect to identify the particular forces by which particular segregations are effected. Among the few instances admitting of tolerably definite interpretation, the best are those in which mechanical pressures and tensions are the agencies at work. We shall discover several on studying the bony frame of the higher animals.

The vertebral column of a man, is subject, as a whole, to certain general strains—the weight of the body, together with the reactions involved by all considerable muscular efforts; and in conformity with this, it has become segregated as a whole. At the same time, being exposed to different forces in the course of those lateral bendings which the movements necessitate, its parts retain a certain separateness. And if we trace up the development of the vertebral column from its primitive form of a cartilaginous cord in the lowest fishes, we see that, throughout, it maintains an integration corresponding to the unity of the incident forces, joined with a division into segments corresponding to the variety of the incident forces. Each segment, considered apart, exemplifies the truth more simply. A vertebra is not a single bone, but consists of a central mass with sundry appendages or processes; and in rudimentary types of vertebræ, these appendages are quite separate from the central mass, and, indeed, exist before it makes its appearance. But these several independent bones, constituting a primitive spinal segment, are subject to a certain aggregate of forces which agree more than they differ: as the fulcrum to a group of muscles habitually acting together, they perpetually undergo certain reactions in common. And accordingly, we see that in the course of development they gradually coalesce. Still clearer is the illustration furnished by spinal segments that become fused together where they are together exposed to some predominant strain. The sacrum consists of a group of vertebræ firmly united. In the ostrich and its congeners there are from seventeen to twenty sacral vertebræ; and besides being confluent with each other, these are confluent with the iliac bones, which run on each side of them. If now we assume these vertebræ to have been originally separate, as they still are in the embryo bird; and if we consider the mechanical conditions to which they must in such case have been exposed; we shall see that their union results in the alleged way. For through these vertebræ the entire weight of the body is transferred to the legs: the legs support the pelvic arch; the pelvic arch supports the sacrum; and to the sacrum is articulated the rest of the spine, with all the limbs and organs attached to it. Hence, if separate, the sacral vertebræ must be held firmly together by strongly-contracted muscles; and must, by implication, be prevented from partaking in those lateral movements which the other vertebræ undergo—they must be subject to a common strain, while they are preserved from strains which would affect them differently; and so they fulfil the conditions under which segregation occurs. But the cases in which cause and effect are brought into the most obvious relation, are supplied by the limbs. The metacarpal bones (those which in man support the palm of the hand) are separate from each other in the majority of mammalia: the separate actions of the toes entailing on them slight amounts of separate movements. This is not so however in the ox-tribe and the horse-tribe. In the ox-tribe, only the middle metacarpals (third and fourth) are developed; and these, attaining massive proportions, coalesce to form the cannon bone. In the horse-tribe, the segregation is what we may distinguish as indirect: the second and fourth metacarpals are present only as rudiments united to the sides of the third, while the third is immensely developed; thus forming a cannon bone which differs from that of the ox in being a single cylinder, instead of two cylinders fused together. The metatarsus in these quadrupeds exhibits parallel changes. Now each of these metamorphoses occurs where the different bones grouped together have no longer any different functions, but retain only a common function. The feet of oxen and horses are used solely for locomotion—are not put like those of unguic-ulate mammals to purposes which involve some relative movements of the metacarpals. Thus there directly or in-directly results a single mass of bone where the incident force is single. And for the inference that these facts have a causal connection, we find confirmation throughout the entire class of birds; in the wings and legs of which, like segregations are found under like conditions. While this sheet is passing through the press, a fact illustrating this general truth in a yet more remarkable manner, has been mentioned to me by Professor Huxley; who kindly allows me to make use of it while still unpublished by him. The *Glyptodon,* an extinct mammal found fossilized in South America, has long been known as a large uncouth creature allied to the Armadillo, but having a massive dermal armor consisting of polygonal plates closely fitted together so as to make a vast box, inclosing the body in such way as effec-tually to prevent it from being bent, laterally or vertically, in the slightest degree. This bony box, which must have weighed several hundredweight, was supported on the spi-nous processes of the vertebræ, and on the adajacent bones of the pelvic and thoracic arches. And the significant fact now to be noted, is, that here, where the trunk vertebræ were together exposed to the pressure of this heavy dermal armor, at the same time that, by its rigidity, they were preserved from all relative movements, the entire series of them were united into one solid, continuous bone.

The formation and maintenance of a species, considered as an essemblage of similar organisms, is interpretable in an analogous way. We have already seen that in so far as the members of a species are subject to different sets of incident forces, they are differentiated, or divided into varieties. And here it remains to add that in so far as they are subject to like sets of incident forces they are segregated, or reduced to, and kept in, the state of a uniform aggregate. For by the process of "natural selection," there is a con-

tinual purification of each species from those individuals
which depart from the common type in ways that unfit
them for the conditions of their existence. Consequently,
there is a continual leaving behind of those individuals
which are in all respects fit for the conditions of their existence; and are therefore very nearly alike. The circumstances to which any species is exposed, being, as we before
saw, an involved combination of incident forces; and the
members of the species having mixed with them some that
differ more than usual from the average structure required
for meeting these forces; it results that these forces are constantly separating such divergent individuals from the rest,
and so preserving the uniformity of the rest—keeping up its
integrity as a species. Jut as the changing autumn leaves
are picked out by the wind from among the green ones
around them, or just as, to use Professor Huxley's simile,
the smaller fragments pass through the sieve while the
larger are kept back; so, the uniform incidence of external
forces affects the members of a group of organisms similarly
in proportion as they are similiar, and differently in proportion as they are different; and thus is ever segregating the
like by parting the unlike from them. Whether these separated members are killed off, as mostly happens, or whether,
as otherwise happens, they survive and multiply into a distinct variety, in consequence of their fitness to certain partially unlike conditions, matters not to the argument. The
one case conforms to the law, that the unlike units of an
aggregate are sorted into their kinds and parted when
uniformly subject to the same incident forces; and the
other to the converse law, that the like units of an aggregate are parted and separately grouped when subject to
different incident forces. And on consulting Mr. Darwin's
remarks on divergence of character, it will be seen that the
segregations thus caused tend ever to become more definite.

§ 167. Mental evolution under one of its leading aspects
we found to consist in the formation of groups of like ob-

jects and like relations—a differentiation of the various things originally confounded together in one assemblage, and an integration of each separate order of things into a separate group (§ 153). Here it remains to point out that while unlikeness in the incident forces is the cause of such differentiations, likeness in the incident forces is the cause of such integrations. For what is the process through which classifications are established? At first, in common with the uninitiated, the botanist recognizes only such conventional divisions as those which agriculture has established—distinguishes a few vegetables and cereals, and groups the rest together into the one miscellaneous aggregate of wild plants. How do these wild plants become grouped in his mind into orders, genera, and species? Each plant he examines yields him a certain complex impression. Every now and then he picks up a plant like one before seen; and the recognition of it is the production in him of a like connected group of sensations, by a like connected group of attributes. That is to say, there is produced throughout the nerves concerned, a combined set of changes, similar to a combined set of changes before produced. Considered analytically, each such combined set of changes is a combined set of molecular modifications wrought in the affected part of the organism. On every repetition of the impression, a like combined set of molecular modifications is superposed on the previous ones, and makes them greater: thus generating an internal idea corresponding to these similar external objects. Meanwhile, another kind of plant produces in the brain of the botanist another set of combined changes or molecular modifications—a set which does not agree with and deepen the one we have been considering, but disagrees with it; and by repetition of such there is generated a different idea answering to a different species. What now is the nature of this process expressed in general terms? On the one hand there are the like and unlike things from which severally emanate the groups of forces by which we perceive them. On the other hand, there are the organs of sense and percipient centres, through which, in the course of observation, these groups of forces pass. In passing through these organs of sense and percipient centres, the like groups of forces are segregated, or separated from the unlike groups of forces; and each such series of groups of forces, parted in this way from others, answering to an external genus or species, constitutes a state of consciousness which we call our idea of the genus or species. We before saw that as well as a separation of mixed matters by the same force, there is a separation of mixed forces by the same matter; and here we may further see that the unlike forces so separated, work unlike structural changes in the aggregate that separates, them—structural changes each of which thus represents, and is equivalent to, the integrated series of motions that has produced it.

By a parallel process, the connections of co-existence and sequence among impressions, become sorted into kinds and grouped simultaneously with the impressions themselves. When two phenomena that have been experienced in a given order, are repeated in the same order, those nerves which before were affected by the transition are again affected; and such molecular modification as they received from the first motion propagated through them, is increased by this second motion along the same route. Each such motion works a structural alteration, which, in conformity with the general law set forth in Chapter IX., involves a diminution of the resistance to all such motions that afterward occur. The segregation of these successive motions (or more strictly, the permanently effective portions of them expended in overcoming resistance) thus becomes the cause of, and the measure of, the mental connection between the impressions which the phenomena produce. Meanwhile, phenomena that are recognized as different from these, being phenomena that therefore affect different nervous elements, will have their connections severally represented by motions along other routes; and along each of these other routes, the nervous discharges will severally take place with a readiness proportionate to the frequency with which experience repeats the connection of phenomena. The classification of relations must hence go on *pari passu* with the classification of the related things. In common with the mixed sensations received from the external world, the mixed relations it presents, cannot be impressed on the organism without more or less segregation of them resulting. And through this continuous sorting and grouping together of changes or motions, which constitutes nervous function, there is gradually wrought that sorting and grouping together of matter, which constitutes nervous structure.

§ 168. In social evolution, the collecting together of the like and the separation of the unlike, by incident forces, is primarily displayed in the same manner as we saw it to be among groups of inferior creatures. The human races tend to differentiate and integrate, as do races of other living forms. Of the forces which effect and maintain the segregations of mankind, may first be named those external ones which we class as physical conditions. The climate and food that are favorable to an indigenous people, are more or less detrimental to a people of different bodily constitution, coming from a remote part of the Earth. In tropical regions the northern races cannot permanently exist: if not killed off in the first generation, they are so in the second; and, as in India, can maintain their footing only by the artificial process of continuous immigration and emigration. That is to say, the external forces acting equally on the inhabitants of a given locality, tend to expel all who are not of a certain type; and so to keep up the integration of those who are of the type. Though elsewhere, as among European nations, we see a certain amount of permanent intermixture, otherwise brought about, we still see that this takes place between races of not very different types, that are naturalized to not very different conditions. The other forces conspiring to produce these national segregations, are those mental ones which show themselves in the affinities of men for others like themselves. Emigrants usually desire to get back among their own people; and where their desire does not take effect, it is only because the restraining ties are too great. Units of one society who are obliged to reside in another, very generally form colonies in the midst of that other—small societies of their own. Races which have been artificially severed, show strong tendencies to reunite. Now though these segregations that result from the mutual affinities of kindred men, do not seem interpretable as illustrations of the general principle above enunciated, they really are thus interpretable. When treating of the direction of motion (§ 80), it was shown that the actions performed by men for the satisfaction of their wants, were always motions along lines of least resistance. The feelings characterizing a member of a given race, are feelings which get complete satisfaction only among other members of that race—a satisfaction partly derived from sympathy with those having like feelings, but mainly derived from the adapted social conditions which grow up where such feelings prevail. When, therefore, a citizen of any nation is, as we see, attracted toward others of his nation, the rationale is, that certain agencies which we call desires, move him in the direction of least resistance. Human motions, like all other motions, being determined by the distribution of forces, it follows that such segregations of races as are not produced by incident external forces, are produced by forces which the units of the races exercise on each other.

During the development of each society, we see analogous segregations caused in analogous ways. A few of them result from minor natural affinities; but those most important ones which constitute political and industrial organization, result from the union of men in whom similiarities have been produced by education—using education in its widest sense, as comprehending all processes by which citizens are molded to special functions. Men brought up to bodily labor, are men who have had wrought in them a certain likeness—a likeness which, in respect of their powers of action, obscures and subordinates their natural differences. Those trained to brain-work, have acquired a certain other community of character which makes them, as social units, more like each other than like those trained to manual occupations. And there arise class-segregations answering to these superinduced likenesses. Much more definite segregations take place among the much more definitely assimilated members of any class who are brought up to the same calling. Even where the necessities of their work forbid concentration in one locality, as among artisans happens with masons and bricklayers, and among traders happens with the retail distributers, and among professionals happens with the medical men; there are not wanting Operative Builders' Unions, and Grocers' Societies, and Medical Associations, to show that these artificially-assimilated citizens become integrated as much as the conditions permit. And where, as among the manufacturing classes, the functions discharged do not require the dispersion of the citizens thus artificially assimilated, there is a progressive aggregation of them in special localities; and a consequent increase in the definiteness of the industrial divisions. If now we seek the causes of these segregations, considered as results of force and motion, we find ourselves brought to the same general principle as before. This likeness generated in any class or sub-class by training, is an aptitude acquired by its members for satisfying their wants in like ways. That is, the occupation to which each man has been brought up, has become to him, in common with those similarly brought up, a line of least resistance. Hence under that pressure which determines all men to activity, these similarly-modified social units are similarly affected, and tend to take similar courses. If then there be any locality which, either by its physical peculiarities or by peculiarities wrought on it during social evolution, is rendered a place where a certain kind of industrial action meets with less resistance than elsewhere; it follows from the law of direction of motion that those social units who have been molded to this kind of industrial action, will move toward this place, or become integrated there. If, for instance, the proximity of coal and iron mines to a navigable river, gives to Glasgow a certain advantage in the building of iron ships—if the total labor required to produce the same vessel, and get its equivalent in food and clothing, is less there than elsewhere; a concentration of iron-ship builders is produced at Glasgow: either by keeping there the population born to iron-ship building; or by immigration of those elsewhere engaged in it; or by both—a concentration that would be still more marked did not other districts offer counterbalancing facilities. The principle equally holds where the occupation is mercantile instead of manufacturing. Stock-brokers cluster together in the city, because the amount of effort to be severally gone through by them in discharging their functions, and obtaining their profits, is less there than in other localities. A place of exchange having once been established, becomes a place where the resistance to be overcome by each is less than elsewhere; and the pursuit of the course of least resistance by each, involves their aggregation around this place.

Of course, with units so complicated as those which constitute a society, and with forces so involved as those which move them, the resulting selections and separations must be far more entangled, or far less definite, than those we have hitherto considered. But though there may be pointed out many anomalies which at first sight seem inconsistent with the alleged law, a closer study shows that they are but subtler illustrations of it. For men's likenesses, being of various kinds, lead to various orders of segregation. There are likenesses of disposition, likenesses of taste, likenesses produced by intellectual culture, likenesses that result from class-training, likenesses of political feeling; and it needs but to glance round at the caste-divisions, the associations for philanthropic, scientific, and artistic purposes, the religious parties and social cliques; to see that some species of likeness among the component members of each body determines their union. Now the different segregative processes by traversing one another, and often by their indirect antagonism, more or less obscure one another's effects; and prevent any one differentiated class from completely integrating. Hence the anomalies referred to. But if this cause of incompleteness be duly borne in mind, social segregations will be seen to conform entirely to the same principle as all other segregations. Analysis will show that either by external incident forces, or by what we may in a sense regard as mutual polarity, there are ever being produced in society segregations of those units which have either a natural likeness or a likeness generated by training.

§ 169. Can the general truth thus variously illustrated be deduced from the persistence of force, in common with foregoing ones? Probably the exposition at the beginning of the chapter will have led most readers to conclude that it can be so deduced.

The abstract propositions involved are these: First, that like units, subject to a uniform force capable of producing motion in them, will be moved to like degrees in the same direction. Second, that like units if exposed to unlike forces capable of producing motion in them, will be differently moved—moved either in different directions or to different degrees in the same direction. Third, that unlike units if acted on by a uniform force capable of producing motion in them, will be differently moved—moved either in different directions or to different degrees in the same direction. Fourth, that the incident forces themselves must be affected in analogous ways: like forces falling on like units must be similarly modified by the conflict; unlike forces falling on like units must be dissimilarly modified; and like forces falling on unlike units must be dissimilarly modified. These propositions admit of reduction to a still more abstract form. They all of them amount to this:—that in the actions and reactions of force and matter, an unlikeness in either of the factors necessitates an unlikeness in the effects;

and that in the absence of unlikeness in either of the factors the effects must be alike.

When thus generalized, the immediate dependence of these propositions on the persistence of force, becomes obvious. Any two forces that are not alike, are forces which differ either in their amounts or directions or both; and by what mathematicians call the resolution of forces, it may be proved that this difference is constituted by the presence in the one of some force not present in the other. Similarly, any two units or portions of matter which are unlike in size, weight, form, or other attribute, can be known by us as unlike only through some unlikeness in the forces they impress on our consciousness; and hence this unlikeness also, is constituted by the presence in the one of some force or forces not present in the other. Such being the common nature of these unlikenesses, what is the inevitable corollary? Any unlikeness in the incident forces, where the things acted on are alike, must generate a difference between the effects; since otherwise, the differential force produces no effect, and force is not persistent. Any unlikeness in the things acted on, where the incident forces are alike, must generate a difference between the effects; since otherwise, the differential force whereby these things are made unlike, produces no effect, and force is not persistent. While, conversely, if the forces acting and the things acted on, are alike, the effects must be alike; since otherwise, a differential effect can be produced without a differential cause, and force is not persistent.

Thus these general truths being necessary implications of the persistence of force, all the redistributions above traced out as characterizing Evolution in its various phases, are also implications of the persistence of force. Such portions of the permanently effective forces acting on any aggregate, as produce sensible motions in its parts, cannot but work the segregations which we see take place. If of the mixed units making up such aggregate, those of the same kind have like motions impressed on them by a uniform force, while units of another kind are moved by this uniform force in ways more or less unlike the ways in which those of the first kind are moved, the two kinds must separate and integrate. If the units are alike and the forces unlike, a division of the differently affected units is equally necessitated. Thus there inevitably arises the demarcated grouping which we everywhere see. By virtue of this segregation that grows ever more decided while there remains any possibility of increasing it, the change from uniformity to multiformity is accompanied by a change from indistinctness in the relations of parts to distinctness in the relations of parts. As we before saw that the transformation of the homogeneous into the heterogeneous is inferable from that ultimate truth which transcends proof; so we here see, that from this same truth is inferable the transformation of an indefinite homogeneity into a definite heterogeneity.

CHAPTER XXII

EQUILIBRATION

§ 170. AND now toward what do these changes tend? Will they go on forever? or will there be an end to them? Can things increase in heterogeneity through all future time? or must there be a degree which the differentiation and integration of Matter and Motion cannot pass? Is it possible for this universal metamorphosis to proceed in the same general course indefinitely? or does it work toward some ultimate state, admitting no further modification of like kind? The last of these alternative conclusions is that to which we are inevitably driven. Whether we watch concrete processes, or whether we consider the question in the abstract, we are alike taught that Evolution has an impassable limit.

The redistributions of matter that go on around us, are ever being brought to conclusions by the dissipation of the motions which effect them. The rolling stone parts with portions of its momentum to the things it strikes, and finally comes to rest; as do also, in like manner, the various things it has struck. Descending from the clouds and trickling over the Earth's surface till it gathers into brooks and rivers, water, still running toward a lower level, is at last arrested by the resistance of other water that has reached the lowest level. In the lake or sea thus formed, every agitation raised by a wind or the immersion of a solid body, propagates itself around in waves that diminish as they widen, and gradually become lost to observation in motions communicated to the atmosphere and the matter on the shores. The impulse given by a player to the harp-string, is transformed through its vibrations into aerial pulses; and these, spreading on all sides, and weakening as they spread, soon cease to be perceptible; and finally die away in generating thermal undulations that radiate into space. Equally in the cinder that falls out of the fire, and in the vast masses of molten lava ejected by a volcano, we see that the molecular agitation known to us as heat, disperses itself by radiation; so that however great its amount, it inevitably sinks at last to the same degree as that existing in surrounding bodies. And if the actions observed be electrical or chemical, we still find that they work themselves out in producing sensible or insensible movements, that are dissipated as before; until quiescence is eventually reached. The proximate rationale of the process exhibited under these several forms, lies in the fact dwelt on when treating of the Multiplication of Effects, that motions are ever being decomposed into divergent motions, and these into redivergent motions. The rolling stone sends off the stones it hits in directions differing more or less from its own; and they do the like with the things they hit. Move water or air, and the movement is quickly resolved into radiating movements. The heat produced by pressure in a given direction, diffuses itself by undulations in all directions; and so do the light and electricity similarly generated. That is to say, these motions undergo division and subdivision; and by continuance of this process without limit, they are, though never lost, gradually reduced to insensible motions.

In all cases then, there is a progress toward equilibration. That universal co-existence of antagonist forces which, as we before saw, necessitates the universality of rhythm, and which, as we before saw, necessitates the decomposition of every force into divergent forces, at the same time necessitates the ultimate establishment of a balance. Every motion being motion under resistance is continually suffering deductions; and these unceasing deductions finally result in the cessation of the motion.

The general truth thus illustrated under its simplest aspect, we must now look at under those more complex aspects it usually presents throughout Nature. In nearly all cases, the motion of an aggregate is compound; and the equilibration of each of its components, being carried on independently, does not affect the rest. The ship's bell that has ceased to vibrate, still continues those vertical and lateral oscillations caused by the ocean-swell. The water of the smooth stream on whose surface have died away the undulations caused by the rising fish, moves as fast as before onward to the sea. The arrested bullet travels with undiminished speed round the Earth's axis. And were the rotation of the Earth destroyed, there would not be implied any diminution of the Earth's movement with respect to the Sun and other external bodies. So that in every case, what we regard as equilibration is a disappearance of some one or more of the many movements which a body possesses, while its other movements continue as before. That this process may be duly realized and the state of things toward which it tends fully understood, it will be well here to cite a case in which we may watch this successive equilibration of combined movements more completely than we can do in those above instanced. Our end will best be served, not by the most imposing, but by the most familiar example. Let us take that of the spinning top. When the string which has been wrapped round a top's axis is violently drawn off, and the top falls on to the table, it usually happens that besides the rapid rotation, two other movements are given to it. A slight horizontal momentum, unavoidably impressed on it when leaving the handle, carries it away bodily from the place on which it drops; and in consequence of its axis being more or less inclined, it falls into a certain oscillation, described by the expressive though inelegant word—"wabbling." These two subordinate motions, variable in their proportions to each other and to the chief motion, are commonly soon brought to a close by separate processes of equilibration. The momentum which carries the top bodily along the table, resisted somewhat by the air, but mainly by the irregularities of the surface, shortly disappears; and the top thereafter continues to spin on one spot. Meanwhile, in consequence of that opposition which the axial momentum of a rotating body makes to any change in the plane of rotation (so beautifully exhibited by the gyroscope), the "wabbling" diminishes; and like the other is quickly ended. These minor motions having been dissipated, the rotatory motion, interfered with only by atmospheric resistance and the friction of the pivot, continues some time with such uniformity that the top appears stationary: there being thus temporarily established a condition which the French mathematicians have termed *equilibrium mobile*. It is true that when the axial velocity sinks below a certain point, new motions commence, and increase till the top falls; but these are merely incidental to a case in which the centre of gravity is above the point of support. Were the top, having an axis of steel, to be suspended from a surface adequately magnetized, all the phenomena described would be displayed, and the moving equilibrium having been once arrived at, would continue until the top became motionless, without any further change of position. Now the facts which it behooves us here to observe, are these. First, that the various motions which an aggregate possesses are separately equilibrated: those which are smallest, or which meet with the greatest resistance, or both, disappearing first; and leaving at last, that which is greatest, or meets with least resistance, or both. Second, that when the aggregate has a movement of its parts with respect to each other, which encounters but little external resistance, there is apt to be established an *equilibrium mobile*. Third, that this moving equilibrium eventually lapses into complete equilibrium.

Fully to comprehend the process of equilibration, is not easy; since we have simultaneously to contemplate various phases of it. The best course will be to glance separately at what we may conveniently regard as its four different orders. The first order includes the comparatively simple motions, as those of projectiles, which are not prolonged enough to exhibit their rhythmical character; but which, being quickly divided and subdivided into motions communicated to other portions of matter, are presently dissipated in the rhythm of ethereal undulations. In the second order, comprehending the various kinds of vibration or oscillation as usually witnessed, the motion is used up in generating a tension which, having become equal to it or momentarily equilibrated with it, thereupon produces a motion in the opposite direction, that is subsequently equilibrated in like manner: thus causing a visible rhythm, that is, however, soon lost in invisible rhythms. The third order of equilibration, not hitherto noticed, obtains in those aggregates which continually receive as much motion as they expend. The steam engine (and especially that kind which feeds its own furnace and boiler) supplies an example. Here the force from moment to moment dissipated in overcoming the resistance of the machinery driven, is from moment to moment replaced from the fuel; and the balance of the two is maintained by a raising or lowering of the expenditure according to the variation of the supply: each increase or decrease in the quantity of steam, resulting in a rise or fall of the engine's movement, such as brings it to a balance with the increased or decreased resistance.

This, which we may fitly call the *dependent* moving equilibrium, should be specially noted; since it is one that we shall commonly meet with throughout various phases of Evolution. The equilibration to be distinguished as of the fourth order, is the *independent* or perfect moving equilibrium. This we see illustrated in the rhythmical motions of the Solar System; which, being resisted only by a medium of inappreciable density, undergo no sensible diminution in such periods of time as we can measure.

All these kinds of equilibration may, however, from the highest point of view, be regarded as different modes of one kind. For in every case the balance arrived at is relative, and not absolute—is a cessation of the motion of some particular body in relation to a certain point or points, involving neither the disappearance of the relative motion lost, which is simply transformed into other motions, nor a diminution of the body's motions with respect to other points. Thus understanding equilibration, it manifestly includes that *equilibrium mobile,* which at first sight seems of another nature. For any system of bodies exhibiting, like those of the Solar System, a combination of balanced rhythms, has this peculiarity—that though the constituents of the system have relative movements, the system as a whole has no movement. The centre of gravity of the entire group remains fixed. Whatever quantity of motion any member of it has in any direction, is from moment to moment counterbalanced by an equivalent motion in some other part of the group in an opposite direction; and so the aggregate matter of the group is in a state of rest. Whence it follows that the arrival at a state of moving equilibrium, is the disappearance of some movement which the aggregate had in relation to external things, and a continuance of those movements only which the different parts of the aggregate have in relation to each other. Thus generalizing the process, it becomes clear that all forms of equilibration are intrinsically the same; since in every aggregate, it is the centre of gravity only that loses its motion: the constituents always retaining some motion with respect to each other—the motion of molecules if none else. Every equilibrium commonly regarded as absolute, is in one sense a moving equilibrium; because along with a motionless state of the whole there is always some relative movement of its insensible parts. And, conversely, every moving equilibrium may be in one sense regarded as absolute; because the relative movements of its sensible parts are accompanied by a motionless state of the whole.

Something has still to be added before closing these somewhat too elaborate preliminaries. The reader must now especially note two leading truths brought out by the foregoing exposition: the one concerning the ultimate, or rather the penultimate, state of motion which the processes described tend to bring about; the other concerning the concomitant distribution of matter. This penultimate state of motion is the moving equilibrium; which, as we have seen, tends to arise in an aggregate having compound motions, as a transitional state on the way toward complete equilibrium. Throughout Evolution of all kinds, there is a continual approximation to, and more or less complete maintenance of, this moving equilibrium. As in the Solar System there has been established an independent moving equilibrium—an equilibrium such that the relative motions of the constituent parts are continually so counterbalanced by opposite motions, that the mean state of the whole aggregate never varies; so is it, though in a less distinct manner, with each form of dependent moving equilibrium. The state of things exhibited in the cycles of terrestrial changes, in the balanced functions of organic bodies that have reached their adult forms, and in the acting and reacting processes of fully-developed societies, is similarly one characterized by compensating oscillations. The involved combination of rhythms seen in each of these cases, has an average condition which remains practically constant during the deviations ever taking place on opposite sides of it. And the fact which we have here particularly to observe, is, that as a corollary from the general law of equilibration above set forth, the evolution of every aggregate must go on until this *equilibrium mobile* is established; since, as we have seen, an excess of force which the aggregate possesses in any direction, must eventually be expended in overcoming resistances to change in that direction: leaving behind only those movements which compensate each other, and so form a moving equilibrium. Respecting the structural state simultaneously reached, it must obviously be one presenting an arrangement of forces that counterbalance all the forces to which the aggregate is subject. So long as there remains a residual force in any direction—be it excess of a force exercised by the aggregate on its environment, or of a force exercised by its environment on the aggregate, equilibrium does not exist; and therefore the redistribution of matter must continue. Whence it follows that the limit of heterogeneity toward which every aggregate progresses, is the formation of as many specializations and combinations of parts, as there are specialized and combined forces to be met.

§ 171. Those successively changed forms which, if the nebular hypothesis be granted, must have arisen during the evolution of the Solar System, were so many transitional kinds of moving equilibrium; severally giving place to more permanent kinds on the way toward complete equilibration. Thus the assumption of an oblate spheroidal figure by condensing nebulous matter, was the assumption of a temporary and partial moving equilibrium among the component parts—a moving equilibrium that must have slowly grown more settled, as local conflicting movements were dissipated. To the formation and detachment of the nebulous rings, which, according to this hypothesis, from time to time took place, we have instances of progressive equilibration ending in the establishment of a complete moving equilibrium. For the genesis of each such ring, implies a perfect balancing of that aggregative force which the whole spheroid exercises on its equatorial portion, by that centrifugal force which the equatorial portion has acquired during previous concentration: so long as these two forces are not equal, the equatorial portion follows the contracting mass; but as soon as the second force has increased up to an equality with the first, the equatorial portion can follow no further, and remains behind. While, however, the resulting ring, regarded as a whole connected by forces with external wholes, has reached a state of moving equilibrium; its parts are not balanced with respect to each other. As we before saw (§ 150), the probabilities against the maintenance of an annular form by nebulous matter, are immense: from the instability of the homogeneous, it is inferable that nebulous matter so distributed must break up into portions; and eventually concentrate into a single mass. That is to say, the ring must progress toward a moving equilibrium of a more complete kind, during the dissipation of that motion which maintained its particles in a diffused form: leaving at length a planetary body, attended perhaps by a group of minor bodies, severally having residuary relative motions that are no longer resisted by sensible media; and there is thus constituted an *equilibrium mobile* that is all but absolutely perfect.[1]

Hypothesis aside, the principle of equilibration is still perpetually illustrated in those minor changes of state which

---

[1] Sir David Brewster has recently been citing with approval a calculation by M. Babinet, to the effect that on the hypothesis of nebular genesis, the matter of the Sun, when it filled the Earth's orbit, must have taken 3181 years to rotate; and that therefore the hypothesis cannot be true. This calculation of M. Babinet may pair-off with that of M. Comte, who, contrariwise, made the time of this rotation agree very nearly with the Earth's period of revolution round the Sun; for if M. Comte's calculation involved a *petitio principii,* that of M. Babinet is manifestly based on two assumptions, both of which are gratuitous, and one of them totally inconsistent with the doctrine to be tested. He has evidently proceeded on the current supposition respecting the Sun's internal density, which is not proved, and from which there are reasons for dissenting; and he has evidently taken for granted that all parts of the nebulous spheroid, when it filled the Earth's orbit, had the same angular velocity; whereas if (as is implied in the nebular hypothesis, rationally understood) this spheroid resulted from the concentration of far more widely diffused matter, the angular velocity of its equatorial portion would obviously be immensely greater than that of its central portion.

the Solar System is undergoing. Each planet, satellite, and comet, exhibits to us at its aphelion a momentary equilibrium between that force which urges it further away from its primary, and that force which retards its retreat; since the retreat goes on until the last of these forces exactly counterpoises the first. In like manner at perihelion a converse equilibrium is momentarily established. The variation of each orbit in size, in eccentricity, and in the position of its plane, has similarly a limit at which the forces producing change in the one direction, are equalled by those antagonizing it; and an opposite limit at which an opposite arrest takes place. Meanwhile, each of these simple perturbations, as well as each of the complex ones resulting from their combination, exhibits, besides the temporary equilibration at each of its extremes, a certain general equilibration of compensating deviations on either side of a mean state. That the moving equilibrium thus constituted, tends, in the course of indefinite time, to lapse into a complete equilibrium by the gradual decrease of planetary motions and eventual integration of all the separate masses composing the Solar System, is a belief suggested by certain observed cometary retardations, and entertained by some of high authority. The received opinion that the appreciable diminution in the period of Encke's comet, implies a loss of momentum caused by resistance of the ethereal medium, commits astronomers who hold it, to the conclusion that this same resistance must cause a loss of planetary motions—a loss which, infinitesimal though it may be in such periods as we can measure, will, if indefinitely continued, bring these motions to a close. Even should there be, as Sir John Herschel suggests, a rotation of the ethereal medium in the same direction with the planets, this arrest, though immensely postponed, would not be absolutely prevented. Such an eventuality, however, must in any case be so inconceivably remote as to have no other than a speculative interest for us. It is referred to here, simply as illustrating the still-continued tendency toward complete equilibrium, through the still-continued dissipation of sensible motion, or transformation of it into insensible motion.

But there is another species of equilibration going on in the Solar System, with which we are more nearly concerned —the equilibration of that molecular motion known as heat. The tacit assumption hitherto current, that the Sun can continue to give off an undiminished amount of light and heat through all future time, is fast being abandoned. Involving as it does, under a disguise, the conception of power produced out of nothing, it is of the same order as the belief that misleads perpetual-motion schemers. The spreading recognition of the truth that force is persistent, and that consequently whatever force is manifested under one shape must previously have existed under another shape, is carrying with it a recognition of the truth that the force known to us in solar radiations, is the changed form of some other force of which the Sun is the seat; and that by the gradual dissipation of these radiations into space, this other force is being slowly exhausted. The aggregative force by which the Sun's substance is drawn to his centre of gravity, is the only one which established physical laws warrant us in suspecting to be the correlate of the forces thus emanating from him: the only source of a known kind that can be assigned for the insensible motions constituting solar light and heat, is the sensible motion which disappears during the progressing concentration of the Sun's substance. We before saw it to be a corollary from the nebular hypothesis, that there is such a progressing concentration of the Sun's substance. And here remains to be added the further corollary, that just as in the case of the smaller members of the Solar System, the heat generated by concentration, long ago in great part radiated into space, has left only a central residue that now escapes but slowly; so in the case of that immensely larger mass forming the Sun, the immensely greater quantity of heat generated and still in process of rapid diffusion, must, as the concentration approaches its limit, diminish in amount, and eventually leave only an inappreciable internal remnant. With or without the accompaniment of that hypothesis of nebular condensation, whence, as we see, it naturally follows, the doctrine that the Sun is gradually losing his heat has now gained considerable currency; and calculations have been made, both respecting the amount of heat and light already radiated, as compared with the amount that remains, and respecting the period during which active radiation is likely to continue. Professor Helmholtz estimates, that since the time when, according to the nebular hypothesis, the matter composing the Solar System extended to the orbit of Neptune, there has been evolved, by the arrest of sensible motion, an amount of heat 454 times as great as that which the Sun still has to give out. He also makes an approximate estimate of the rate at which this remaining $\frac{1}{454}$th is being diffused: showing that a diminution of the Sun's diameter to the extent of $\frac{1}{10,000}$, would produce heat, at the present rate, for more than 2000 years; or, in other words, that a contraction of $\frac{1}{20,000,000}$ of his diameter suffices to generate the amount of light and heat annually emitted; and that thus, at the present rate of expenditure, the Sun's diameter will diminish by something like $\frac{1}{20}$ in the lapse of the next million years.[1] Of course these conclusions are not to be considered as more than rude approximations to the truth. Until quite recently, we have been totally ignorant of the Sun's chemical composition; and even now have obtained but a superficial knowledge of it. We know nothing of his internal structure; and it is quite possible (probable, I believe) that the assumptions respecting central density, made in the foregoing estimates, are wrong. But no uncertainty in the data on which these calculations proceed, and no consequent error in the inferred rate at which the Sun is expending his reserve of force, militates against the general proposition that this reserve of force *is* being expended; and must in time be exhausted. Though the residue of undif-

---

[1] See paper "On the Inter-action of Natural Forces," by Prof. Helmholtz, translated by Prof. Tyndall, and published in the "Philosophical Magazine," supplement to Vol. XI., fourth series.

fused motion in the Sun, may be much greater than is above concluded; though the rate of radiation cannot, as assumed, continue at a uniform rate, but must eventually go on with slowly-decreasing rapidity; and though the period at which the Sun will cease to afford us adequate light and heat, is very possibly far more distant than above implied; yet such a period must some time be reached, and this is all which it here concerns us to observe.

Thus while the Solar System, if evolved from diffused matter, has illustrated the law of equilibration in the establishment of a complete moving equilibrium; and while, as at present constituted, it illustrates the law of equilibration in the balancing of all its movements; it also illustrates this law in the processes which astronomers and physicists infer are still going on. That motion of masses produced during Evolution, is being slowly re-diffused in molecular motion of the ethereal medium; both through the progressive integration of each mass, and the resistance to its motion through space. Infinitely remote as may be the state when all the motions of masses shall be transformed into molecular motion, and all the molecular motion equilibrated; yet such a state of complete integration and complete equilibration, is that toward which the changes now going on throughout the Solar System inevitably tend.

§ 172. A spherical figure is the one which can alone equilibrate the forces of mutually-gravitating atoms. If the aggregate of such atoms has a rotatory motion, the form of equilibrium becomes a spheroid of greater or less oblateness, according to the rate of rotation; and it has been ascertained that the Earth is an oblate spheroid, diverging just as much from sphericity as is requisite to counterbalance the centrifugal force consequent on its velocity round its axis. That is to say, during the evolution of the Earth, there has been reached a complete equilibrium of those forces which affect its general outline. The only other process of equilibration which the Earth as a whole can exhibit, is the loss of its axial motion; and that any such loss is going on we have no direct evidence. It has been contended, however, by Professor Helmholtz, that inappreciable as may be its effect within known periods of time, the friction of the tidal wave must be slowly diminishing the Earth's rotatory motion, and must eventually destroy it. Now though it seems an oversight to say that the Earth's rotation can thus be destroyed, since the extreme effect, to be reached only in infinite time by such a process, would be an extension of the Earth's day to the length of a lunation; yet it seems clear that this friction of the tidal wave is a real cause of decreasing rotation. Slow as its action is, we must recognize it as exemplifying, under another form, the universal progress toward equilibrium.

It is needless to point out, in detail, how those movements which the Sun's rays generate in the air and water on the Earth's surface, and through them in the Earth's solid substance,[1] one and all teach the same general truth. Evidently the winds and waves and streams, as well as the denudations and depositions they effect, perpetually illustrate on a grand scale, and in endless modes, that gradual dissipation of motions described in the first section; and the consequent tendency toward a balanced distribution of forces. Each of these sensible motions, produced directly or indirectly by integration of those insensible motions communicated from the Sun, becomes, as we have seen, divided and subdivided into motions less and less sensible; until it is finally reduced to insensible motions, and radiated from the Earth in the shape of thermal undulations. In their totality, these complex movements of aerial, liquid, and

---

[1] Until I recently consulted his "Outlines of Astronomy" on another question, I was not aware that so far back as 1833, Sir John Herschel had enunciated the doctrine that "the sun's rays are the ultimate source of almost every motion which takes place on the surface of the earth." He expressly includes all geologic, meteorologic, and vital actions; as also those which we produce by the combustion of coal. The late George Stephenson appears to have been wrongly credited with this last idea.

solid matter on the Earth's crust, constitute a dependent moving equilibrium. As we before saw, there is traceable throughout them an involved combination of rhythms. The unceasing circulation of water from the ocean to the land, and from the land back to the ocean, is a type of these various compensating actions; which, in the midst of all the irregularities produced by their mutual inter-ferences, maintain an average. And in this, as in other equilibrations of the third order, we see that the power from moment to moment in course of dissipation, is from moment to moment renewed from without: the rises and falls in the supply being balanced by rises and falls in the expenditure; as witness the correspondence between the magnetic variations and the cycle of the solar spots. But the fact it chiefly concerns us to observe, is, that this process must go on bringing things ever nearer to complete rest. These mechanical movements, meteorologic and geologic, which are continually being equilibrated, both temporarily by counter-movements and permanently by the dissipation of such movements and counter-movements, will slowly diminish as the quantity of force received from the Sun diminishes. As the insensible motions propagated to us from the centre of our system become feebler, the sensible motions here produced by them must decrease; and at that remote period when the solar heat has ceased to be appreci-able, there will no longer be any appreciable redistributions of matter on the surface of our planet.

Thus from the highest point of view, all terrestrial changes are incidents in the course of cosmical equilibra-tion. It was before pointed out (§ 69), that of the incessant alterations which the Earth's crust and atmosphere undergo, those which are not due to the still-progressing motion of the Earth's substance toward its centre of gravity, are due to the still-progressing motion of the Sun's substance toward its centre of gravity. Here it is to be remarked, that this continuance of integration in the Earth and in the Sun, is a continuance of that transformation of sensible motion into insensible motion which we have seen ends in equilibration; and that the arrival in each case at the extreme of integration, is the arrival at a state in which no more sensible motion remains to be transformed into insensible motion —a state in which the forces producing integration and the forces opposing integration have become equal.

§ 173. Every living body exhibits, in a fourfold form, the process we are tracing out—exhibits it from moment to moment in the balancing of mechanical forces; from hour to hour in the balancing of functions; from year to year in the changes of state that compensate changes of condition; and finally in the complete arrest of vital movements at death. Let us consider the facts under these heads.

The sensible motion constituting each visible action of an organism, is soon brought to a close by some adverse force within or without the organism. When the arm is raised, the motion given to it is antagonized partly by gravity and partly by the internal resistances consequent on structure; and its motion, thus suffering continual deduction, ends when the arm has reached a position at which the forces are equilibrated. The limits of each systole and diastole of the heart, severally show us a momentary equilibrium between muscular strains that produce opposite movements; and each gush of blood requires to be immediately followed by another, because the rapid dissipation of its momentum would otherwise soon bring the mass of circulating fluid to a stand. As much in the actions and reactions going on among the internal organs, as in the mechanical balancing of the whole body, there is at every instant a progressive equilibration of the motions at every instant produced. Viewed in their aggregate, and as forming a series, the organic functions constitute a dependent moving equilibrium—a moving equilibrium, of which the motive power is ever being dissipated through the special equilibrations just exemplified, and is ever being renewed by the taking in of additional motive power. Food is a store of force which continually adds to the momentum of the vital actions, as much as is continually deducted from them by the forces overcome. All the functional movements thus maintained, are, as we have seen, rhythmical (§ 85); by their union compound rhythms of various lengths and complexities are produced; and in these simple and compound rhythms, the process of equilibration, besides being exemplified at each extreme of every rhythm, is seen in the habitual preservation of a constant mean, and in the re-establishment of that mean when accidental causes have produced divergence from it. When, for instance, there is a great expenditure of motion through muscular activity, there arises a reactive demand on those stores of latent motion which are laid up in the form of consumable matter throughout the tissues: increased respiration and increased rapidity of circulation, are instrumental to an extra genesis of force, that counterbalances the extra dissipation of force. This unusual transformation of molecular motion into sensible motion, is presently followed by an unusual absorption of food—the source of molecular motion; and in proportion as there has been a prolonged draft upon the spare capital of the system, is there a tendency to a prolonged rest, during which that spare capital is replaced. If the deviation from the ordinary course of the functions has been so great as to derange them, as when violent exertion produces loss of appetite and loss of sleep, an equilibration is still eventually effected. Providing the disturbance is not such as to overturn the balance of the functions, and destroy life (in which case a complete equilibration is suddenly effected), the ordinary balance is by and by re-established: the returning appetite is keen in proportion as the waste has been large; while sleep, sound and prolonged, makes up for previous wakefulness. Not even in those extreme cases where some excess has wrought a derangement that is never wholly rectified, is there an exception to the general law; for in such cases the cycle of the functions is, after a time, equilibrated about a new mean state, which thenceforth becomes the normal state of the individual. Thus, among the involved rhythmical changes constituting organic life, any disturbing force that works an excess of change in some direction, is gradually diminished and finally neutralized by antagonistic forces; which thereupon work a compensating change in the opposite direction, and so, after more or less of oscillation, restore the medium condition. And this process it is, which constitutes what physicians call the *vis medicatrix naturæ*. The third form of equilibration displayed by organic bodies, is a necessary sequence of that just illustrated. When through a change of habit or circumstance, an organism is permanently subject to some new influence, or different amount of an old influence, there arises, after more or less disturbance of the organic rhythms, a balancing of them around the new average condition produced by this additional influence. As temporary divergences of the organic rhythms are counteracted by temporary divergences of a reverse kind; so there is an equilibration of their permanent divergences by the genesis of opposing divergences that are equally permanent. If the quantity of motion to be habitually generated by a muscle, becomes greater than before, its nutrition becomes greater than before. If the expenditure of the muscle bears to its nutrition, a greater ratio than expenditure bears to nutrition in other parts of the system; the excess of nutrition becomes such that the muscle grows. And the cessation of its growth is the establishment of a balance between the daily waste and the daily repair—the daily expenditure of force, and the amount of latent force daily added. The like must manifestly be the case with all organic modifications consequent on change of climate or food. This is a conclusion which we may safely draw without knowing the special rearrangements that effect the equilibration. If we see that a different mode of life is followed, after a period of functional derangement, by some altered condition of the system—if we see that this altered condition, becoming by and by established, continues without further change; we have no alternative but to say, that the new forces brought to bear on the system have been compensated by the opposing forces they have evoked. And this is the interpretation of the process which we call *adaptation*. Finally, each organism illustrates the law in the *ensemble* of its life. At the outset it daily absorbs under the form of food, an amount of force greater than it daily expends; and the surplus is daily equilibrated by growth. As maturity is approached, this surplus diminishes; and in the perfect organism, the day's absorption of potential motion balances the day's expenditure of actual motion. That is to say, during adult life there is continuously exhibited an equilibration of the third order. Eventually, the daily loss, beginning to outbalance the daily gain, there results a diminishing amount of functional action; the organic rhythms extend less and less widely on each side of the medium state; and there finally results that complete equilibration which we call death.

The ultimate structural state accompanying that ultimate functional state toward which an organism tends, both individually and as a species, may be deduced from one of the propositions set down in the opening section of this chapter. We saw that the limit of heterogeneity is arrived at whenever the equilibration of any aggregate becomes complete—that the redistribution of matter can continue so long only as there continues any motion unbalanced. Whence we found it to follow that the final structural arrangements, must be such as will meet all the forces acting on the aggregate, by equivalent antagonist forces. What is the implication in the case of organic aggregates; the equilibrium of which is a moving one? We have seen that the maintenance of such a moving equilibrium requires the habitual genesis of internal forces corresponding in number, directions, and amounts to the external incident forces—as many inner functions, single or combined, as there are single or combined outer actions to be met. But functions are the correlatives of organs; amounts of functions are, other things equal, the correlatives of sizes of organs; and combinations of functions are correlatives of connections of organs. Hence the structural complexity accompanying functional equilibration, is definable as one in which there are as many specialized parts as are capable, separately and jointly, of counteracting the separate and joint forces amid which the organism exists. And this is the limit of organic heterogeneity; to which man has approached more nearly than any other creature.

Groups of organisms display this universal tendency toward a balance very obviously. In § 85, every species of plant and animal was shown to be perpetually undergoing a rhythmical variation in number—now from abundance of food and absence of enemies rising above its average, and then by a consequent scarcity of food and abundance of enemies being depressed below its average. And here we have to observe that there is thus maintained an equilibrium between the sum of those forces which result in the increase of each race, and the sum of those forces which result in its decrease. Either limit of variation is a point at which the one set of forces, before in excess of the other, is counterbalanced by it. And amid these oscillations produced by their conflict, lies that average number of the species at which its expansive tendency is in equilibrium with surrounding repressive tendencies. Nor can it be questioned that this balancing of the preservative and destructive forces which we see going on in every race, must necessarily go on. Since increase of number cannot but continue until increase of mortality stops it; and decrease of number cannot but continue until it is either arrested by fertility or extinguishes the race entirely.

§ 174. The equilibrations of those nervous actions which constitute what we know as mental life, may be classified in like manner with those which constitute what we distinguish as bodily life. We may deal with them in the same order.

Each pulse of nervous force from moment to moment generated (and it was shown in § 86 that nervous currents are not continuous but rhythmical) is met by counteracting forces; in overcoming which it is dispersed and equilibrated. When tracing out the correlation and equivalence of forces, we saw that each sensation and emotion, or rather such part of it as remains after the excitation of associated ideas and feelings, is expended in working bodily changes—contractions of the involuntary muscles, the voluntary muscles, or both; as also in a certain stimulation of secreting organs. That the movements thus initiated are ever being brought to a close by the opposing forces they evoke, was pointed out above; and here it is to be observed that the like holds with the nervous changes thus initiated. Various facts prove that the arousing of a thought or feeling, always involves the overcoming of a certain resistance: instance the fact that where the association of mental states has not been frequent, a sensible effort is needed to call up the one after the other; instance the fact that during nervous prostration there is a comparative inability to think—the ideas will not follow one another with the habitual rapidity; instance the converse fact that at times of unusual energy, natural or artificial, the friction of thought becomes relatively small, and more numerous, more remote, or more difficult connections of ideas are formed. That is to say, the wave of nervous energy each instant generated, propagates itself throughout body and brain, along those channels which the conditions at the instant render lines of least resistance; and spreading widely in proportion to its amount, ends only when it is equilibrated by the resistances it everywhere meets. If we contemplate mental actions as extending over hours and days, we discover equilibrations analogous to those hourly and daily established among the bodily functions. In the one case as in the other, there are rhythms which exhibit a balancing of opposing forces at each extreme, and the maintenance of a certain general balance. This is seen in the daily alternation of mental activity and mental rest—the

forces expended during the one being compensated by
the forces acquired during the other. It is also seen in the
recurring rise and fall of each desire: each desire, reaching
a certain intensity, is equilibrated either by expenditure of
the force it embodies, in the desired actions, or, less completely, in the imagination of such actions: the process ending in that satiety, or that comparative quiescence, forming
the opposite limit of the rhythm. And it is further manifest under a twofold form, on occasions of intense joy or
grief: each paroxysm of passion, expressing itself in vehement bodily actions, presently reaches an extreme whence
the counteracting forces produce a return to a condition of
moderate excitement; and the successive paroxysms, finally
diminishing in intensity, end in a mental equilibrium either
like that before existing, or partially differing from it in its
medium state. But the species of mental equilibration to
be more especially noted, is that shown in the establishment
of a correspondence between relations among our states of
consciousness and relations in the external world. Each
outer connection of phenomena which we are capable of
perceiving, generates, through accumulated experiences, an
inner connection of mental states; and the result toward
which this process tends, is the formation of a mental connection having a relative strength that answers to the relative constancy of the physical connection represented. In
conformity with the general law that motion pursues the
line of least resistance, and that, other things equal, a line
once taken by motion is made a line that will be more
readily pursued by future motion; we have seen that the
ease with which nervous impressions follow one another,
is, other things equal, great in proportion to the number
of times they have been repeated together in experience.
Hence, corresponding to such an invariable relation as that
between the resistance of an object and some extension possessed by it, there arises an indissoluble connection in consciousness; and this connection, being as absolute internally
as the answering one is externally, undergoes no further

change—the inner relation is in perfect equilibrium with the outer relation. Conversely, it hence happens that to such uncertain relations of phenomena as that between clouds and rain, there arise relations of ideas of a like uncertainty; and if, under given aspects of the sky, the tendencies to infer fair or foul weather correspond to the frequencies with which fair or foul weather follow such aspects, the accumulation of experiences has balanced the mental sequences and the physical sequences. When it is remembered that between these extremes there are countless orders of external connections having different degrees of constancy, and that during the evolution of intelligence there arise answering internal associations having different degrees of cohesion; it will be seen that there is a progress toward equilibrium between the relations of thought and the relations of things. This equilibration can end only when each relation of things has generated in us a relation of thought, such that on the occurrence of the conditions, the relation in thought arises as certainly as the relation in things. Supposing this state to be reached (which however it can be only in infinite time), experience will cease to produce any further mental evolution—there will have been reached a perfect correspondence between ideas and facts; and the intellectual adaptation of man to his circumstances will be complete. The like general truths are exhibited in the process of moral adaptation; which is a continual approach to equilibrium between the emotions and the kinds of conduct necessitated by surrounding conditions. The connections of feelings and actions are determined in the same way as the connections of ideas: just as repeating the association of two ideas facilitates the excitement of the one by the other; so does each discharge of feeling into action render the subsequent discharge of such feeling into such action more easy. Hence it happens that if an individual is placed permanently in conditions which demand more action of a special kind than has before been requisite, or than is natural to him—if the pressure of the painful feelings which these conditions entail when disregarded, impels him to perform this action to a greater extent—if by every more frequent or more lengthened performance of it under such pressure, the resistance is somewhat diminished; then, clearly, there is an advance toward a balance between the demand for this kind of action and the supply of it. Either in himself, or in his descendants continuing to live under these conditions, enforced repetition must eventually bring about a state in which this mode of directing the energies will be no more repugnant than the various other modes previously natural to the race. Hence the limit toward which emotional modification perpetually tends, and to which it must approach indefinitely near (though it can absolutely reach it only in infinite time), is a combination of desires that correspond to all the different orders of activity which the circumstances of life call for— desires severally proportionate in strength to the needs for these orders of activity; and severally satisfied by these orders of activity. In what we distinguish as acquired habits, and in the moral differences of races and nations produced by habits that are maintained through successive generations, we have countless illustrations of this progressive adaptation; which can cease only with the establishment of a complete equilibrium between constitution and conditions.

Possibly some will fail to see how the equilibrations described in this section can be classed with those preceding them; and will be inclined to say that what are here set down as facts, are but analogies. Nevertheless such equilibrations are as truly physical as the rest. To show this fully, would require a more detailed analysis than can now be entered on. For the present it must suffice to point out, as before (§ 71), that what we know subjectively as states of consciousness, are, objectively, modes of force; that so much feeling is the correlate of so much motion; that the performance of any bodily action is the transformation of a certain amount of feeling into its equivalent amount of motion; that this bodily action is met by forces which it is expended in overcoming; and that the necessity for the frequent repetition of this action implies the frequent recurrence of forces to be so overcome. Hence the existence in any individual of an emotional stimulus that is in equilibrium with certain external requirements, is literally the habitual production of a certain specialized portion of nervous energy, equivalent in amount to a certain order of external resistances that are habitually met. And thus the ultimate state, forming the limit toward which Evolution carries us, is one in which the kinds and quantities of mental energy daily generated and transformed into motions, are equivalent to, or in equilibrium with, the various orders and degrees of surrounding forces which antagonize such motions.

§ 175. Each society taken as a whole, displays the process of equilibration in the continuous adjustment of its population to its means of subsistence. A tribe of men living on wild animals and fruits is manifestly, like every tribe of inferior creatures, always oscillating about that average number which the locality can support. Though by artificial production, and by successive improvements in artificial production, a superior race continually alters the limit which external conditions put to population; yet there is ever a checking of population at the temporary limit reached. It is true that where the limit is being so rapidly changed as among ourselves, there is no actual stoppage: there is only a rhythmical variation in the rate of increase. But in noting the causes of this rhythmical variation—in watching how, during periods of abundance, the proportion of marriages increases, and how it decreases during periods of scarcity; it will be seen that the expansive force produces unusual advance whenever the repressive force diminishes, and *vice versâ;* and thus there is as near a balancing of the two as the changing conditions permit.

The internal actions constituting social functions, exemplify the general principle no less clearly. Supply and demand are continually being adjusted throughout all industrial processes; and this equilibration is interpretable in the same way as preceding ones. The production and distribution of a commodity, is the expression of a certain aggregate of forces causing special kinds and amounts of motion. The price of this commodity, is the measure of a certain other aggregate of forces expended by the laborer who purchases it, in other kinds and amounts of motion. And the variations of price represent a rhythmical balancing of these forces. Every rise or fall in the rate of interest, or change in the value of a particular security, implies a conflict of forces in which some, becoming temporarily predominant, cause a movement that is presently arrested or equilibrated by the increase of opposing forces; and amid these daily and hourly oscillations, lies a more slowly-varying medium, into which the value ever tends to settle; and would settle but for the constant addition of new influences. As in the individual organism so in the social organism, functional equilibrations generate structural equilibrations. When on the workers in any trade there comes an increased demand, and when in return for the increased supply, there is given to them an amount of other commodities larger than was before habitual—when, consequently, the resistances overcome by them in sustaining life are less than the resistances overcome by other workers; there results a flow of other workers into this trade. This flow continues until the extra demand is met, and the wages so far fall again that the total resistance overcome in obtaining a given amount of produce, is as great in this newly-adopted occupation as in the occupations whence it drew recruits. The occurrence of motion along lines of least resistance, was before shown to necessitate the growth of population in those places where the labor required for self-maintenance is the smallest; and here we further see that those engaged in any such advantageous locality, or advantageous business, must multiply till there arises an approximate balance between this locality or business and others accessible to the same citizens. In determining the career of every youth, we see an estimation by parents of the respective advantages offered by all that are available, and a choice of the one which promises best; and through the consequent influx into trades that are at the time most profitable, and the withholding of recruits from overstocked trades, there is insured a general equipoise between the power of each social organ and the function it has to perform.

The various industrial actions and reactions thus continually alternating, constitute a dependent moving equilibrium like that which is maintained among the functions of an individual organism. And this dependent moving equilibrium parallels those already contemplated, in its tendency to become more complete. During early stages of social evolution, while yet the resources of the locality inhabited are unexplored, and the arts of production undeveloped, there is never anything more than a temporary and partial balancing of such actions, under the form of acceleration or retardation of growth. But when a society approaches the maturity of that type on which it is organized, the various industrial activities settle down into a comparatively constant state. Moreover, it is observable that advance in organization, as well as advance in growth, is conducive to a better equilibrium of industrial functions. While the diffusion of mercantile information is slow, and the means of transport deficient, the adjustment of supply to demand is extremely imperfect: great overproduction of each commodity followed by great underproduction, constitute a rhythm having extremes that depart very widely from the mean state in which demand and supply are equilibrated. But when good roads are made, and there is a rapid diffusion of printed or written intelligence, and still more when railways and telegraphs come into existence—when the periodical fairs of early days lapse into weekly markets, and these into daily markets; there is gradually produced a better balance of production and consumption. Extra demand is much more quickly followed by augmented supply; and the rapid oscillations of price within narrow limits on either side of a comparatively uniform mean indicate a near approach to equilibrium. Evidently this industrial progress has for its limit, that which Mr. Mill has called "the stationary state." When population shall have become dense over all habitable parts of the globe; when the resources of every region have been fully explored; and when the productive arts admit of no further improvements; there must result an almost complete balance, both between the fertility and mortality of each society, and between its producing and consuming activities. Each society will exhibit only minor deviations from its average number, and the rhythm of its industrial functions will go on from day to day and year to year with comparatively insignificant perturbations. This limit, however, though we are inevitably advancing toward it, is indefinitely remote; and can never indeed be absolutely reached. The peopling of the Earth up to the point supposed cannot take place by simple spreading. In the future, as in the past, the process will be carried on rhythmically, by waves of emigration from new and higher centres of civilization successively arising; and by the supplanting of inferior races by the superior races they beget; and the process so carried on must be extremely slow. Nor does it seem to me that such an equilibration will, as Mr. Mill suggests, leave scope for further mental culture and moral progress; but rather that the approximation to it must be simultaneous with the approximation to complete equilibrium between man's nature and the conditions of his existence.

One other kind of social equilibration has still to be considered:—that which results in the establishment of governmental institutions, and which becomes complete as these institutions fall into harmony with the desires of the people. There is a demand and supply in political affairs as in industrial affairs; and in the one case as in the other, the antagonist forces produce a rhythm which, at first extreme in its oscillations, slowly settles down into a moving equilibrium of comparative regularity. Those aggressive impulses inherited from the pre-social state—those tendencies to seek self-satisfaction regardless of injury to other beings, which are essential to a predatory life, constitute an anti-social force, tending ever to cause conflict and eventual separation of citizens. Contrariwise, those desires whose ends can be achieved only by union, as well as those sentiments which find satisfaction through intercourse with fellow men, and those resulting in what we call loyalty, are forces tending to keep the units of a society together. On the one hand, there is in each citizen more or less of resistance against all restraints imposed on his actions by other citizens: a resistance which, tending continually to widen each individual's sphere of action, and reciprocally to limit the spheres of action of other individuals, constitutes a repulsive force mutually exercised by the members of a social aggregate. On the other hand, the general sympathy of man for man, and the more special sympathy of each variety of man for others of the same variety, together with sundry allied feelings which the social state gratifies, act as an attractive force, tending ever to keep united those who have a common ancestry. And since the resistances to be overcome in satisfying the totality of their desires when living separately, are greater than the resistances to be overcome in satisfying the totality of their desires when living together, there is a residuary force that prevents their separation. Like all other opposing forces, those exerted by citizens on each other are ever producing alternating movements, which, at first extreme, undergo a gradual diminution on the way to ultimate equilibrium. In small, undeveloped societies, marked rhythms result from these conflicting tendencies. A tribe whose members have held together for a generation or two, reaches a size at which it will not hold together; and on the occurrence of some event causing unusual antagonism among its members, divides.

Each primitive nation, depending largely for its continued union on the character of its chief, exhibits wide oscillations between an extreme in which the subjects are under rigid restraint, and an extreme in which the restraint is not enough to prevent disorder. In more advanced nations of like type, we always find violent actions and reactions of the same essential nature—"despotism tempered by assassination," characterizing a political state in which unbearable repression from time to time brings about a bursting of all bonds. In this familiar fact, that a period of tyranny is followed by a period of license and *vice versâ,* we see how these opposing forces are ever equilibrating each other; and we also see, in the tendency of such movements and counter-movements to become more moderate, how the equilibration progresses toward completeness. The conflicts between Conservatism (which stands for the restraints of society over the individual) and Reform (which stands for the liberty of the individual against society), fall within slowly approximating limits; so that the temporary predominance of either produces a less marked deviation from the medium state. This process, now so far advanced among ourselves that the oscillations are comparatively unobtrusive, must go on till the balance between the antagonist forces approaches indefinitely near perfection. For, as we have already seen, the adaptation of man's nature to the conditions of his existence cannot cease until the internal forces which we know as feelings are in equilibrium with the external forces they encounter. And the establishment of this equilibrium is the arrival at a state of human nature and social organization, such that the individual has no desires but those which may be satisfied without exceeding his proper sphere of action, while society maintains no restraints but those which the individual voluntarily respects. The progressive extension of the liberty of citizens, and the reciprocal removal of political restrictions, are the steps by which we advance toward this state. And the ultimate abolition of all limits to the freedom of each, save those imposed by the like freedom of all, must result from the complete equilibration between man's desires and the conduct necessitated by surrounding conditions.

Of course in this case, as in the preceding ones, there is thus involved a limit to the increase of heterogeneity. A few pages back, we reached the conclusion that each advance in mental evolution, is the establishment of some further internal action, corresponding to some further external action—some additional connection of ideas or feelings, answering to some before unknown or unantagonized connection of phenomena. We inferred that each such new function, involving some new modification of structure, implies an increase of heterogeneity; and that thus, increase of heterogeneity must go on, while there remain any outer relations affecting the organism which are unbalanced by inner relations. Whence we saw it to follow that increase of heterogeneity can come to an end only as equilibration is completed. Evidently the like must simultaneously take place with society. Each increment of heterogeneity in the individual must directly or indirectly involve, as cause or consequence, some increment of heterogeneity in the arrangements of the aggregate of individuals. And the limit to social complexity can be arrived at only with the establishment of the equilibrium, just described, between social and individual forces.

§ 176. Here presents itself a final question, which has probably been taking a more or less distinct shape in the minds of many, while reading this chapter. "If Evolution of every kind, is an increase in complexity of structure and function that is incidental to the universal process of equilibration, and if equilibration must end in complete rest; what is the fate toward which all things tend? If the Solar System is slowly dissipating its forces—if the Sun is losing his heat at a rate which will tell in millions of years—if with diminution of the Sun's radiations there must go on a diminution in the activity of geologic and meteorologic processes

as well as in the quantity of vegetal and animal existence—
if Man and Society are similarly dependent on this supply
of force that is gradually coming to an end; are we not
manifestly progressing toward omnipresent death?"

That such a state must be the outcome of the processes
everywhere going on, seems beyond doubt. Whether any
ulterior process may reverse these changes, and initiate
a new life, is a question to be considered hereafter. For
the present it must suffice that the proximate end of all the
transformations we have traced is a state of quiescence.
This admits of *à priori* proof. It will soon become apparent that the law of equilibration, not less than the
preceding general laws, is deducible from the persistence
of force.

We have seen (§ 74) that phenomena are interpretable
only as the results of universally-coexistent forces of attraction and repulsion. These universally-coexistent forces
of attraction and repulsion, are, indeed, the complementary
aspects of that absolutely persistent force which is the ultimate datum of consciousness. Just in the same way that
the equality of action and reaction is a corollary from the
persistence of force, since their inequality would imply
the disappearance of the differential force into nothing, or
its appearance out of nothing; so, we cannot become conscious of an attractive force without becoming simultaneously conscious of an equal and opposite repulsive force.
For every experience of a muscular tension (under which
form alone we can immediately know an attractive force),
presupposes an equivalent resistance—a resistance shown in
the counterbalancing pressure of the body against neighboring objects, or in that absorption of force which gives motion to the body, or in both—a resistance which we cannot
conceive as other than equal to the tension, without conceiving force to have either appeared or disappeared, and
so denying the persistence of force. And from this necessary correlation results our inability, before pointed out, of
interpreting any phenomena save in terms of these correla-

tives—an inability shown alike in the compulsion we are under to think of the statical forces which tangible matter displays, as due to the attraction and repulsion of its atoms, and in the compulsion we are under to think of dynamical forces exercised through space, by regarding space as filled with atoms similarly endowed. Thus from the existence of a force that is forever unchangeable in quantity, there follows, as a necessary corollary, the co-extensive existence of these opposite forms of force—forms under which the conditions of our consciousness oblige us to represent that absolute force which transcends our knowledge.

But the forces of attraction and repulsion being universally co-existent, it follows, as before shown, that all motion is motion under resistance. Units of matter, solid, liquid, aeriform, or ethereal, filling the space which any moving body traverses, offer to such body the resistance consequent on their cohesion, or their inertia, or both. In other words, the denser or rarer medium which occupies the places from moment to moment passed through by such moving body, having to be expelled from them, as much motion is abstracted from the moving body as is given to the medium in expelling it from these places. This being the condition under which all motion occurs, two corollaries result. The first is, that the deductions perpetually made by the communication of motion to the resisting medium, cannot but bring the motion of the body to an end in a longer or shorter time. The second is, that the motion of the body cannot cease until these deductions destroy it. In other words, movement must continue till equilibration takes place; and equilibration must eventually take place. Both these are manifest deductions from the persistence of force. To say that the whole or part of a body's motion can disappear, save by transfer to something which resists its motion, is to say that the whole or part of its motion can disappear without effect; which is to deny the persistence of force. Conversely, to say that the medium traversed can be moved out of the body's path, without deducting from the body's motion, is to say that motion of the medium can arise out of nothing; which is to deny the persistence of force. Hence this primordial truth is our immediate warrant for the conclusions, that the changes which Evolution presents cannot end until equilibrium is reached, and that equilibrium must at last be reached.

Equally necessary, because equally deducible from this same truth that transcends proof, are the foregoing propositions respecting the establishment and maintenance of moving equilibria, under their several aspects. It follows from the persistence of force, that the various motions possessed by any aggregate, either as a whole or among its parts, must be severally dissipated by the resistances they severally encounter; and that thus, such of them as are least in amount, or meet with greatest opposition, or both, will be brought to a close while the others continue. Hence in every diversely moving aggregate, there results a comparatively early dissipation of motions which are smaller and much resisted; followed by long-continuance of the larger and less-resisted motions; and so there arise dependent and independent moving equilibria. Hence also may be inferred the tendency to conservation of such moving equilibria. For the new motion given to the parts of a moving equilibrium by a disturbing force, must either be of such kind and amount that it cannot be dissipated before the pre-existing motions, in which case it brings the moving equilibrium to an end; or else it must be of such kind and amount that it can be dissipated before the pre-existing motions, in which case the moving equilibrium is re-established.

Thus from the persistence of force follow, not only the various direct and indirect equilibrations going on around, together with that cosmical equilibration which brings Evolution under all its forms to a close; but also those less manifest equilibrations shown in the readjustments of moving equilibria that have been disturbed. By this ultimate principle is provable the tendency of every organism, disordered by some unusual influence, to return to a balanced state. To it also may be traced the capacity, possessed in a slight degree by individuals, and in a greater degree by species, of becoming adapted to new circumstances. And not less does it afford a basis for the inference, that there is a gradual advance toward harmony between man's mental nature and the conditions of his existence. After finding that from it are deducible the various characteristics of Evolution, we finally draw from it a warrant for the belief, that Evolution can end only in the establishment of the greatest perfection and the most complete happiness.

CHAPTER XXIII

DISSOLUTION

§ 177. WHEN, in Chapter XII., we glanced at the cycle of changes through which every existence passes, in its progress from the imperceptible to the perceptible and again from the perceptible to the imperceptible—when these opposite redistributions of matter and motion were severally distinguished as Evolution and Dissolution; the natures of the two, and the conditions under which they respectively occur, were specified in general terms. Since then, we have contemplated the phenomena of Evolution in detail; and have followed them out to those states of equilibrium in which they all end. To complete the argument we must now contemplate, somewhat more in detail than before, the complementary phenomena of Dissolution. Not, indeed, that we need dwell long on Dissolution, which has none of those various and interesting aspects which Evolution presents; but something more must be said than has yet been said.

It was shown that neither of these two antagonist processes ever goes on absolutely unqualified by the other; and that a change toward either is a differential result of the conflict between them. An evolving aggregate, while on the average losing motion and integrating, is always, in one way or other, receiving some motion and to that extent disintegrating; and after the integrative changes have ceased to predominate, the reception of motion, though perpetually checked by its dissipation, constantly tends to produce a reverse transformation, and eventually does produce it. When Evolution has run its course—when the aggregate has at length parted with its excess of motion, and habitually receives as much from its environment as it habitually loses—when it has reached that equilibrium in which its changes end; it thereafter remains subject to all actions in its environment which may increase the quantity of motion it contains, and which in the lapse of time are sure, either slowly or suddenly, to give its parts such excess of motion as will cause disintegration. According as its equilibrium is a very unstable or a very stable one, its dissolution may come quickly or may be indefinitely delayed—may occur in a few days or may be postponed for millions of years. But exposed as it is to the contingencies not simply of its immediate neighborhood but of a Universe everywhere in motion, the period must at last come when, either alone or in company with surrounding aggregates, it has its parts dispersed.

The process of dissolution so caused we have here to look at as it takes place in aggregates of different orders. The course of change being the reverse of that hitherto traced, we may properly take the illustrations of it in the reverse order—beginning with the most complex and ending with the most simple.

§ 178. Regarding the evolution of a society as at once an increase in the number of individuals integrated into a corporate body, an increase in the masses and varieties of the parts into which this corporate body divides as well as of the actions called their functions, and an increase in the degree of combination among these masses and their functions; we shall see that social dissolution conforms to the general law in being, materially considered, a disintegration, and, dynamically considered, a decrease in the movements of wholes and an increase in the movements of parts; while it further conforms to the general law in being caused by an excess of motion in some way or other received from without.

It is obvious that the social dissolution which follows the aggression of another nation, and which, as history shows us, is apt to occur when social evolution has ended and decay has begun, is, under its broadest aspect, the incidence of a new external motion; and when, as sometimes happens, the conquered society is dispersed, its dissolution is literally a cessation of those corporate movements which the society, both in its army and in its industrial bodies, presented, and a lapse into individual or uncombined movements—the motion of units replaces the motion of masses.

It cannot be questioned, either, that when plague or famine at home, or a revolution abroad, gives to any society an unusual shock that causes disorder, or incipient dissolution, there results a decrease of integrated movements and an increase of disintegrated movements. As the disorder progresses, the political actions previously combined under one government become uncombined: there arise the antagonistic actions of riot or revolt. Simultaneously, the industrial and commercial processes that were co-ordinated throughout the whole body politic, are broken up; and only the local, or small, trading transactions continue. And each further disorganizing change diminishes the joint operations by which men satisfy their wants, and leaves them to satisfy their wants, so far as they can, by separate operations. Of the way in which such disintegrations are liable to be set up in a society that has evolved to the limit of its type, and reached a state of moving equilibrium, a good illustration is furnished by Japan. The finished fabric into which its people had organized themselves, maintained an almost constant state so long as it was preserved from fresh external forces. But as soon as it received an impact from European civilization, partly by armed aggression, partly by commercial impulse, partly by the influence of ideas, this fabric began to fall to pieces. There is now in progress a political dissolution. Probably a political reorganization will follow; but, be this as it may, the change thus far produced by an outer action is a change toward dissolution—a change from integrated motions to disintegrated motions.

Even where a society that has developed into the highest form permitted by the characters of its units, begins thereafter to dwindle and decay, the progressive dissolution is still essentially of the same nature. Decline of numbers is, in such case, brought about partly by emigration; for a society having the fixed structure in which evolution ends, is necessarily one that will not yield and modify under pressure of population: so long as its structure will yield and modify, it is still evolving. Hence the surplus population continually produced, not held together by an organization that adapts itself to an augmenting number, is continually dispersed: the influences brought to bear on the citizens by other societies, cause their detachment, and there is an increase in the uncombined motions of units instead of an increase of combined motions. Gradually as rigidity becomes greater, and the society becomes still less capable of being remolded into the form required for successful competition with growing and more plastic societies, the number of citizens who can live within its unyielding framework becomes positively smaller. Hence it dwindles both through continued emigration and through the diminished multiplication that follows innutrition. And this further dwindling or dissolution, caused by the number of those who die becoming greater than the number of those who survive long enough to rear offspring, is similarly a decrease in the total quantity of combined motion and an increase in the quantity of uncombined motion—as we shall presently see when we come to deal with individual dissolution.

Considering, then that social aggregates differ so much

from aggregates of other kinds, formed as they are of units held together loosely and indirectly, in such variable ways by such complex forces, the process of dissolution among them conforms to the general law quite as clearly as could be expected.

§ 179. When from these super-organic aggregates we descend to organic aggregates, the truth that Dissolution is a disintegration of matter, caused by the reception of additional motion from without, becomes easily demonstrable. We will look first at the transformation and afterward at its cause.

Death, or that final equilibration which precedes dissolution, is the bringing to a close of all those conspicuous integrated motions that arose during evolution. The impulsions of the body from place to place first cease; presently the limbs cannot be stirred; later still the respiratory actions stop; finally the heart becomes stationary, and, with it, the circulating fluids. That is, the transformation of molecular motion into the motion of masses, comes to an end; and each of these motions of masses, as it ends, disappears into molecular motions. What next takes place? We cannot say that there is any further transformation of sensible movements into insensible movements; for sensible movements no longer exist. Nevertheless, the process of decay involves an increase of insensible movements; since these are far greater in the gases generated by decomposition, than they are in the fluid-solid matters out of which the gases arise. Each of the complex chemical units composing an organic body, possesses a rhythmic motion in which its many component units jointly partake. When decomposition breaks up these complex molecules, and their constituents assume gaseous forms, there is, besides that increase of motion implied by the diffusion, a resolution of such motions as the aggregate molecules possessed, into motions of their constituent molecules. So that in organic dissolution we have, first, an end put to that trans-

formation of the motion of units into the motion of aggregates, which constitutes evolution, dynamically considered;
and we have also, though in a subtler sense, a transformation of the motion of aggregates into the motion of units.
Still it is not thus shown that organic dissolution fully
answers to the general definition of dissolution—the absorption of motion and concomitant disintegration of matter.
The disintegration of matter is, indeed, conspicuous enough;
but the absorption of motion is not conspicuous. True, the
fact that motion has been absorbed may be inferred from
the fact that the particles previously integrated into a solid
mass, occupying a small space, have most of them moved
away from one another and now occupy a great space; for
the motion implied by this transposition must have been
obtained from somewhere. But its source is not obvious.
A little search, however, will bring us to its derivation.

At a temperature below the freezing-point of water,
decomposition of organic matter does not take place—the
integrated motions of the highly integrated molecules are
not resolved into the disintegrated motions of their component molecules. Dead bodies kept at this temperature for
an indefinitely long period, are prevented from decomposing
for an indefinitely long period: witness the frozen carcases
of Mammoths—Elephants of a species long ago extinct—
that are found imbedded in the ice at the mouths of Siberian
rivers; and which, though they have been there for many
thousands of years, have flesh so fresh that when at length
exposed, it is devoured by wolves. What now is the meaning of such exceptional preservations? A body kept below
freezing-point is a body which receives very little heat by
radiation or conduction; and the reception of but little heat
is the reception of but little molecular motion. That is to
say, in an environment which does not furnish it with molecular motion passing a certain amount, an organic body
does not undergo dissolution. Confirmatory evidence is
yielded by the variations in rate of dissolution which accompany variations of temperature. All know that in cool

weather the organic substances used in our households keep longer, as we say, than in hot weather. Equally certain, if less familiar, is the fact that in tropical climates decay proceeds much more rapidly than in temperate climates. Thus, in proportion as the molecular motion of surrounding matter is great, the dead organism receives an abundant supply of motion to replace the motion continually taken up by the dispersing molecules of the gases into which it is being disintegrated. The still quicker decompositions produced by exposure to artificially-raised temperatures, afford further proofs; as instance those which occur in cooking. The charred surfaces of parts that have been much heated, show us that the molecular motion absorbed has served to dissipate in gaseous forms all the elements but the carbon.

The nature and cause of Dissolution are thus clearly displayed by the aggregates which so clearly display the nature and cause of Evolution. One of these aggregates being composed of that peculiar matter to which a large quantity of constitutional motion gives great plasticity, and the ability to evolve into a highly compound form (§ 103); we see that after evolution has ceased, a very moderate amount of molecular motion, added to that already locked up in its peculiar matter, suffices to cause dissolution. Though at death there is reached a stable equilibrium among the sensible masses, or organs, which make up the body; yet, as the insensible units or molecules of which these organs consist are in unstable equilibrium, small incident forces suffice to overthrow them, and hence disintegration proceeds rapidly.

§ 180. Most inorganic aggregates, having arrived at dense forms in which comparatively little motion is retained, remain long without marked changes. Each has lost so much motion in passing from the disintegrated to the integrated state, that much motion must be given to it to cause resumption of the disintegrated state; and an immense time may elapse before there occur in the environment changes great enough to communicate to it the requisite quantity of motion. We will look first at those exceptional inorganic aggregates which retain much motion, and therefore readily undergo dissolution.

Among these are the liquids and volatile solids which dissipate under ordinary conditions—water that evaporates, carbonate of ammonia that wastes away by the dispersion of its molecules. In all such cases motion is absorbed; and always the dissolution is rapid in proportion as the quantity of heat or motion which the aggregated mass receives from its environment is great. Next come the cases in which the molecules of a highly integrated or solid aggregate are dispersed among the molecules of a less integrated or liquid aggregate; as in aqueous solutions. One evidence that this disintegration of matter has for its concomitant the absorption of motion, is that soluble substances dissolve the more quickly the hotter the water: supposing always that no elective affinity comes into play. Another and still more conclusive evidence is, that when crystals of a given temperature are placed in water of the same temperature, the process of solution is accompanied by a fall of temperature—often a very great one. Omitting instances in which some chemical action takes place between the salt and the water, it is a uniform law that the motion which disperses the molecules of the salt through the water, is at the expense of the molecular motion possessed by the water.

Masses of sediment accumulated into strata, afterward compressed by many thousands of feet of superincumbent strata, and reduced in course of time to a solid state, may remain for millions of years unchanged; but in subsequent millions of years they are inevitably exposed to disintegrating actions. Raised along with other such masses into a continent, denuded and exposed to rain, frost, and the grinding actions of glaciers, they have their particles gradually separated, carried away, and widely dispersed. Or when, as otherwise happens, the encroaching sea reaches them, the undermined cliffs which they form fall from time to time, breaking into fragments of all sizes; the waves, rolling about the small pieces, and in storms turning over and knocking together the larger blocks, reduce them to bowlders and pebbles, at last to sand and mud. Even if portions of the disintegrated strata accumulate into shingle banks, which afterward become solidified, the process of dissolution, arrested though it may be for some enormous geologic period, is finally resumed. As many a shore shows us, the conglomerate itself is sooner or later subject to the like processes; and its cemented masses of heterogeneous components, lying on the beach, are broken up and worn away by impact and attrition—that is, by communicated mechanical motion.

When not thus effected, the disintegration is effected by communicated molecular motion. The consolidated stratum, located in some area of subsidence, and brought down nearer and nearer to the regions occupied by molten matter, comes eventually to have its particles brought to a plastic state by heat, or finally melted down into liquid. Whatever may be its subsequent transformations, the transformation then exhibited by it is an absorption of motion and disintegration of matter.

Be it simple or compound, small or large, a crystal or a mountain-chain, every inorganic aggregate on the Earth, thus, at some time or other, undergoes a reversal of those changes undergone during its evolution. Not that it usually passes back completely from the perceptible into the imperceptible; as organic aggregates do in great part, if not wholly. But still its disintegration and dispersion carry it some distance on the way toward the imperceptible; and there are reasons for thinking that its arrival there is but delayed. At a period immeasurably remote, every such inorganic aggregate, along with all undissipated remnants of organic aggregates, must be reduced to a state of gaseous diffusion, and so complete the cycle of its changes.

§ 181. For the Earth as a whole, when it has gone through the entire series of its ascending transformations,

must remain, like all smaller aggregates, exposed to the
contingencies of its environment; and in the course of those
ceaseless changes in progress throughout a Universe of
which all parts are in motion, must, at some period beyond
the utmost stretch of imagination, be subject to forces sufficient to cause its complete disintegration. Let us glance at
the forces competent to disintegrate it.

In his essay on "The Inter-action of Natural Forces,"
Professor Helmholtz states the thermal equivalent of the
Earth's movement through space as calculated on the now
received datum of Mr. Joule. "If our Earth," he says,
"were by a sudden shock brought to rest in her orbit—
which is not to be feared in the existing arrangement of our
system—by such a shock a quantity of heat would be generated equal to that produced by the combustion of fourteen
such Earths of solid coal. Making the most unfavorable
assumption as to its capacity for heat, that is, placing it
equal to that of water, the mass of the Earth would thereby
be heated 11,200 degrees; it would therefore be quite fused,
and for the most part reduced to vapor. If then the Earth,
after having been thus brought to rest, should fall into the
Sun, which of course would be the case, the quantity of
heat developed by the shock would be 400 times greater."
Now though this calculation seems to be nothing to the purpose, since the Earth is not likely to be suddenly arrested
in its orbit and not likely therefore suddenly to fall into the
Sun; yet, as before pointed out (§ 171), there is a force at
work which it is held must at last bring the Earth into the
Sun. This force is the resistance of the ethereal medium.
From ethereal resistance is inferred a retardation of all moving bodies in the Solar System—a retardation which certain
astronomers contend even now shows its effects in the
relative nearness to one another of the orbits of the older
planets. If, then, retardation is going on, there must come
a time, no matter how remote, when the slowly diminishing orbit of the Earth will end in the Sun; and though
the quantity of molar motion to be then transformed into

molecular motion, will not be so great as that which the calculation of Helmholtz supposes, it will be great enough to reduce the substance of the Earth to a gaseous state.

The dissolution of the Earth, and, at intervals, of every other planet, is not, however, a dissolution of the Solar System. Viewed in their *ensemble,* all the changes exhibited throughout the Solar System, are incidents accompanying the integration of the entire matter composing it: the local integration of which each planet is the scene, completing itself long before the general integration is complete. But each secondary mass having gone through its evolution and reached a state of equilibrium among its parts, thereafter continues in its extinct state, until by the still progressing general integration it is brought into the central mass. And though each such union of a secondary mass with the central mass, implying transformation of molar motion into molecular motion, causes partial diffusion of the total mass formed, and adds to the quantity of motion that has to be dispersed in the shape of light and heat; yet it does but postpone the period at which the total mass must become completely integrated, and its excess of contained motion radiated into space.

[1] § 182. Here we come to the question raised at the close of the last chapter—Does Evolution as a whole, like Evolution in detail, advance toward complete quiescence? Is that motionless state called death, which ends Evolution in organic bodies, typical of the universal death in which Evolution at large must end? And have we thus to contemplate as the outcome of things, a boundless space holding here and there extinct suns, fated to remain forever without further change?

To so speculative an inquiry, none but a speculative

---

[1] Though this chapter is new, this section, and the one following it, are not new. In the first edition they were included in the final section of the foregoing chapter. While substantially the same as before, the argument has been in some places abbreviated and in other places enforced by additional matter.

answer is to be expected. Such answer as may be ventured, must be taken less as a positive answer than as a demurrer to the conclusion that the proximate result must be the ultimate result. If, pushing to its extreme the argument that Evolution must come to a close in complete equilibrium or rest, the reader suggests that for aught which appears to the contrary, the Universal Death thus implied will continue indefinitely, it is legitimate to point out how, on carrying the argument still further, we are led to infer a subsequent Universal Life. Let us see what may be assigned as grounds for inferring this.

It has been already shown that all equilibration, so far as we can trace it, is relative. The dissipation of a body's motion by communication of it to surrounding matter, solid, liquid, gaseous, and ethereal, brings the body to a fixed position in relation to the matter that abstracts its motion. But all its other motions continue. Further, this motion, the disappearance of which causes relative equilibration, is not lost but simply transferred. Whether it is directly transformed into insensible motion, as happens in the case of the Sun; or, whether, as in the sensible motions going on around us, it is directly transformed into smaller sensible motions, and these into still smaller, until they become insensible, matters not. In every instance the ultimate result is, that whatever motion of masses is lost, reappears as molecular motion pervading space. Thus the questions we have to consider, are—Whether after the completion of all the relative equilibrations which bring Evolution to a close, there remain any further equilibrations to be effected?—Whether there are any other motions of masses that must eventually be transformed into molecular motion?—And if there are such other motions, what must be the consequence when the molecular motion generated by their transformation is added to that which already exists?

To the first of these questions the answer is, that there *do* remain motions which are undiminished by all the relative equilibrations we have considered; namely, the motions of translation possessed by those vast masses of matter called stars—remote suns that are probably, like our own, surrounded by circling groups of planets. The belief that the stars are fixed, has long since been abandoned: observation has proved many of them to have sensible proper motions. Moreover, it has been ascertained by measurement that in relation to the stars nearest to us, our own star travels at the rate of about half a million miles per day; and if, as is admitted to be not improbable, our own star is moving in the same direction with adjacent stars, its absolute velocity may be, and most likely is, immensely greater than this. Now no such changes as those taking place within the Solar System, even when carried to the extent of integrating the whole of its matter into one mass, and diffusing all its relative motions in an insensible form through space, can affect these sidereal motions. Hence, there appears no alternative but to infer that they must remain to be equilibrated by some subsequent process.

The next question that arises is—To what law do sidereal motions conform? And to this question Astronomy replies —the law of gravitation. The movements of binary stars have proved this. The periodic times of sundry binary stars have been calculated on the assumption that their revolutions are determined by a force like that which regulates the revolutions of planets and satellites; and the subsequent performances of their revolutions in the predicted periods have verified the assumption. If, then, these remote bodies are centres of gravitation—if we infer that all other stars are centres of gravitation, as we may fairly do—and if we draw the unavoidable corollary, that the gravitative force which so conspicuously affects stars that are near one another, also affects remote stars; we must conclude that all the members of our Sidereal System gravitate, individually and collectively.

But if these widely dispersed moving masses mutually gravitate, what must happen? There appears but one tenable answer. They cannot preserve their present arrangement: the irregular distribution of our Sidereal System being such as to render even a temporary moving equilibrium impossible. If the stars are centres of an attractive force that varies inversely as the square of the distance, there is no escape from the inference that the structure of our galaxy is undergoing change, and must continue to undergo change.

Thus, in the absence of tenable alternatives, we are brought to the positions:—1, that the stars are in motion; 2, that they move in conformity with the law of gravitation; 3, that, distributed as they are, they cannot move in conformity with the law of gravitation without undergoing rearrangement. If now we ask the nature of this rearrangement, we find ourselves obliged to infer a progressive concentration. Stars at present dispersed, must become locally aggregated; existing aggregations (excepting, perhaps, the globular clusters) must grow more dense; and aggregations must coalesce with one another. That integration has been progressing throughout past eras we found to be indicated by the structure of the heavens, in general and in detail; and of the extent to which it has in some places already gone, remarkable instances are furnished by the Magellanic clouds—two closely-packed agglomerations, not, indeed, of single stars only, but of single stars, of clusters regular and irregular, of nebulæ, and of diffused nebulosity. That these have been formed by mutual gravitation of parts once widely scattered there is evidence in the barrenness of the surrounding celestial spaces: the nubecula minor, especially, being seated, as Humboldt says, in "a kind of starless desert."

What must be the limit of such concentrations? The mutual attraction of two stars, when it so far predominates over other attractions as to cause approximation, almost certainly ends in the formation of a binary star; since the motions generated by other attractions prevent the two stars from moving in straight lines to their common centre of gravity. Between small clusters, too, having also certain proper motions as clusters, mutual attraction may lead, not to complete union, but to the formation of binary clusters. As the process continues, however, and the clusters become larger, they must move more directly toward each other: thus forming clusters of increasing density. While, therefore, during the earlier stages of concentration, the probabilities are immense against the actual contact of these mutually-gravitating masses; it is tolerably manifest that, as the concentration increases, collision must become probable, and ultimately certain. This is an inference not lacking the support of high authority. Sir John Herschel, treating of those numerous and variously-aggregated clusters of stars revealed by the telescope, and citing with apparent approval his father's opinion, that the more diffused and irregular of these, are "globular clusters in a less advanced state of condensation"; subsequently remarks, that "among a crowd of solid bodies of whatever size, animated by independent and partially opposing impulses, motions opposite to each other *must* produce collision, destruction of velocity, and subsidence or near approach toward the centre of preponderant attraction; while those which conspire, or which remain outstanding after such conflicts, *must* ultimately give rise to circulation of a permanent character." Now what is here alleged of these minor clusters cannot be denied of larger clusters; and thus the above-inferred process of concentration, appears certain to bring about an increasingly-frequent integration of masses.

We have next to consider the consequences of the accompanying loss of velocity. The sensible motion which disappears cannot be destroyed, but must be transformed into insensible motion. What will be the effect of this insensible motion? Already we have seen that were the Earth arrested, dissipation of its substance would result. And if so relatively small a momentum as that acquired by the Earth in falling to the Sun, would be equivalent to a molecular motion sufficient to reduce the Earth to gases of extreme rarity; what must be the molecular motion generated by the mutually-arrested momenta of two stars, that have moved to their common centre of gravity through spaces immeasurably greater? There seems no alternative but to conclude, that it would be great enough to reduce the matter of the stars to an almost inconceivable tenuity—a tenuity like that which we ascribe to nebular matter. Such being the immediate effect, what would be the ulterior effect? Sir John Herschel, in the passage above quoted, describing the collisions that must arise in a concentrating group of stars, adds that those stars "which remain outstanding after such conflicts *must* ultimately give rise to circulation of a permanent character." The problem, however, is here dealt with purely as a mechanical one: the assumption being that the mutually-arrested masses will continue as masses—an assumption to which no objection appeared at the time when Sir John Herschel wrote this passage; since the correlation of forces was not then recognized. But obliged as we now are to conclude, that stars moving at the high velocities acquired during concentration, will, by mutual arrest, be dissipated into gases, the problem becomes different; and a different inference seems unavoidable. For the diffused matter produced by such conflicts must form a resisting medium, occupying that central region of the cluster through which its members from time to time pass in describing their orbits—a resisting medium which they cannot move through without having their velocities diminished. Every additional collision, by augmenting this resisting medium, and making the losses of velocity greater, must aid in preventing the establishment of that equilibrium which would else arise; and so must conspire to produce more frequent collisions. And the nebulous matter thus formed, presently enveloping the whole cluster, must, by continuing to shorten the gyrations of the moving masses, entail an increasingly active integration and reactive disintegration of them; until they are all dissipated. Whether this process completes itself independently in different parts of our Sidereal System; or whether it completes itself only by aggregating the whole matter of our Sidereal System; or whether, as seems not unlikely, local integrations and disintegrations run their courses while the general integration is going on; are questions that need not be discussed. In any case the conclusion to be drawn is, that the integration must continue until the conditions which bring about disintegration are reached; and that there must then ensue a diffusion that undoes the preceding concentration. This, indeed, is the conclusion which presents itself as a deduction from the persistence of force. If stars concentrating to a common centre of gravity eventually reach it, then the quantities of motion they have acquired must suffice to carry them away again to those remote regions whence they started. And since, by the conditions of the case, they cannot return to these remote regions in the shape of concrete masses, they must return in the shape of diffused masses. Action and reaction being equal and opposite, the momentum producing dispersion must be as great as the momentum acquired by aggregation; and being spread over the same quantity of matter, must cause an equivalent distribution through space, whatever be the form of the matter. One condition, however, essential to the literal fulfilment of this result, must be specified; namely, that the quantity of molecular motion radiated into space by each star in the course of its formation from diffused matter, shall either not escape from our Sidereal System or shall be compensated by an equal quantity of molecular motion radiated from other parts of space into our Sidereal System. In other words, if we set out with that amount of molecular motion implied by the existence of the matter of our Sidereal System in a nebulous form; then it follows from the persistence of force, that if this matter undergoes the redistribution constituting Evolution, the quantity of molecular motion given out during the integration of each mass, plus the quantity of molecular motion given out during the integration of all the masses, must suffice again to reduce it to the same nebulous form.

Here, indeed, we arrive at a barrier to our reasonings; since we cannot know whether this condition is or is not fulfilled. If the ether which fills the interspaces of our Sidereal System has a limit somewhere beyond the outermost stars, then it is inferable that motion is not lost by radiation beyond this limit; and if so, the original degree of diffusion may be resumed. Or supposing the ethereal medium to have no such limit, yet, on the hypothesis of an unlimited space, containing, at certain intervals, Sidereal Systems like our own, it may be that the quantity of molecular motion radiated into the region occupied by our Sidereal System, is equal to that which our Sidereal System radiates; in which case the quantity of motion possessed by it, remaining undiminished, it may continue during unlimited time its alternate concentrations and diffusions. But if, on the other hand, throughout boundless space filled with ether, there exist no other Sidereal Systems subject to like changes, or if such other Sidereal Systems exist at more than a certain average distance from one another; then it seems an unavoidable conclusion that the quantity of motion possessed, must diminish by radiation; and that so, on each successive resumption of the nebulous form, the matter of our Sidereal System will occupy a less space; until it reaches either a state in which its concentrations and diffusions are relatively small, or a state of complete aggregation and rest. Since, however, we have no evidence showing the existence or non-existence of Sidereal Systems throughout remote space; and since, even had we such evidence, a legitimate conclusion could not be drawn from premises of which one element (unlimited space) is inconceivable; we must be forever without answer to this transcendent question.

But confining ourselves to the proximate and not necessarily insoluble question, we find reason for thinking that after the completion of those various equilibrations which bring to a close all the forms of Evolution we have contemplated, there must continue an equilibration of a far wider kind. When that integration everywhere in progress throughout our Solar System has reached its climax, there will remain to be effected the immeasurably greater integration of our Solar System, with other such systems. There must then reappear in molecular motion what is lost in the motion of masses; and the inevitable transformation of this motion of masses into molecular motion, cannot take place without reducing the masses to a nebulous form.

§ 183. Thus we are led to the conclusion that the entire process of things, as displayed in the aggregate of the visible Universe, is analogous to the entire process of things as displayed in the smallest aggregates.

Motion as well as Matter being fixed in quantity, it would seem that the change in the distribution of Matter which Motion effects, coming to a limit in whichever direction it is carried, the indestructible Motion thereupon necessitates a reverse distribution. Apparently, the universally-coexistent forces of attraction and repulsion, which, as we have seen, necessitate rhythm in all minor changes throughout the Universe, also necessitate rhythm in the totality of its changes—produce now an immeasurable period during which the attractive forces predominating, cause universal concentration, and then an immeasurable period during which the repulsive forces predominating, cause universal diffusion—alternate eras of Evolution and Dissolution. And thus there is suggested the conception of a past during which there have been successive Evolutions analogous to that which is now going on; and a future during which successive other such Evolutions may go on—ever the same in principle but never the same in concrete result.

CHAPTER XXIV

SUMMARY AND CONCLUSION

§ 184. At the close of a work like this, it is more than usually needful to contemplate as a whole that which the successive chapters have presented in parts. A coherent knowledge implies something more than the establishment of connections; we must not rest after seeing how each minor group of truths falls into its place within some major group, and how all the major groups fit together. It is requisite that we should retire a space, and, looking at the entire structure from a distance at which details are lost to view, observe its general character.

Something more than recapitulation—something more even than an organized restatement, will come within the scope of the chapter. We shall find that in their *ensemble* the general truths reached exhibit, under certain aspects, a oneness not hitherto observed.

There is, too, a special reason for noting how the various divisions and sub-divisions of the argument consolidate; namely, that the theory at large thereby obtains a final illustration. The reduction of the generalizations that have been set forth to a completely integrated state, exemplifies once more the process of Evolution, and strengthens still further the general fabric of conclusions.

§ 185. Here, indeed, we find ourselves brought round unexpectedly, and very significantly, to the truth with which we set out, and with which our resurvey must commence. For this integrated form of knowledge is the form which, apart from the doctrine of Evolution, we decided to be the highest form.

When we inquired what constitutes Philosophy—when we compared men's various conceptions of Philosophy, so that, eliminating the elements in which they differed we might see in what they agreed; we found in them all, the tacit implication that Philosophy is completely unified knowledge. Apart from each particular scheme of unified knowledge, and apart from the proposed methods by which unification is to be effected, we traced in every case the belief that unification is possible, and that the end of Philosophy is the achievement of it.

Accepting this conclusion, we went on to consider the data with which Philosophy must set out. Fundamental propositions, or propositions not deducible from deeper ones, can be established only by showing the complete congruity of all the results reached through the assumption of them; and, premising that they were assumed till so established, we took as our data, those organized components of our intelligence without which there cannot go on the mental processes implied by philosophizing.

From the specification of these we passed to certain primary truths—"The Indestructibility of Matter," "The Continuity of Motion," and "The Persistence of Force"; of which the last is ultimate and the others derivative. Having previously seen that our experiences of Matter and Motion are resolvable into experiences of Force; we further saw the truths that Matter and Motion are unchangeable in quantity, to be implications of the truth that Force is unchangeable in quantity. This we discovered is the truth by derivation from which all other truths are to be proved.

The first of the truths which presented itself to be so proved, was "The Persistence of the Relations among Forces." This, which is ordinarily called Uniformity of Law, we found to be a necessary implication of the fact that Force can neither arise out of nothing nor lapse into nothing.

The deduction next drawn, was that forces which seem to be lost are transformed into their equivalents of other forces; or, conversely, that forces which become manifest, do so by disappearance of pre-existing equivalent forces. Of these truths we found illustrations in the motions of the heavenly bodies, in the changes going on over the Earth's surface, and in all organic and super-organic actions.

It turned out to be the same with the law that everything moves along the line of least resistance, or the line of greatest traction, or their resultant. Among movements of all orders, from those of stars down to those of nervous discharges and commercial currents, it was shown both that this is so, and that, given the Persistence of Force, it must be so.

So, too, we saw it to be with "The Rhythm of Motion." All motion alternates—be it the motion of planets in their orbits or ethereal molecules in their undulations—be it the cadences of speech or the rises and falls of prices; and, as before, it became manifest that, Force being persistent, this perpetual reversal of Motion between limits is inevitable.

§ 186. These truths holding of all existences, were recognized as of the kind required to constitute what we distinguished as Philosophy. But, on considering them, we perceived that as they stand they do not form anything like a Philosophy; and that a Philosophy cannot be formed by any number of such truths separately known. Each such truth expresses the general law of some one factor by which phenomena, as we habitually experience them, are produced; or, at most, expresses the law of co-operation of some two factors. But knowing what are the elements of a process, is not knowing how these elements combine to effect it. That which alone can unify knowledge must be the law of co-operation of all the factors—a law expressing simultaneously the complex antecedents and the complex consequents which any phenomenon as a whole presents.

A further inference was that Philosophy, as we understand it, must not unify separate concrete phenomena only; and must not stop short with unifying separate classes of concrete phenomena; but must unify all concrete phenomena. If the law of operation of each factor holds true throughout the Cosmos; so, too, must the law of their co-operation. And hence in comprehending the Cosmos as conforming to this law of co-operation, must consist that highest unification which Philosophy seeks.

Descending from this abstract statement to a concrete one, we saw that the law sought must be the law of the continuous redistribution of Matter and Motion. The changes everywhere going on, from those which are slowly altering the structure of our galaxy down to those which constitute a chemical decomposition, are changes in the relative positions of component parts; and everywhere necessarily imply that, along with a new arrangement of Matter, there has arisen a new arrangement of Motion. Hence we may be certain, *à priori,* that there must be a law of the concomitant redistribution of Matter and Motion, which holds of every change; and which, by thus unifying all changes, must be the basis of a Philosophy.

In commencing our search for this universal law of redistribution, we contemplated from another point of view the problem of Philosophy; and saw that its solution could not but be of the nature indicated. It was shown that a Philosophy stands self-convicted of inadequacy if it does not formulate the whole series of changes passed through by every existence in its passage from the imperceptible to the perceptible and again from the perceptible to the imperceptible. If it begins its explanations with existences that already have concrete forms, or leaves off while they still retain concrete forms; then, manifestly, they had preceding histories, or will have succeeding histories, or both, of which no account is given. And as such preceding and succeeding histories are subjects of possible knowledge, a Philosophy which says nothing about them, falls short of the required unification. Whence we saw it to follow that the formula sought, equally applicable to existences taken singly and in their totality, must be applicable to the whole history of each and to the whole history of all.

By these considerations we were brought within view of the formula. For if it had to comprehend the entire progress from the imperceptible to the perceptible and from the perceptible to the imperceptible; and if it was also to express the continuous redistribution of Matter and Motion; then, obviously, it could be no other than one defining the opposite processes of concentration and diffusion in terms of Matter and Motion. And if so, it must be a statement of the truth that the concentration of Matter implies the dissipation of Motion, and that, conversely, the absorption of Motion implies the diffusion of Matter.

Such, in fact, we found to be the law of the entire cycle of changes passed through by every existence—loss of motion and consequent integration, eventually followed by gain of motion and consequent disintegration. And we saw that besides applying to the whole history of each existence, it applies to each detail of the history. Both processes are going on at every instant; but always there is a differential result in favor of the first or the second. And every change, even though it be only a transposition of parts, inevitably advances the one process or the other.

Evolution and Dissolution, as we name these opposite transformations, though thus truly defined in their most general characters, are but incompletely defined; or, rather, while the definition of Dissolution is sufficient, the definition of Evolution is extremely insufficient. Evolution is always an integration of Matter and dissipation of Motion; but it is in most cases much more than this. The primary redistribution of Matter and Motion is usually accompanied by secondary redistributions.

Distinguishing the different kinds of Evolution so produced as simple and compound, we went on to consider under what conditions the secondary redistributions which make Evolution compound take place. We found that a concentrating aggregate which loses its contained motion rapidly, or integrates quickly, exhibits only simple Evolution; but in proportion as its largeness, or the peculiar constitution of its components, hinders the dissipation of its motion, its parts, while undergoing that primary redistribution which results in integration, undergo secondary redistributions producing more or less complexity.

§ 187. From this conception of Evolution and Dissolution as together making up the entire process through which things pass; and from this conception of Evolution as dividing into simple and compound; we went on to consider the law of Evolution, as exhibited among all orders of existences, in general and in detail.

The integration of Matter and concomitant dissipation of Motion, was traced not in each whole only, but in the parts into which each whole divides. By the aggregate Solar System, as well as by each planet and satellite, progressive concentration has been, and is still being, exemplified. In each organism that general incorporation of dispersed materials which causes growth, is accompanied by local incorporations, forming what we call organs. Every society while it displays the aggregative process by its increasing mass of population, displays it also by the rise of dense masses in special parts of its area. And in all cases, along with these direct integrations, there go the indirect integrations by which parts are made mutually dependent.

From this primary redistribution we were led on to consider the secondary redistributions, by inquiring how there came to be a formation of parts during the formation of a whole. It turned out that there is habitually a passage from homogeneity to heterogeneity, along with the passage from diffusion to concentration. While the matter composing the Solar System has been assuming a denser form, it has changed from unity to variety of distribution. Solidification of the Earth has been accompanied by a progress from comparative uniformity to extreme multiformity. In the course of its advance from a germ to a mass of relatively great bulk, every plant and animal also advances from simplicity to complexity. The increase of a society in numbers and consolidation has for its concomitant an increased heterogeneity both of its political and its industrial organization. And the like holds of all super-organic products—Language, Science, Art, and Literature.

But we saw that these secondary redistributions are not thus completely expressed. At the same time that the parts into which each whole is resolved become more unlike one another, they also become more sharply marked off. The result of the secondary redistributions is therefore to change an indefinite homogeneity into a definite heterogeneity. This additional trait also we found to be traceable in evolving aggregates of all orders. Further consideration, however, made it apparent that the increasing definiteness which goes along with increasing heterogeneity, is not an independent trait; but that it results from the integration which progresses in each of the differentiating parts, while it progresses in the whole they form.

Further, it was pointed out that in all evolutions, inorganic, organic, and super-organic, this change in the arrangement of Matter is accompanied by a parallel change in the arrangement of Motion: every increase in structural complexity involving a corresponding increase in functional complexity. It was shown that along with the integration of molecules into masses, there arises an integration of molecular motion into the motion of masses; and that as fast as there results variety in the sizes and forms of aggregates and their relations to incident forces, there also results variety in their movements.

The transformation thus contemplated under separate aspects, being in itself but one transformation, it became needful to unite these separate aspects into a single conception—to regard the primary and secondary redistributions as simultaneously working their various effects. Everywhere the change from a confused simplicity to a distinct complexity, in the distribution of both matter and motion, is incidental to the consolidation of the matter and the loss of its motion. Hence the redistribution of the matter and of its retained motion, is from a diffused, uniform, and indeterminate arrangement, to a concentrated, multiform, and determinate arrangement.

§ 188. We come now to one of the additions that may be made to the general argument while summing it up. Here is the fit occasion for observing a higher degree of unity in the foregoing inductions, than we observed while making them.

The law of Evolution has been thus far contemplated as holding true of each order of existences, considered as a separate order. But the induction as so presented, falls short of that completeness which it gains when we contemplate these several orders of existences as forming together one natural whole. While we think of Evolution as divided into astronomic, geologic, biologic, psychologic, sociologic, etc., it may seem to a certain extent a coincidence that the same law of metamorphosis holds throughout all its divisions. But when we recognize these divisions as mere conventional groupings, made to facilitate the arrangement and acquisition of knowledge—when we regard the different existences with which they severally deal as component parts of one Cosmos; we see at once that there are not several kinds of Evolution having certain traits in common, but one Evolution going on everywhere after the same manner. We have repeatedly observed that while any whole is evolving, there is always going on an evolution of the parts into which it divides itself; but we have not observed that this equally holds of the totality of things, as made up of parts within parts from the greatest down to the smallest. We know that while a physically-cohering aggregate like the human body is getting larger and taking on its general shape, each of its organs is doing the same; that while each organ is growing and becoming unlike others, there is going on a differentiation and integration of its component tissues and vessels; and that even the components of these components are sever-

ally increasing and passing into more definitely heterogeneous structures. But we have not duly remarked that, setting
out with the human body as a minute part, and ascending
from it to greater parts, this simultaneity of transformation
is equally manifest—that while each individual is developing, the society of which he is an insignificant unit is developing too; that while the aggregate mass forming a society
is becoming more definitely heterogeneous, so likewise is that
total aggregate, the Earth, of which the society is an inappreciable portion; that while the Earth, which in bulk is not
a millionth of the Solar System, progresses toward its concentrated and complex structure, the Solar System similarly
progresses; and that even its transformations are but those
of a scarcely appreciable portion of our Sidereal System,
which has at the same time been going through parallel
changes.

So understood, Evolution becomes not one in principle
only, but one in fact. There are not many metamorphoses
similarly carried on; but there is a single metamorphosis
universally progressing, wherever the reverse metamorphosis
has not set in. In any locality, great or small, throughout
space, where the occupying matter acquires an appreciable
individuality, or distinguishableness from other matter,
there Evolution goes on; or rather, the acquirement of this
appreciable individuality is the commencement of Evolution. And this holds uniformly; regardless of the size of
the aggregate, regardless of its inclusion in other aggregates,
and regardless of the wider evolutions within which its own
is comprehended.

§ 189. After making them, we saw that the inductions
which, taken together, establish the law of Evolution, do
not, so long as they remained inductions, form coherent
parts of that whole rightly named Philosophy; nor does
even the foregoing passage of these inductions from agreement into identity, suffice to produce the unity sought.
For, as was pointed out at the time, to unify the truths thus

reached with other truths, it is requisite to deduce them from the Persistence of Force. Our next step, therefore, was to show why, Force being persistent, the transformation which Evolution shows us necessarily results.

The first conclusion arrived at was, that any finite homogeneous aggregate must inevitably lose its homogeneity, through the unequal exposure of its parts to incident forces. It was pointed out that the production of diversities of structure by diverse forces, and forces acting under diverse conditions, has been illustrated in astronomic evolution; and that a like connection of cause and effect is seen in the large and small modifications undergone by our globe. The early changes of organic germs supplied further evidence that unlikenesses of structure follow unlikenesses of relations to surrounding agencies—evidence enforced by the tendency of the differently-placed members of each species to diverge into varieties. And we found that the contrasts, political and industrial, which arise between the parts of societies, serve to illustrate the same principle. The instability of the homogeneous thus everywhere exemplified we also saw holds in each of the distinguishable parts into which any uniform whole lapses; and that so the less heterogeneous tends continually to become more heterogeneous.

A further step in the inquiry disclosed a secondary cause of increasing multiformity. Every differentiated part is not simply a seat of further differentiations, but also a parent of further differentiations; since, in growing unlike other parts, it becomes a centre of unlike reactions on incident forces, and by so adding to the diversity of forces at work, adds to the diversity of effects produced. This multiplication of effects proved to be similarly traceable throughout all Nature—in the actions and reactions that go on throughout the Solar System, in the never-ceasing geologic complications, in the involved symptoms produced in organisms by disturbing influences, in the many thoughts and feelings generated by single impressions, and in the ever-ramifying results of each new agency brought to bear on a society. To which was added the corollary, confirmed by abundant facts, that the multiplication of effects advances in a geometrical progression along with advancing heterogeneity.

Completely to interpret the structural changes constituting Evolution, there remained to assign a reason for that increasingly-distinct demarcation of parts which accompanies the production of differences among parts. This reason we discovered to be, the segregation of mixed units under the action of forces capable of moving them. We saw that when unlike incident forces have made the parts of an aggregate unlike in the natures of their component units, there necessarily arises a tendency to separation of the dissimilar units from one another, and to a clustering of those units which are similar. This cause of the local integrations that accompany local differentiations, turned out to be likewise exemplified by all kinds of Evolution—by the formation of celestial bodies, by the molding of the Earth's crust, by organic modifications, by the establishment of mental distinctions, by the genesis of social divisions.

At length, to the query whether these processes have any limit, there came the answer that they must end in equilibrium. That continual division and subdivision of forces, which changes the uniform into the multiform and the multiform into the more multiform, is a process by which forces are perpetually dissipated; and dissipation of them, continuing as long as there remain any forces unbalanced by opposing forces, must end in rest. It was shown that when, as happens in aggregates of various orders, many movements are going on together, the earlier dispersion of the smaller and more resisted movements, establishes moving equilibria of different kinds: forming transitional stages on the way to complete equilibrium. And further inquiry made it apparent that, for the same reason, these moving equilibria have certain self-conserving powers; shown in the neutralization of perturbations, and the adjustment to new conditions. This general principle of equilibration, like the preceding general principles, was traced throughout all forms of Evolution—astronomic, geo-logic, biologic, mental and social. And our concluding inference was, that the penultimate stage of equilibration, in which the extremest multiformity and most complex moving equilibrium are established, must be one imply-ing the highest conceivable state of humanity.

But the fact which it here chiefly concerns us to re-member, is that each of these laws of the redistribution of Matter and Motion was found to be a derivative law—a law deducible from the fundamental law. The Persistence of Force being granted, there follow as inevitable inferences "The Instability of the Homogeneous" and "The Multipli-cation of Effects"; while "Segregation" and "Equilibra-tion" also become corollaries. And thus discovering that the processes of change formulated under these titles are so many different aspects of one transformation, determined by an ultimate necessity, we arrive at a complete unifica-tion of them—a synthesis in which Evolution in general and in detail becomes known as an implication of the law that transcends proof. Moreover, in becoming thus unified with one another, the complex truths of Evolution become simultaneously unified with those simpler truths shown to have a like affiliation—the equivalence of transformed forces, the movement of every mass and molecule along its line of least resistance, and the limitation of its motion by rhythm. Which further unification brings us to a con-ception of the entire plexus of changes presented by each concrete phenomenon, and by the aggregate of concrete phenomena, as a manifestation of one fundamental fact—a fact shown alike in the total change and in all the sepa-rate changes composing it.

§ 190. Finally we turned to contemplate, as exhibited throughout Nature, that process of Dissolution which forms the complement of Evolution; and which inevitably, at some time or other, undoes what Evolution has done.

Quickly following the arrest of Evolution in aggregates

that are unstable, and following it at periods often long delayed but reached at last in the stable aggregates around us, we saw that even to the vast aggregate of which all these are parts—even to the Earth as a whole—Dissolution must eventually arrive. Nay we even saw grounds for the belief that the far vaster masses dispersed at almost immeasurable intervals through space, will, at a time beyond the reach of finite imaginations, share the same fate; and that so universal Evolution will be followed by universal Dissolution—a conclusion which, like those preceding it, we saw to be deducible from the Persistence of Force.

It may be added that in so unifying the phenomena of Dissolution with those of Evolution, as being manifestations of the same ultimate law under opposite conditions, we also unify the phenomena presented by the existing Universe with the like phenomena that have preceded them and will succeed them—so far, at least, as such unification is possible to our limited intelligences. For if, as we saw reason to think, there is an alternation of Evolution and Dissolution in the totality of things—if, as we are obliged to infer from the Persistence of Force, the arrival at either limit of this vast rhythm brings about the conditions under which a counter-movement commences—if we are hence compelled to entertain the conception of Evolutions that have filled an immeasurable past and Evolutions that will fill an immeasurable future; we can no longer contemplate the visible creation as having a definite beginning or end, or as being isolated. It becomes unified with all existence before and after; and the Force which the Universe presents, falls into the same category with its Space and Time, as admitting of no limitation in thought.

§ 191. So rounding off the argument, we find its result brought into complete coalescence with the conclusion reached in Part I.; where, independently of any inquiry like the foregoing, we dealt with the relation between the Knowable and the Unknowable.

It was there shown by analysis of both our religious and our scientific ideas, that while knowledge of the cause which produces effects on our consciousness is impossible, the existence of a cause for these effects is a datum of consciousness. We saw that the belief in a Power of which no limit in Time or Space can be conceived is that fundamental element in Religion which survives all its changes of form. We saw that all Philosophies avowedly or tacitly recognize this same ultimate truth—that while the Relativist rightly repudiates those definite assertions which the Absolutist makes respecting existence transcending perception, he is yet at last compelled to unite with him in predicating existence transcending perception. And this inexpugnable consciousness in which Religion and Philosophy are at one with Common Sense, proved to be likewise that on which all exact Science is based. We found that subjective Science can give no account of those conditioned modes of being which constitute consciousness, without postulating unconditioned being. And we found that objective Science can give no account of the world which we know as external, without regarding its changes of form as manifestations of something that continues constant under all forms. This is also the implication to which we are now led back by our completed synthesis. The recognition of a persistent Force, ever changing its manifestations but unchanged in quantity throughout all past time and all future time, is that which we find alone makes possible each concrete interpretation, and at last unifies all concrete interpretations. Not, indeed, that this coincidence adds to the strength of the argument as a logical structure. Our synthesis has proceeded by taking for granted at every step this ultimate truth; and the ultimate truth cannot, therefore, be regarded as in any sense an outcome of the synthesis. Nevertheless, the coincidence yields a verification. For when treating of the data of Philosophy, it was pointed out that we cannot take even a first step without making assumptions; and that the only course is to proceed with them as provisional, until they are proved true by the congruity of all the results reached. This congruity we here see to be perfect and all-embracing—holding throughout that entire structure of definite consciousness of relations which we call Knowledge, and harmonizing with it that indefinite consciousness of existence transcending relations which forms the essence of Religion.

§ 192. Toward some result of this order, inquiry, scientific, metaphysical, and theological, has been, and still is, manifestly advancing. The coalescence of polytheistic conceptions into the monotheistic conception, and the reduction of the monotheistic conception to a more and more general form in which personal superintendence becomes merged in universal immanence, clearly shows this advance. It is equally shown in the fading away of old theories about "essences," "potentialities," "occult virtues," etc.; in the abandonment of such doctrines as those of "Platonic Ideas," "Pre-established Harmonies," and the like; and in the tendency toward the identification of Being as present to us in consciousness, with Being as otherwise conditioned beyond consciousness. Still more conspicuous is it in the progress of Science; which from the beginning has been grouping isolated facts under laws, uniting special laws under more general laws, and so reaching on to laws of higher and higher generality; until the conception of universal laws has become familiar to it.

Unification being thus the characteristic of developing thought of all kinds, and eventual arrival at unity being fairly inferable, there arises yet a further support to our conclusion. Since, unless there is some other and higher unity, the unity we have reached must be that toward which developing thought tends; and that there is any other and higher unity is scarcely supposable. Having grouped the changes which all orders of existences display into inductions; having merged these inductions into a single induction; having interpreted this induction deductively; having seen that the ultimate truth from which it is deduced is one transcending proof: it seems, to say the least, very improbable that there can be established a fundamentally different way of unifying that entire process of things which Philosophy has to interpret. That the foregoing accumulated verifications are all illusive, or that an opposing doctrine can show a greater accumulation of verifications, is not easy to conceive.

Let no one suppose that any such implied degree of trustworthiness is alleged of the various minor propositions brought in illustration of the general argument. Such an assumption would be so manifestly absurd, that it seems scarcely needful to disclaim it. But the truth of the doctrine as a whole, is unaffected by errors in the details of its presentation. If it can be shown that the Persistence of Force is not a datum of consciousness; or if it can be shown that the several laws of force above specified are not corollaries from it; or if it can be shown that, given these laws, the redistribution of Matter and Motion does not necessarily proceed as described; then, indeed, it will be shown that the theory of Evolution has not the high warrant here claimed for it. But nothing short of this can shake the general conclusions arrived at.

§ 193. If these conclusions be accepted—if it be agreed that the phenomena going on everywhere are parts of the general process of Evolution, save where they are parts of the reverse process of Dissolution; then we may infer that all phenomena receive their complete interpretation, only when recognized as parts of these processes. Whence it follows that the limit toward which Knowledge is advancing, must be reached when the formulæ of these processes are so applied as to yield a total and specific interpretation of each phenomenon in its entirety, as well as of phenomena in general.

The partially-unified knowledge distinguished as Science

does not yet include such total interpretations. Either, as in the more complex sciences, the progress is almost exclusively inductive; or, as in the simpler sciences, the deductions are concerned with the component phenomena; and at present there is scarcely a consciousness that the ultimate task is the deductive interpretation of phenomena in their state of composition. The Abstract Sciences, dealing with the forms under which phenomena are presented, and the Abstract-Concrete Sciences, dealing with the factors by which phenomena are produced, are, philosophically considered, the handmaids of the Concrete Sciences, which deal with the produced phenomena as existing in all their natural complexity. The laws of the forms and the laws of the factors having been ascertained, there then comes the business of ascertaining the laws of the products, as determined by the interaction of the co-operative factors. Given the Persistence of Force, and given the various derivative laws of Force, and there has to be shown not only how the actual existences of the inorganic world necessarily exhibit the traits they do, but how there necessarily result the more numerous and involved traits exhibited by organic and superorganic existences—how an organism is evolved? what is the genesis of human intelligence? whence social progress arises?

It is evident that this development of Knowledge into an organized aggregate of direct and indirect deductions from the Persistence of Force, can be achieved only in the remote future; and, indeed, cannot be completely achieved even then. Scientific progress is progress in that equilibration of thought and things which we saw is going on, and must continue to go on; but which cannot arrive at perfection in any finite period. Still, though Science can never be entirely reduced to this form; and though only at a far distant time can it be brought nearly to this form; much may even now be done in the way of approximation.

Of course, what may now be done, can be done but very imperfectly by any single individual. No one can possess that encyclopedic information required for rightly organizing even the truths already established. Nevertheless as progress is effected by increments—as all organization, beginning in faint and blurred outlines, is completed by successive modifications and additions; advantage may accrue from an attempt, however rude, to reduce the facts now accumulated—or rather certain classes of them—to something like co-ordination. Such must be the plea for the several volumes which are to succeed this; dealing with the respective divisions of what we distinguished at the outset as Special Philosophy.

§ 194. A few closing words must be said, concerning the general bearings of the doctrines that are now to be further developed. Before proceeding to interpret the detailed phenomena of Life, and Mind, and Society, in terms of Matter, Motion, and Force, the reader must be reminded in what sense the interpretations are to be accepted.

It is true that their purely relative character has been repeatedly insisted upon; but the liability to misinterpretation is so great, that notwithstanding all evidence to the contrary, there will probably have arisen in not a few minds, the conviction that the solutions which have been given, along with those to be derived from them, are essentially materialistic. Having, throughout life, constantly heard the charge of materialism made against those who ascribed the more involved phenomena to agencies like those which produce the simplest phenomena, most persons have acquired repugnance to such modes of interpretation; and the universal application of them, even though it is premised that the solutions they give can be but relative, will probably rouse more or less of the habitual feeling. Such an attitude of mind, however, is significant, not so much of a reverence for the Unknown Cause, as of an irreverence for those familiar forms in which the Unknown Cause is manifested to us. Men who have not risen above that vulgar conception which unites with Matter the contemptuous epithets "gross" and "brute," may naturally feel dismay at the proposal to reduce the phenomena of Life, of Mind, and of Society, to a level with those which they think so degraded. But whoever remembers that the forms of existence which the uncultivated speak of with so much scorn, are shown by the man of science to be the more marvellous in their attributes the more they are investigated, and are also proved to be in their ultimate natures absolutely incomprehensible—as absolutely incomprehensible as sensation, or the conscious something which perceives it—whoever clearly recognizes this truth, will see that the course proposed does not imply a degradation of the so-called higher, but an elevation of the so-called lower. Perceiving, as he will, that the Materialist and Spiritualist controversy is a mere war of words, in which the disputants are equally absurd—each thinking he understands that which it is impossible for any man to understand—he will perceive how utterly groundless is the fear referred to. Being fully convinced that whatever nomenclature is used, the ultimate mystery must remain the same, he will be as ready to formulate all phenomena in terms of Matter, Motion, and Force, as in any other terms; and will rather indeed anticipate, that only in a doctrine which recognizes the Unknown Cause as co-extensive with all orders of phenomena, can there be a consistent Religion, or a consistent Philosophy.

Though it is impossible to prevent misrepresentations, especially when the questions involved are of a kind that excite so much animus, yet to guard against them as far as may be, it will be well to make a succinct and emphatic restatement of the Philosophico-Religious doctrine which pervades the foregoing pages. Over and over again it has been shown in various ways, that the deepest truths we can reach are simply statements of the widest uniformities in our experience of the relations of Matter, Motion, and Force; and that Matter, Motion, and Force are but symbols of the Unknown Reality. A Power of which the nature remains forever inconceivable, and to which no limits in Time or Space can be imagined, works in us certain effects. These effects have certain likenesses of kind, the most general of which we class together under the names of Matter, Motion, and Force; and between these effects there are likenesses of connection, the most constant of which we class as laws of the highest certainty. Analysis reduces these several kinds of effect to one kind of effect; and these several kinds of uniformity to one kind of uniformity. And the highest achievement of Science is the interpretation of all orders of phenomena, as differently-conditioned manifestations of this one kind of effect, under differently-conditioned modes of this one kind of uniformity. But when Science has done this, it has done nothing more than systematize our experience; and has in no degree extended the limits of our experience. We can say no more than before, whether the uniformities are as absolutely necessary, as they have become to our thought relatively necessary. The utmost possibility for us, is an interpretation of the process of things as it presents itself to our limited consciousness; but how this process is related to the actual process we are unable to conceive, much less to know. Similarly, it must be remembered that while the connection between the phenomenal order and the ontological order is forever inscrutable; so is the connection between the conditioned forms of being and the unconditioned form of being forever inscrutable. The interpretation of all phenomena in terms of Matter, Motion, and Force, is nothing more than the reduction of our complex symbols of thought, to the simplest symbols; and when the equation has been brought to its lowest terms the symbols remain symbols still. Hence the reasonings contained in the foregoing pages, afford no support to either of the antagonist hypotheses respecting the ultimate nature of things. Their implications are no more materialistic than they are spiritualistic; and no more spiritualistic than they are materialistic. Any argument which is apparently furnished to either hypothesis, is neutralized by as good an argument furnished to the other. The Materialist, seeing it to be a necessary deduction from the law of correlation, that what exists in consciousness under the form of feeling, is transformable into an equivalent of mechanical motion, and by consequence into equivalents of all the other forces which matter exhibits; may consider it therefore demonstrated that the phenomena of consciousness are material phenomena. But the Spiritualist, setting out with the same data, may argue with equal cogency, that if the forces displayed by matter are cognizable only under the shape of those equivalent amounts of consciousness which they produce, it is to be inferred that these forces, when existing out of consciousness, are of the same intrinsic nature as when existing in consciousness; and that so is justified the spiritualistic conception of the external world, as consisting of something essentially identical with what we call mind. Manifestly, the establishment of correlation and equivalence between the forces of the outer and the inner worlds may be used to assimilate either to the other; according as we set out with one or other term. But he who rightly interprets the doctrine contained in this work, will see that neither of these terms can be taken as ultimate. He will see that though the relation of subject and object renders necessary to us these antithetical conceptions of Spirit and Matter; the one is no less than the other to be regarded as but a sign of the Unknown Reality which underlies both.

APPENDIX

DEALING WITH CERTAIN CRITICISMS

One way of estimating the validity of a critic's judgments, is that of studying his mental peculiarities as generally displayed. If he betrays idiosyncrasies of thought in his writings at large, it may be inferred that these idiosyncrasies possibly, if not probably, give a character to the verdicts he passes upon the productions of others. I am led to make this remark by considering the probable connection between Professor Tait's habit of mind as otherwise shown, and as shown in the opinion he has tacitly expressed respecting the formula of Evolution.

Daily carrying on experimental researches, Professor Tait is profoundly impressed with the supreme value of the experimental method; and has reached the conviction that by it alone can any physical knowledge be gained. Though he calls the ultimate truths of physics "axioms," yet, not very consistently, he alleges that only by observation and experiment can these "axioms" be known as such. Passing over this inconsistency, however, we have here to note the implied proposition that where no observation or experiment is possible; no physical truth can be established; and, indeed, that in the absence of any possibility of experiment or observation there is no basis for any physical belief at all. Now "The Unseen Universe," a work written by him in conjunction with Professor Balfour-Stewart, contains an elaborate argument concerning the relations between the Universe which is visible to us and an invisible Universe. This argument, carried on in pursuance of physical laws established by converse with the Universe we know, extends them to the Universe we do not know: the law of the Conservation of Energy, for example, being regarded as common to the two, and the principle of Continuity, which is traced among perceptible phenomena, being assumed to hold likewise of the imperceptible. On the strength of these reasonings, conclusions are drawn which are considered as at least probable: support is found for certain theological beliefs. Now, clearly, the relation between the seen and the unseen Universes cannot be the subject of any observation or experiment; since, by the definition of it, one term of the relation is absent. If we have, then, no warrant for asserting a physical axiom save as a generalization of results of experiments—if, consequently, where no observation or experiment is possible, reasoning after physical methods can have no place; then there can be no basis for any conclusion respecting the physical relations of the seen and the unseen Universes. Not so, however, concludes Professor Tait. He thinks that while no validity can be claimed for our judgments respecting perceived forces, save as experimentally justified, some validity can be claimed for our judgments respecting unperceived forces, where no experimental justification is possible.

The peculiarity thus exhibited in Professor Tait's general thinking, is exhibited also in some of his thinking on those special topics with which he is directly concerned as a Professor of Physics. An instance was given by Professor Clerk-Maxwell when reviewing, in "Nature" for July 3, 1879, the new edition (1879) of Thomson and Tait's "Treatise on Natural Philosophy." Professor Clerk-Maxwell writes:

"Again at p. 222, the capacity of the student is called upon to accept the following statement:

" 'Matter has an innate power of resisting external influences, so that every body, as far as it can, remains at rest or moves uniformly in a straight line.'

"Is it a fact that 'matter' has any power, either innate or acquired, of resisting external influences?"

And to Professor Clerk-Maxwell's question thus put, the answer of one not having a like mental peculiarity with Professor Tait, must surely be—No.

But the most remarkable example of Professor Tait's mode of thought, as exhibited in his own department, is contained in a lecture which he gave at Glasgow when the British Association last met there (see "Nature," September 21, 1876)—a lecture given for the purpose of dispelling certain erroneous conceptions of force commonly entertained. Asking how the word force "is to be correctly used" he says:

> "Here we cannot but consult Newton. The sense in which he uses the word 'force,' and therefore the sense in which we must continue to use it if we desire to avoid intellectual confusion, will appear clearly from a brief consideration of his simple statement of the laws of motion. The first of these laws is: *Every body continues in its state of rest or of uniform motion in a straight line, except in so far as it is compelled by impressed forces to change that state.*"

Thus Professor Tait quotes, and fully approves, that conception of force which regards it as something which changes the state of a body. Later on in the course of his lecture, after variously setting forth his views of how force is rightly to be conceived, he says "force is the rate at which an agent does work per unit of length." Now let us compare these two definitions of force. It is first, on the authority of Newton emphatically indorsed, said to be that which changes the state of a body. Then it is said to be the rate at which an agent does work (doing work being equivalent to changing a body's state). In the one case, therefore, force itself is the agent which does the work or changes the state; in the other case, force is the rate at which some other agent does the work or changes the state. How are these statements to be reconciled? Otherwise put the difficulty stands thus—force is that which changes the state of a body; force is a rate, and a rate is a relation (as between time and distance, interest and capital); therefore a relation changes the state of a body. A relation is no longer a *nexus* among phenomena, but becomes a producer of phenomena. Whether Professor Tait succeeded in dispelling "the widespread ignorance as to some of the most important elementary principles of physics"—whether his audience went away with clear ideas of the "much abused and misunderstood term" force, the report does not tell us.

Let us pass now from these illustrations of Professor Tait's judgment as exhibited in his special department, to the consideration of his judgment on a wider question here before us—the formula of Evolution. In "Nature" for July 17, 1879, while reviewing Sir Edmund Beckett's "Origin of the Laws of Nature" and praising it, he says of the author:

"He follows in fact, in his own way, the hint given by a great mathematician (Kirkman), who made the following exquisite translation of a well-known definition: Evolution is a change from an indefinite, incoherent, homogeneity to a definite, coherent, heterogeneity, through continuous differentiations and integrations.[1]

[*Translation into plain English.*] Evolution is a change from a nohowish, untalkaboutable, all-alikeness, to a somehowish and in-general-talkaboutable not-all-alikeness, by continuous somethingelseifications, and sticktogetherations."

Professor Tait, proceeding then to quote from Sir Edmund Beckett's book passages in which, as he thinks, there is a kindred tearing off of disguises from the expressions used by other authors, winds up by saying—"When the purposely vague statements of the materialists and agnostics are thus stripped of the tinsel of high-flown and unintelligible language, the eyes of the thoughtless who have

---

[1] A conscientious critic usually consults the latest edition of the work he criticises, so that the author may have the benefit of any corrections or alterations he has made. Apparently Mr. Kirkman does not think such a precaution needful. Publishing in 1876 his "Philosophy without Assumptions," from which the above passage is taken, he quotes from the first edition of "First Principles" published in 1862; though in the edition of 1867, and all subsequent ones, the definition is, in expression, considerably modified—two of the leading words being no longer used.

accepted them on authority (!) are at last opened, and they are ready to exclaim with Titania, methinks, 'I was enamored of an ass.' " And that Mr. Kirkman similarly believes that his travesty proves the formula of Evolution to be meaningless, is shown by the sentence which follows it— "Can any man show that my translation is unfair?"

One would have thought that Mr. Kirkman and Profesor Tait, however narrowly they limited themselves to their special lines of inquiry, could hardly have avoided observing that in proportion as scientific terms express wider generalities, they necessarily lose that vividness of suggestion which words of concrete meanings have; and therefore, to the uninitiated, seem vague, or even empty. If Professor Tait enunciated to a rustic the physical axiom, "action and reaction are equal and opposite," the rustic might not improbably fail to form any corresponding idea. And he might, if his self-confidence were akin to that of Mr. Kirkman, conclude that where he saw no meaning there could be no meaning. Further, if, after the axiom had been brought partially within his comprehension by an example, he were to laugh at the learned words used and propose to say instead—"shoving and back-shoving are one as strong as the other"; it would possibly be held by Professor Tait that this way of putting it is hardly satisfactory. If he thought it worth while to enlighten the rustic, he might perhaps point out to him that his statement did not include all the facts—that not only shoving and back-shoving, but also pulling and back-pulling, are one as strong as the other. Supposing the rustic were not too conceited, he might eventually be taught that the abstract, and to him seemingly vague, formula "action and reaction are equal and opposite," was chosen because by no words of a more specific kind could be expressed the truth in its entirety. Professor Tait however, and Mr. Kirkman, though the physical and mathematical terms they daily employ are so highly abstract as to prove meaningless to those who are unfamiliar with the concrete facts covered by them, seem not to have drawn any general inference from this habitual experience. For had they done so, they must have been aware that a formula expressing all orders of changes in their general course—astronomic, geologic, biologic, psychologic, sociologic—could not possibly be framed in any other than words of the highest abstractness. Perhaps there may come the rejoinder that they do not believe any such universal formula is possible. Perhaps they will say that the on-going of things as shown in our planetary system, has nothing in common with the on-going of things which has brought the Earth's crust to its present state, and that this has nothing in common with the on-going of things which the growths and actions of living bodies show us; although, considering that the laws of molar motion and the laws of molecular action are proved to hold true of them all, it requires considerable courage to assert that the modes of co-operation of the physical forces in these several regions of phenomena present no traits in common. But unless they allege that there is one law for the redistribution of matter and motion in the heavens, and another law for the redistribution of matter and motion in the Earth's inorganic masses, and another law for its organic masses— unless they assert that the transformation everywhere in progress follows here one method and there another; they must admit that the proposition which expresses the general course of the transformation can do it only in terms remote in the extremest degree from words suggesting definite objects and actions.

After noting the unconsciousness thus betrayed by Mr. Kirkman and Professor Tait, that the expression of highly abstract truths necessitates highly abstract words, we may go on to note a scarcely less remarkable anomaly of thought shown by them. Mr. Kirkman appears to think, and Professor Tait apparently agrees with him in thinking, that when one of these abstract words coined from Greek or Latin roots, is transformed into an uncouth-looking combination of equivalents of Saxon, or rather Old English, origin, what they regard as its misleading glamour is thereby dissipated and its meaninglessness made manifest. We may conveniently observe the nature of Mr. Kirkman's belief, by listening to an imaginary addition to that address before the Literary and Philosophical Society of Liverpool, in which he first set forth the leading ideas of his volume; and we may fitly, in this imaginary addition, adopt the manner in which he delights.

"Observe, gentlemen," we may suppose him saying, "I have here the yolk of an egg. The evolutionists, using their jargon, say that one of its characters is 'homogeneity'; and if you do not examine your thoughts, perhaps you may think that the word conveys some idea. But now if I translate it into plain English and say that one of the characters of this yolk is 'all-alikeness,' you at once perceive how nonsensical is their statement. You see that the substance of the yolk is not all-alike, and that therefore all-alikeness cannot be one of its attributes. Similarly with the other pretentious term 'heterogeneity,' which, according to them, describes the state things are brought to by what they call evolution. It is mere empty sound, as is manifest if I do but transform it, as I did the other, and say instead 'not-all-alikeness.' For on showing you this chick into which the yolk of the egg turns, you will see that 'not-all-alikeness' is a character which cannot be claimed for it. How can any one say that the parts of the chick are not-all-alike? Again, in their blatant language we are told that evolution is carried on by continuous 'differentiations'; and they would have us believe that this word expresses some fact. But if we put instead of it 'somethingelseifications' the delusion they try to practice on us becomes clear. How can they say that while the parts have been forming themselves, the heart has been becoming something else than the stomach, and the leg something else than the wing, and the head something else than the tail? The like manifestly happens when for 'integrations' we read 'sticktogetherations': what sense the term might seem to have, becomes obvious nonsense when the substituted word is used. For nobody dares assert that the parts of the chick stick together any more than do the parts of the yolk. I need hardly show you that now when I take a portion of the yolk between my fingers and pull, and now when I take any part of the chick, as the leg, and pull, the first resists just as much as the last—the last does not stick together any more than the first; so that there has been no progress in 'sticktogetherations.' And thus, gentlemen, you perceive that these big words which, to the disgrace of the Royal Society, appear even in papers published by it, are mere empty bladders which these would-be philosophers use to buoy up their ridiculous doctrines."

There is a further curious mental trait exhibited by Mr. Kirkman and which Professor Tait appears to have in common with him. Very truly it has been remarked that there is a great difference between disclosing the absurdities contained *in* a thing and piling absurdities *upon* it; and a remark to be added is that some minds appear incapable of distinguishing between intrinsic absurdity and extrinsic absurdity. The case before us illustrates this remark; and at the same time shows us how analytical faculties of one kind may be constantly exercised without strengthening analytical faculties of another kind—how mathematical analysis may be daily practiced without any skill in psychological analysis being acquired. For if these gentlemen had analyzed their own thoughts to any purpose, they would have known that incongruous juxtapositions may, by association of ideas, suggest characters that do not at all belong to the things juxtaposed. Did Mr. Kirkman ever observe the result of putting a bonnet on a nude statue? If he ever did, and if he then reasoned after the manner exemplified above, he doubtless concluded that the obscene effect belonged intrinsically to the statue, and only required the addition of the bonnet to make it conspicuous. The alternative conclusion, however, which perhaps most will draw, is that not in the statue itself was there anything of an obscene suggestion, but that this effect was purely adventitious: the bonnet, connected in daily experience with living women, calling up the thought of a living woman with the head dressed but otherwise naked. Similarly though, by clothing an idea in words which excite a feeling of the ludicrous by their oddity, any one may associate this feeling of the ludicrous with the idea itself, yet he does not thereby make the idea ludicrous; and if he thinks he does, he shows that he has not practiced introspection to much purpose.

By way of a lesson in mental discipline, it may be not uninstructive here to note a curious kinship of opinion between these two mathematicians and two litterateurs. At first sight it appears strange that men whose lives are passed in studies so absolutely scientific as those which Professor Tait and Mr. Kirkman pursue, should, in their judgments on the formula of Evolution, be at one with two men of exclusively literary culture—a North American Reviewer and Mr. Matthew Arnold. In the "North American Review," vol. 120, page 202, a critic, after quoting the formula of Evolution, says: "This may be all true, but it seems at best rather the blank form for a universe than anything corresponding to the actual world about us." On which the comment may be that one who had studied celestial mechanics as much as the reviewer has studied the general course of transformations, might similarly have remarked that the formula—"bodies attract one another directly as their masses and inversely as the squares of their distances," was at best but a blank form for solar systems and sidereal clusters. With this parenthetical comment I pass to the fact above hinted, that Mr. Matthew Arnold obviously coincides with the reviewer's estimate of the formula. In Chapter V. of his work "God and the Bible," when preparing the way for a criticism on German theologians as losing themselves in words, he quotes a saying from Homer. This he introduces by remarking that it "is not at all a grand one. We are almost ashamed to quote it to readers who may have come fresh from the last number of the 'North American Review,' and from the great sentence there quoted as summing up Mr. Herbert Spencer's theory of evolution: 'Evolution is,' etc. Homer's poor little saying comes not in such formidable shape. It is only this: *Wide is the range of words! words may make this way or that way.*" And then he proceeds with his reflections upon German logomachies. All of which makes it manifest that, going out of his way, as he does, to quote this formula from the "North American Review," he intends tacitly to indicate his agreement in the reviewer's estimate of it.

That these two men of letters, like the two mathematicians, are unable to frame ideas answering to the words in which evolution at large is expressed, seems manifest. In all four the verbal symbols used call up either no images, or images of the vaguest kinds, which, grouped together, form but the most shadowy thoughts. If, now, we ask what is the common trait in the education and pursuits of all four, we see it to be lack of familiarity with those complex processes of change which the concrete sciences bring before us. The men of letters, in their early days dieted on grammars and lexicons, and in their later days occupied with *belles-lettres,* Biography, and a History made up mainly of personalities, are by their education and course of life left almost without scientific ideas of a definite kind. The universality of physical causation—the interpretation of all things in terms of a never-ceasing redistribution of matter and motion, is naturally to them an idea utterly alien. The mathematician, too, and the mathematical physicist, occupied exclusively with the phenomena of number, space, and time, or, in dealing with forces, dealing with them in the abstract, carry on their researches in such ways as may, and often do, leave them quite unconscious of the traits exhibited by the general transformations which things, individually and in their totality, undergo. In a chapter on "Discipline" in the "Study of Sociology," I have commented upon the uses of the several groups of Sciences—Abstract, Abstract-Concrete, and Concrete—in cultivating different powers of mind; and have argued that, while, for complete preparation, the discipline of each group of sciences is indispensable, the discipline of any one group alone, or any two groups, leaves certain defects of judgment. Especially have I contrasted the analytical habit of thought which study of the Abstract and Abstract-Concrete Sciences produces, with the synthetical habit of thought produced by study of the Concrete Sciences. And I have exemplified the defects of judgment to which the analytical habit unqualified by the synthetical habit, leads. Here we meet with a striking illustration. Scientific culture of the analytical kind, almost as much as absence of scientific culture, leaves the mind bare of those ideas with which the Concrete Sciences deal. Exclusive familiarity with the *forms* and *factors* of phenomena, no more fits men for dealing with the *products* in their totalities, than does mere literary study.

An objection made to the formula of evolution by a sympathetic critic, Mr. T. E. Cliffe Leslie, calls for notice. It is urged in a spirit widely different from that displayed by Mr. Kirkman and his applauder Professor Tait; and it has an apparent justification. Indeed many readers who before accepted the formula of Evolution in full, will, after reading Mr. Cliffe Leslie's comments, agree with him in thinking that it is to be taken with the qualifications he points out. We shall find, however, that a clearer apprehension of the meanings of the words used, and a clearer apprehension of the formula in its totality, excludes the criticisms Mr. Leslie makes.

In the first place he dissociates from one another those traits of Evolution which I have associated, and which I have alleged to be true only when associated. He quotes me as saying that a change from the homogeneous to the heterogeneous characterizes all evolution; and he puts this at the outset of his criticism as though I made this change the primary characteristic. But if he will refer to "First

Principles," Part II. chap. 14 (in the second and subsequent editions), he will find it shown that under its *primary* aspect, Evolution "is a change from a less coherent form to a more coherent form, consequent on the dissipation of motion and integration of matter." The next chapter contains proofs that the change from homogeneity to heterogeneity is a *secondary* change, which, when conditions allow, accompanies the change from the incoherent to the coherent. At the beginning of the chapter after that, come the sentences— "But now, does this generalization express the whole truth? Does it include everything essentially characterizing Evolution and exclude everything else? . . . A critical examination of the facts will show that it does neither." And the chapter then goes on to show that the change is from an *indefinite* incoherent homogeneity to a *definite* coherent heterogeneity. Further qualifications contained in a succeeding chapter, bring the formula to this final form—"Evolution is an integration of matter and concomitant dissipation of motion; during which the matter passes from an indefinite, incoherent homogeneity to a definite, coherent heterogeneity; and during which the retained motion undergoes a parallel transformation."

Now if these various traits of the process of Evolution are kept simultaneously in view, it will be seen that most of Mr. Cliffe Leslie's objections fail to apply. He says:

"The movement of language, law, and political and civil union, is for the most part in an opposite direction. In a savage country like Africa, speech is in a perpetual flux, and new dialects spring up with every swarm from the parent hive. In the civilized world the unification of language is rapidly proceeding."

Here two different ideas are involved—the evolution of a language considered singly, and the evolution of languages considered as an aggregate. Nothing which he says implies that any one language becomes, during its evolution, less heterogeneous. The disappearance of dialects is not a progress toward the homogeneity of a language, but is the final triumph of one variety of a language over the other varieties, and the extinction of them: the conquering variety meanwhile becoming within itself more heterogeneous. This, too, is the process which Mr. Leslie refers to as likely to end in an extinction of the Celtic languages. Advance toward homogeneity would be shown if the various languages in Europe, having been previously unlike, were, while still existing, to become gradually more like. But the supplanting of one by another, or of some by others, no more implies any tendency of languages to become alike, than does the supplanting of species, genera, orders, and classes of animals, one by another, during the evolution of life, imply the tendency of organisms to assimilate in their natures. Even if the most heterogeneous creature, Man, should overrun the Earth and extirpate the greater part of its other inhabitants, it would not imply any tendency toward homogeneity in the proper sense. It would remain true that organisms tend perpetually toward heterogeneity, individually and as an assemblage. Of course if all kinds but one were destroyed, they could no longer display this tendency. Display of it would be limited to the remaining kind, which would continue, as now, to show it in the formation of local varieties, becoming gradually more divergent; and the like is true of languages.

In the next case Mr. Leslie identifies progressing unification with advance toward homogeneity. His words are:

"Already Europe has nearly consolidated itself into a Heptarchy, the number of states into which England itself was once divided; and the result of the American War exemplifies the prevalence of the forces tending to homogeneity over those tending to heterogeneity."

To this the reply is that these cases exemplify, rather, the prevalence of the forces which change the incoherent into the coherent—which effect integration. That is, they exemplify Evolution under its primary aspect. In the "Principles of Sociology," Part II. chap. 3, Mr. Leslie will find

numerous kindred cases brought in illustration of this law
of Evolution. To which add that such integrations bring
after them greater heterogeneity, not greater homogeneity.
The divisions of the Heptarchy were societies substantially
like one another in their structures and activities; but the
parts of the nation which correspond to them, have been
differentiated into parts carrying on varieties of occupations
with entailed unlikenesses of structures—here purely agricultural, there manufacturing; here predominantly given to
coal mining and iron smelting, there to weaving; here distinguished by scattered villages, there by clusters of large
towns.

Again, it is alleged that an increasing homogeneity is
shown in fashion. "Once every rank, profession, and district had a distinctive garb; now all such distinctions, save
with the priest and the soldier, have almost disappeared
among men." But while for a reason to be presently pointed
out, there has occurred a change which has abolished one
order of differences, differences of another order, far more
multitudinous, have arisen. Nothing is more striking than
the extreme heterogeneity of dress at the present day. As
Mr. Leslie alleges, the dresses of those forming each class
were once all alike; now no two dresses are alike. Within
the vague limits of the current fashion, the degree of variety
in women's costumes is infinite; and even men's costumes,
though having average resemblances, diverge from one another in colors, materials, and detailed forms in innumerable ways.

Other instances given by Mr. Leslie concern the organizations for carrying on production and distribution. He
argues that—

"In the industrial world a generation ago a constant movement toward a differentiation of employments and functions
appeared; now some marked tendencies to their amalgamation
have begun to disclose themselves. Joint Stock Companies
have almost effaced all real division of labor in the wide region of
trade within their operation."

Here, as before, Mr. Leslie represents amalgamation as
equivalent to increase of homogeneity; whereas amalgamation is but another name for integration, which is the primary process in Evolution, and which may, and does, go
along with increasing heterogeneity in the amalgamated
things. It cannot be said that a Joint Stock Banking Company, with its proprietory and directors in addition to its
officers, contains fewer unlike parts than does a private
Banking establishment: the contrary must be said. A Railway Company has far more numerous functionaries with
different duties, than had the one, or the many, coaching
establishments it replaced. And then, apart from the fact
that the larger aggregate of co-operators who, as a Company,
carry on, say a process of manufacture, is more complex as
well as more extensive; there is the fact, here chiefly to be
noted, that the entire assemblage of industrial structures is,
by the addition of these new structures, made more heterogeneous than before. Had all the smaller manufacturing
establishments, carried on by individuals or firms, been destroyed, the contrary might have been alleged; but as it is,
we see that in addition to all the old forms there have come
these new forms, making the totality of them more multiform than before. Mr. Leslie further illustrates his interpretation by saying:

"Many of the things for sale in a village huckster's shop
were formerly the subjects of distinct branches of business in a
large town; now the wares in which scores of different retailers
dealt, are all to be had in great establishments in New York,
Paris, and London, which sometimes buy direct from the producers, thus also eliminating the wholesale dealer."

Replies akin to the preceding ones are readily made. The
first is that wholesale dealers have not been at present eliminated; and cannot be so long as the ordinary shopkeepers
survive, as they will certainly do. In the smaller places,
forming the great majority of places, these vast establishments cannot exist; and in them, shopkeepers carrying on

business as at present will continue to necessitate wholesale dealers. Even in large places the same thing will hold. It is only people of a certain class, able to pay ready money and willing to go great distances to purchase, who frequent these large establishments. Those who live from hand to mouth, and those who prefer to buy at adjacent places, will maintain a certain proportion of shops, and the wholesale distributing organization needed for them. Again, we have to note that one of these great stores, such as Whiteley's or Shoolbred's, does not within itself display any advance toward homogeneity or despecialization; for it is made up of many separate departments, with their separate heads, carrying on businesses substantially separate—all superintended by one owner. It is nothing but an aggregate of shops under one roof instead of under the many roofs covering the side of a street; and exhibits just as much heterogeneity as the shops do when arranged in line instead of massed together. That which it really illustrates is a new form of integration, which is the primary evolutionary process. And then, lastly, comes the fact that the distributing organization of the country, considered as a whole, is by the addition of these establishments made more heterogeneous than before. All the old types of trading concerns continue to exist; and here are new types added, making the entire assemblage of them more varied.

From these objections made by Mr. Leslie which I have endeavored to show result from misapprehensions, I pass to two others which are to be met by taking account of certain complicating facts liable to be overlooked. Mr. Leslie remarks that—

"In the early stages of social progress, again, a differentiation takes place, as Mr. Spencer has observed, between political and industrial functions, which fall to distinct classes; now a man is a merchant in the morning and a legislator at night; in mercantile business one year, and the next perhaps head of the Navy, like Mr. Goschen or Mr. W. H. Smith."

Nothing contained in this volume explains the seeming anomaly here exemplified; but any one who turns to a chapter in the second part of the "Principles of Sociology," entitled "Social Types and Metamorphoses," will there find a clew to the explanation of it; and will see that it is a phenomenon consequent on the progressing dissolution of one type and evolution of another. The doctrine of Evolution, currently regarded as referring only to the development of species, is erroneously supposed to imply some intrinsic proclivity in every species towerd a higher form; and, similarly, a majority of readers make the erroneous assumption that the transformation which constitutes Evolution in its wider sense, implies an intrinsic tendency to go through those changes which the formula of Evolution expresses. But all who have fully grasped the argument of this work, will see that the process of Evolution is not necessary, but depends on conditions; and that the prevalence of it in the Universe around, is consequent on the prevalence of these conditions: the frequent occurrence of Dissolution showing us that where the conditions are not maintained, the reverse process is quite as readily gone through. Bearing in mind this truth, we shall be prepared to find that the progress of a social organism toward more heterogeneous and more definite structures of a certain type, continues only as long as the actions which produce these effects continue in play. We shall expect that if these actions cease, the progressing transformation will cease. We shall infer that the particular structures which have been formed by the activities carried on, will not grow more heterogeneous and more definite; and that if other orders of activities, implying other sets of forces, commence, answering structures of another kind will begin to make their appearance, to grow more heterogeneous and definite, and to replace the first. And it will be manifest that while the transition is going on—while the first structures are dissolving and the second evolving—there must be a mixture of structures causing apparent confusion of traits. Just as during the metamorphoses of an

animal which, having during its earlier existence led one
kind of life, has to develop structures fitting it for another
kind of life, there must occur a blurring of the old organization while the new organization is becoming distinct, leading
to transitory anomalies of structure; so, during the metamorphoses undergone by a society in which the militant
activities and structures are dwindling while the industrial
are growing, the old and new arrangements must be mingled
in a perplexing way. On reading the chapter in the "Principles of Sociology" which I have named, Mr. Leslie will
see that the above facts referred to by him are interpretable
as consequent on the transition from that type of regulative
organization proper to militant life, to that type of regulative organization proper to industrial life; and that so long
as these two modes of life, utterly alien in their natures,
have to be jointly carried on, there will continue this jum-
bling of the regulative systems they respectively require.

The second of the objections above noted as needing to
be otherwise dealt with than by further explanation of the
formula of Evolution, concerns the increase of likeness
among developing systems of Civil Law; in proof of which
increase of likeness Mr. Leslie quotes Sir Henry Maine to
the effect that "all laws, however dissimilar in their infancy,
tend to resemble each other in their maturity": the implication to which Mr. Leslie draws attention, being that in respect of their laws societies become not more heterogeneous
but more homogeneous. Now though in their details, systems of Law will, I think, be found to acquire, as they
evolve, an increasing number of differences from one another; yet in their cardinal traits it is probably true that
they usually approximate. How far this militates against
the formula of Evolution we shall best see by first considering the analogy furnished by animal organisms. Low down
in the animal kingdom there are simple mollusks with but
rudimentary nervous systems—a ganglion or two and a few
fibres. Diverging from this low type we have the great sub-
kingdom constituted by the higher Mollusca and the still

greater subkingdom constituted by the Vertebrata. As these two types evolve, their nervous systems develop; and though in the highest members of the two they remain otherwise unlike, yet they approximte in so far that each acquires great nervous centres: the large cephalopods have clustered ganglia which simulate brains. Compare, again, the Mollusca and the Articulata in respect of their vascular systems. Fundamentally unlike as these are orginally, and remaining unlike as they do throughout many successive stages of ascent in these two subkingdoms, they nevertheless are made similar in the highest forms of both by each having a central propelling organ—a heart. Now in these and in some cases which the external organs furnish, such as the remarkable resemblance Evolution has produced between the eyes of the highest Mollusca and those of the Vertebrata, it may be said that there is implied a change toward homogeneity. No zoologist, however, would admit that these facts really conflict with the general law of Organic Evolution. As already explained, the tendency to progress from homogeneity to heterogeneity is not intrinsic but extrinsic. Structures become unlike in consequence of unlike exposures to incident forces. This is so with organisms as wholes, which, as they multiply and spread, are ever falling into new sets of conditions; and it is so with the parts of each organism. These pass from primitive likeness into unlikeness, as fast as the mode of life places them in different relations to actions—primarily external and secondarily internal; and with each successive change in mode of life new unlikenesses are superposed. One of the implications is that if, in organisms otherwise different, there arise like sets of conditions to which certain parts are subject, such parts will tend toward likeness; and this is what happens with their nervous and vascular systems. Duly to co-ordinate the actions of all parts of an active organism, there requires a controlling apparatus; and the conditions to be fulfilled for perfect co-ordination are conditions common to all active organisms. Hence, in proportion as fulfilment approaches completeness in the highest organisms, however otherwise unlike their types are, this apparatus acquires in all of them certain common characters—especially extreme centralization. Similarly with the apparatus for distributing nutriment. The relatively high activity accompanying superior organization implies great waste; great waste implies active circulation of blood; active circulation of blood implies efficient propulsion; so that a heart becomes a common need for highly evolved creatures, however otherwise unlike their structures may be. Thus is it, too, with societies. As they evolve there arise certain conditions to be fulfilled for the maintenance of social life; and in proportion as the social life becomes high, these conditions need to be more effectually fulfilled. A legal code expresses one set of these conditions. It formulates certain regulative principles to which the conduct of citizens must conform that social activities may be harmoniously carried on. And these regulative principles being in essentials the same everywhere, it results that systems of Law acquire certain general similarities as the most developed social life is approached.

These special replies to Mr. Leslie's objections are, however, but introductory to the general reply; which would be, I think, adequate even in their absence. Mr. Leslie's method is that of taking detached groups of social phenomena, as those of language, of fashion, of trade, and arguing (though, as I have sought to show, not effectually) that their later transformations do not harmonize with the alleged general law of Evolution. But the real question is, not whether we find advance to a more definite coherent heterogeneity in these taken separately, but whether we find this advance in the structures and actions of the entire society. Even were it true that the law does not hold in certain orders of social processes and products, it would not follow that it does not hold of social processes and products in their totality. The law is a law of the transformation of aggregates; and must be tested by the entire assemblages of phenomena which the aggregates present. Omitting societies in states of decay and dissolution, which exhibit the converse change, and contemplating only societies which are growing, Mr. Leslie will, I think, scarcely allege of any one of them that its structures and functions do not, taken altogether, exhibit increasing heterogeneity. And if, instead of taking each society as an aggregate, he takes the entire aggregate of societies which the Earth supports, from primitive hordes up to highly civilized nations, he will scarcely deny that this entire aggregate has been becoming more various in the forms of societies it includes, and is still becoming more various.

Criticism would be greatly diminished in bulk if there were excluded from it all that part devoted to disproving statements which have not been made; and were this course pursued, the work "On Mr. Spencer's Formula of Evolution," by Malcolm Guthrie, would disappear bodily. It is little else than a misstatement of certain fundamental views of mine, and then an elaborate refutation of the views as misstated.

Let me first show by brief extracts from "First Principles" what these views are. In a chapter on "Ultimate Scientific Ideas," after showing how the hypothesis that matter consists of solid atoms commits us to alternative impossibilities of thought, I have shown how the hypothesis of Boscovich, that matter consists of centres of force without extension, is unthinkable. In the course of the argument I have pointed out that though Boscovich's hypothesis cannot be realized in thought, yet, on the other hand, the hypothesis of extended atoms itself implies an imaginary separableness of each atom into parts, and again of these into parts, and so on without limit until unextended centres of force are reached: the consciousness of force being that which alone perpetually emerges. And I have ended by saying that "Matter then, in its ultimate nature, is as absolutely incomprehensible as Space and Time." In the second part of the work, in chapters treating of "The Indestructibility of Matter," "The Continuity of Motion," and "The Persist-

ence of Force," I have at some length elaborated the view
that Force is the ultimate component of thought into which
our conceptions of external existences are resolvable. Summing up the first of these chapters I have said—"thus, then,
by the indestructibility of matter, we really mean the indestructibility of the *force* with which matter affects us." At
the close of the second of these chapters I have argued that
"the continuity of motion, as well as the indestructibility of
matter, is really known to us in terms of *force*" . . . "that
which defies suppression in thought, is really the force
which the motion indicates." And then in the third chapter, having shown how the truths that matter is indestructible and motion continuous, can be known to us only as
corollaries from the truth that force is persistent—that force
is that "out of which our conceptions of Matter and Motion
are built"—I have gone on to say that "by the Persistence
of Force, we really mean the persistence of some Power
which transcends our knowledge and conception." Throughout all which arguments the implication is that I hold Matter and Motion to be conditioned manifestations of this unknown Power. Being aware of the perversity of critics, I
have, in the "Summary and Conclusion," again endeavored
to bar out misinterpretations. Here is one of the sentences
it contains:

"Over and over again it has been shown in various ways,
that the deepest truths we can reach, are simply statements of
the widest uniformities in our experience of the relations of
Matter, Motion, and Force; and that Matter, Motion, and Force
are but symbols of the Unknown Reality. A Power of which the
nature remains forever inconceivable, and to which no limits in
Time or Space can be imagined, works in us certain effects. These
effects have certain likenesses of kind, the most general of which
we class together under the names of Matter, Motion, and Force."

In which sentences it is distinctly stated that I have throughout regarded Matter under the form present to consciousness, as a *symbol*—a certain conditioned *effect* wrought in us

by the Unknown Power; and I have gone on to say that "the interpretation of all phenomena in terms of Matter, Motion, and Force, is nothing more than the reduction of our complex symbols of thought, to the simplest symbols; and when the equation has been brought to its lowest terms the symbols remain symbols still."

It will scarcely be believed, and yet it is true, that notwithstanding all this, Mr. Guthrie ascribes to me the vulgar conceptions of Matter and Motion; argues as though I really think they are in themselves what they seem to our consciousness; and proceeds to criticise my views on this assumption. He ignores the conspicuous fact that Matter and Motion are both regarded by me as modes of manifestation of Force, and that Force as we are conscious of it when by our own efforts we produce changes, is the correlative of that Universal Power which transcends consciousness. And then he ends the criticisms forming the second part of his work by saying "if this is not materialistic I do not know what is." He does not do this by inadvertence, though there would be little excuse even then; but he does it deliberately and with his eyes open. His next chapter begins:

"It will have been observed that in the preceding part of this criticism I have employed the term 'matter in motion,' and have avoided the use of the word 'force,' although it appears so prominently in the pages of Mr. Spencer's work. This has not been accidental, but by design, indicating as it does one of my main criticisms of Mr. Spencer.

"I can logically take up one of two positions. The first recognizes matter, whose properties are merely those of extension, which are capable of being described in terms of geometry and arithmetic. I can also recognize as the sole active properties of matter its modes and rates of motion—the motion, that is to say, of ultimate units, atoms, molecules, or masses, also capable of measurement.

"The second position recognizes matter and its activity or activities—matter as endowed with force or forces."

Thus it will be observed that having avowedly dealt with Matter and Motion as modes of Force, I am "by design"

criticised as though I had not so dealt with them. Having
distinctly said what I mean by Matter and Motion, I am
practically told that I shall not mean that, but shall mean
what Mr. Guthrie means; and shall be dealt with accordingly. And then, further, it will be observed that of the
two positions which Mr. Guthrie lays down as possible, and
proceeds to argue upon as alternatives, one or other of which
I must accept, both speak of Matter and units of Matter as
though actually existing under the forms thought by us;
and the last, speaking of "matter as endowed with force or
forces," implies that whether in mass or in units, Matter is a
space-occupying something which is in the one case inert
and the other case made active by force with which it is
"endowed"—force which is added to the inert something.
Spite of all the pains I have taken to show that I regard
Matter as *itself* a localized manifestation of Force—spite of
all the evidence that our idea of a unit of Matter, or atom,
is regarded by me simply as a symbol which the form of our
thought obliges us to use, but which we cannot suppose answers to the reality without committing ourselves to alternative impossibilities of thought; I am debited with the belief
that Matter actually consists "of space-occupying units, having shape and measurement." Though I have repeatedly
made it clear that our ideas of Matter, Motion and Force are
but the x, y, and z with which we work our equations, and
formulate the various relations among phenomena in such
way as to express their order in terms of x, y and z—though
I have shown that the realities for which x, y and z stand,
cannot be conceived by us as actually existing thus or thus
without committing ourselves to alternative absurdities; yet
questions are put implying that I must hold one or other
hypothesis concerning these actual existences, and I am supposed to be involved in all the difficulties which arise.

Another work devoted to the refutation of my views, is
that of Professor Birks—"Modern Physical Fatalism and
the Doctrine of Evolution, including an examination of Mr.

H. Spencer's First Principles." Having dealt with the work of Mr. Guthrie, I cannot pass by that of Professor Birks without raising the suspicion that I find some difficulty in dealing with it. Indeed, I do find a difficulty—a difficulty illustrated by that found in disentangling a skein of silk which has been pulled about by a child for half an hour. And just as the patience of a bystander would fail were he asked to look on until, by unravelling the tangled skein, its continuity was proved; so would the reader's attention be exhausted before I had rectified one-tenth part of the meshes and knots into which Professor Birks has twisted my statements.

Abundant warrant for this assertion is furnished by the very first paragraph succeeding the one in which Professor Birks announces that he is about to take "First Principles" as representative of the "fatalistic theory." In this paragraph he represents me as asserting that ultimate religious ideas are "incapable of being conceived." He further says that ultimate scientific ideas are by me "pronounced equally inconceivable." Now any clear-headed reader who accepted Professor Birks' version of my views, would be led to debit me with the absurdity of saying that certain things which are put together in consciousness (ideas) cannot be put together in consciousness (conceived). To conceive is to frame in thought; and as every idea is framed in thought, it is nonsense to say of any idea that it cannot be conceived— nonsense which I have nowhere uttered. My statement is that "Ultimate Scientific Ideas, then, are all representative of realities that cannot be comprehended"; and the like is alleged of ultimate religious ideas. The things which I say cannot be comprehended or conceived are not the *ideas*, but the *realities* beyond consciousness for which the ideas in consciousness stand. In Professor Birks' statement, however, inconceivableness of the realities is transformed into inconceivableness of the answering ideas! Further, at the end of this first paragraph which deals with me, I am represented as teaching that religion "is equivalent to Nescience or

Ignorance alone." This statement is as far removed from the truth as the others. I have argued at considerable length, and in such various ways that I thought it impossible to misunderstand me, that though the Power universally manifest to us through phenomena, alike in the surrounding world and in ourselves—the Power "in which we live and move and have our being"—is, and must ever remain, inscrutable; yet that the existence of this Inscrutable Power is the most certain of all truths. I have contended that while, to the intellectual consciousness, this Power, though unknowable in nature, must be ever present as existing, it must be, to the emotional consciousness, an object to the sentiment we call religious; since, in substance if not in form, it answers to the creating and sustaining Power toward which the religious sentiment is in other cases drawn out. Yet though in the most emphatic way I have represented this unknown and unknowable Power as the object-matter of religion, Professor Birks represents me as saying that the unknowableness of it is the object-matter of religion! Though I hold that an Ultimate Being, known with absolute certainty as existing, but of whose nature we are in ignorance, is the sphere for religious feeling; he says I hold that the ignorance alone is the sphere for religious feeling!

When in the first sixteen lines specifically treating of my views, these three cases occur, it may be imagined what an intricate plexus of misrepresentations, misunderstandings, and perversions, fills the three hundred and odd pages forming the volume. Especially may it be anticipated that the metaphysical discussions, occupying five chapters, are so confused that it is next to impossible to deal with them. I must limit myself to giving a sample or two from this part of the work: one of them illustrating Professor Birks' critical fairness, and the other his philosophic capacity.

In his chapter on "The Reality of Matter," he says (page 111), "The sense of reality in things around us, Mr. Spencer has truly said, is one which no metaphysical criticisms can shake in the least"; and the rest of the paragraph is devoted to enlarging upon this proposition. The next paragraph begins—" 'Permanent possibilities of sensation' is merely an ingenious phrase to disguise and conceal a self-contradiction": sundry antagonistic criticisms upon this phrase being appended. And then the opening words of the paragraph which succeeds are quoted from "First Principles." Now since the refutation of my views is the aim of the work; and since both the preceding and succeeding passages specifically refer to my work; and since no other name is mentioned; every reader, not otherwise better instructed, will conclude that as a matter of course the phrase "permanent possibilities of sensation" is mine; and that the criticisms upon it tell against me. Even were there evidence that this phrase "permanent possibilities of sensation," expressed, or harmonized with, a doctrine entertained by me; yet as the phrase is not mine, the quoting it as mine would have been a literary misdemeanor. What then must be said of it when, instead of standing for any view of mine, it stands for an opposite view? Mr. Mill's expression, quoted by Professor Birks as though it were my expression, belongs to a theory of knowledge entirely at variance with that set forth and everywhere implied in "First Principles"; and a theory which, where the occasion was fit, I have persistently combated (see "Principles of Psychology," Part VII. "General Analysis"). And yet Professor Birks tacitly makes me responsible for the incongruities which result from uniting this theory with the opposed theory.

From this sample of critical truthfulness let us pass now to a sample of critical acumen.

In arguing against Hamilton and Mansel in § 26, I have said, "It is rigorously impossible to conceive that our knowledge is a knowledge of appearances only, without at the same time conceiving a Reality of which they are appearances; for appearance without reality is unthinkable." On page 121 of his work, Professor Birks, quoting the last five words of this sentence, continues—"This is true, when once the conception of distance has been gained by actual experience." And he then proceeds to comment upon visual impressions, illusive and other. Again on page 135, when criticising my argument concerning the indestructibility of matter, Professor Birks says:

"Matter, as knowable, is declared to be not the unseen reality, but the sensible appearances, or phenomenal matter alone. Phenomenal matter, it appears from daily and hourly experience, appears and disappears, perishes and is new-created continually. . . . The cloud vanishes, the star sets, or a mist blots it out, the drop evaporates, the ship melts into the yeast of waves, the candle is burned away and comes to an end. The substance may last in another form, but the phenomenon or appearance is gone. . . . Thus, by the theory, of Matter, the Noumenon, we know nothing, and therefore cannot know that it is indestructible. Of Matter, the Phenomenon, we may know much. And one main thing we know of it, proved by hourly experience, is that it both may be and continually is destroyed. For an appearance is destroyed and perishes, when it ceases to appear."

In which sentences, as in all accompanying sentences covering several pages, the implication is that Professor Birks identifies appearance in the philosophical sense with appearance in the popular sense! Everywhere his expressions and arguments make manifest the fact that Professor Birks thinks the meaning of phenomenon, in metaphysical discussion, is no wider than that implied by its derivation—something visible! Sounds, smells, tastes, are in his view not phenomena; nor are touches, pressures, tensions. And hence it results that since when a pound of salt is dissolved in water it ceases to be visible, its existence, phenomenally considered, ends: its continued power of affecting our senses by its weight, to the same extent as before the solution, not being considered as a phenomenal manifestation of its existence!

In § 46, when commenting on the mental confusion which metaphysical discussions often produce, I have ascribed this in part to the misleading connotations of the words "appearance" and "phenomena"; and after illustrating this have said:

"So that the implication of uncertainty has infected the very word *appearance*. Hence, Philosophy, by giving it an extended meaning, leads us to think of all our senses as deceiving us in the same way that the eyes do; and so makes us feel ourselves floating in a world of phantasms. Had *phenomenon* and *appearance* no such misleading associations, little, if any, of this mental confusion would result. Or did we in place of them use the term *effect,* which is equally applicable to all impressions produced on consciousness through any of the senses, and which carries with it in thought the necessary correlative *cause,* with which it is equally real, we should be in little danger of falling into the insanities of idealism."

This caution was intended for the general reader. That it might be needed by one who should undertake to deal with the work critically, never occurred to me. Not only, however, does it seem that Professor Birks (who quotes the last three words of the paragraph) needs such a caution, but it further seems that the caution is thrown away upon him. For just those misinterpretations of the words above pointed out, are the misinterpretations he makes. After this I shall, I think, be absolved from examining further his metaphysical criticisms.

Of his criticisms upon various of the physical doctrines which this work contains, I will notice two only—the one because I wish to repudiate a view which, spite of abundant evidence to the contrary, he ascribes to me; and the other because, based as his statement is on a fact which he misinterprets, it is desirable to give the right interpretation of it. On page 188, Professor Birks says:

"The Essence of the doctrine held by Mr. Grove, Dr. Tyndall, and Mr. Spencer, and which the last has made the foundation of his whole theory of Physical Fatalism, is that there is, every moment, an unchanging total of Force, which never varies in amount, while it incessantly changes its form. The Force, then, which persists, must be a present existence. But Potential

Energy is nothing of the kind. It is the sum of trillions of trillions of future possibilities of force, ranging through trillions of trillions of different future intervals of time."

Now the tacit implication here is, that I accept the doctrine of Potential Energy. The men of science named, with many others who might be added, hold that the total quantity of force remains constant. Against these it is urged that energy, in becoming potential, ceases to exist; and that therefore the doctrine is untrue. And being represented as holding this doctrine in common with them, I am said to have based my general fabric of conclusions upon a fallacy. In the first place I have to ask on what authority Professor Birks assumes that I hold the doctrine of Potential Energy in the way in which it is held by those named? And in the second place I have to ask how it happens that Professor Birks, elaborately criticising my views step by step, deliberately ignores the passages in which I have repudiated this doctrine? In the chapter on "The Continuity of Motion," I have, at considerable length, given reasons for regarding the conception of Potential Energy as an illegitimate one; and have distinctly stated that I am at issue with scientific friends on the matter. Devoting, as Professor Birks does, his chapter entitled "The Transformation of Force and Motion," to the incongruities which result when the doctrine of the Persistence of Force is joined with the doctrine of Potential Energy, as commonly received, it was doubtless convenient to assume, spite of the direct evidence to the contrary, that I accept this doctrine, and am implicated in all the consequences. But there can be but one opinion respecting the honesty of making the assumption. Let me add that my rejection of this doctrine is not without other warrant than my own. Since the issue of the last edition of this work, containing the passages I have referred to, Mr. James Croll, no mean authority as a mathematician and physicist, has published, in the "Philosophical Magazine" for October, 1876, p. 241, a paper in which he shows, I think conclusively, that the commonly accepted view of Potential

Energy cannot be sustained, but that energy invariably remains actual. I learn from him that he had in 1867 indicated briefly this same view.

The remaining case, above adverted to as calling for comment, concerns my motive for suppressing a certain passage in the chapter on "Ultimate Scientific Ideas," and substituting another passage. Before proceeding to state the reasons for this substitution, and to disprove the inferences which Professor Birks draws from it, I may remark that it is usual in literary criticism to judge an author by the latest expression of his views. It is commonly thought nothing but fair that if he has made an error (I say this hypothetically, for in this case I have no error to acknowledge) he should be allowed the benefit of any correction he makes. Professor Birks, however, apparently thinks that, moved by the high motive of "doing God service," he is warranted in taking the opposite course—perhaps thinks, indeed, that he would fail of his duty did any regard for generous dealing prevent him from making a point against an opponent of his creed.

But now, saying no more about the ethics of criticism, I pass to the substantial question. In the first place, I have to point out that in the passage suppressed I have not said that which Professor Birks alleges. He represents me as asserting "that gravitation is a necessary result of the laws of space" (p. 227). I have asserted no such thing. He says, "There can be no *à priori* necessity that every particle should act on every other at all at every distance" (p. 222). I have nowhere said, or even hinted, that there is any such *à priori* necessity. The notion "that gravitation results by a fatal necessity from the laws of space," which he ascribes to me (p. 229), is one which I should repudiate as utterly absurd, and one which is not in the remotest way implied by anything I have said. What I have said is that "Light, Heat, Gravitation, and all central forces, vary inversely as the squares of the distances," and that "this law is not simply an empirical one, but one deducible mathematically from the relations of space." Now what is here said to be "deducible mathematically from the relations of space"? Not a thing, or a force, but a *law*. What is the law here said to be knowable *à priori?* The *law of variation* of any or every central force. And what is alone included in the assertion of this *à priori* law? Simply this, that *given* a central force and such is the law according to which it will vary. Nothing is alleged respecting the existence of any central force. Does Professor Birks contend that if I say that light, proceeding from a centre, necessarily varies inversely as the square of the distance, I thereby say that the existence of light itself is known *à priori* as a result of space relations? When I assert that of the heat radiating in all directions from a point, the quantity falling on a given surface necessarily decreases as the square of the distance increases, do I thereby assert the necessary existence of the heat which conforms to this law? Why then do I, in asserting that the *law of variation* of gravity "results by a fatal necessity from the laws of space" simultaneously assert "that *gravitation* results by a fatal necessity from the laws of space"? Professor Birks, however, because I assert the first says I assert the second. My proposition—Central forces vary inversely as the squares of the distances, he actually transforms into the proposition—There is a cosmical force which varies inversely as the squares of the distances. And debiting me with the last as identical with the first, proceeds, after his manner, to debit me with various resulting absurdities.

Having thus shown that the passage in question contains no such statement as that which Professor Birks says it contains, I go on to show that I have not removed this passage because I have abandoned the belief it embodies. Clear proof is at hand. If Professor Birks will turn to the "Replies to Criticisms," contained in the third volume of my "Essays: Scientific, Political and Speculative"(pp. 334–337), he will find that I have there defended the above proposition against a previous attack; and assigning, as I have done, justification for it, I have shown no sign of relinquishing it. Why, then, Professor Birks will ask, did I make the change in question? Had his mental attitude been other than it is, he might readily have divined the reason. Knowing, as he seemingly does, that this doctrine which he criticises had been already criticised in a similar manner (for otherwise he would scarcely have discovered the change I have made), he might have seen clearly enough that the passage was suppressed simply to deprive opponents of the opportunity of evading the general argument of the chapter by opening a side issue on a point not essential to its argument.

The chapter has for its subject, certain incapacities of the human mind—a subject, by the way, on which theologians are never tired of enlarging when it suits their own purpose, but on which an antagonist may not enlarge without exciting their anger. Various examples of these incapacities are given, to justify and enforce the conclusion drawn. Among these was originally included the example in question. Misrepresenting it as Professor Birks misrepresents it, another writer had before him similarly based on his mis-representation sundry animadversions. Though still regarding the statement I had actually made (not the one ascribed to me) as valid, I concluded that it would be best to remove the stumbling-block out of the way of future readers; and therefore decided to replace the illustration by another. The rest of the chapter remains exactly as it was, and its argument is not in the remotest degree affected by this substitution. Nevertheless, Professor Birks, wrongly describing the nature of the illustration, and wrongly attributing the removal of the illustration to change in my belief, also wrongly conveys the impression that the doctrine which the illustration contained had some vital connection with the general argument of the chapter and with the doctrine of the work; and by conveying this impression calls forth exultation from religious periodicals.

Were I to deal with Professor Birks' book page by page, a much larger book than his would be required to expose his misstatements, perversions, confusions. The above examples must suffice. I will add only that in one belief of his I cordially agree with him. At the close of his preface he says—"I think that those who take the pains to read my strictures, and compare them with the statements of the work to which they are a reply, will find the effort repaid by a clearer apprehension of the topics in debate." And I venture to join with this the expression of my belief that if readers follow Professor Birks' tacit suggestion, "a clearer apprehension of the topics in debate" will not result from acceptance of his criticisms.

SUBJECT-INDEX

(for this index the author is indebted to f. howard
collins, esq., of edgbaston, birmingham)

B

BABINET, J., on nebular hypothesis, 485.

Baer, K.E.von, the formula of, 336.

Ball and string, perceptible and latent activity shown by, 189.

Beckett, Sir E., *Origin of the Laws of Nature,* 554.

Bees, the sex of, 439.

Beliefs: usually founded on fact, 17–19; the common groundwork of opposed, 19–25 (*see also* Religion).

Biology: relativity of knowledge and the nature of life, 93–98; definition of life, 95; transformation and equivalence of forces, 214–217; laws of motion, 236–240; rhythm of motion, 265–268; universal presence of integration and disintegration, 287; amount of contained motion in animals and plants, 302–306; and their mutual interdependence, 311–316; heterogeneity of evolving organisms, 333–336; 340–341; Von Baer's formula, 336; increasing definiteness of mammalian development, 366–368; has increasing definiteness characterized evolving flora and fauna? 368–370; redistributions of motion of evolving functions, 385–388; instability of the homogeneous, 409–416; multiplication of effects, 437–444; probable effects of upheavals in East Indian Archipelago, 440–443; segregation, 465–468; equilibration, 492–496; dissolution, 515–517.

Bird, wounded, apologue, 81–83, 444–445.

Birks, T. R., on *First Principles,* 574–584.

Blood, mental effects of cerebral supply, 221.

Body: distinguishable from space, 194, 229.

Bones: integration in ossifying, 313; heterogeneity in various races, 341; increased definiteness, 368; segregation in ossifying, 465–468.

Boscovich, R. J., theory of matter, 65–67, 72.

Botany: transformation and equivalence of forces, 214–217; laws of motion, 236–240; contained motion, 302–306; mutual interdependence of animals and plants, 312, 315–316; heterogeneity of evolving plants, 333–336; has increasing definiteness characterized evolving flora? 368–370; instability of the homogeneous, 409–416; effects of upheavals in East Indian Archipelago, 440–443; plant classification showing psychical segregation, 468–471.

Brain: causes influencing action of, 221; integration of growth, 312.

Brewster, Sir D., on the nebular hypothesis, 485 note.

Bronze, effects of substitution for stone, 449.

Bullets, projection of, 201.

Burney, Dr. C., on musical development, 355.

C

CANDLE: chemical explanation of burning, not philosophical, 278–280; effects on igniting, 428–429.

Cannon, rhythm consequent upon discharge, 256.

Caoutchouc, introduction in England of, 451.

Cause, the First: infinite and abso-

K

KANT, Immanuel, space and time forms of the intellect, 62.

Kirkman, T. P., on the formula of evolution, 554–559.

Knowledge: thought transcended by, 30; *résumé* showing limitations, 78–79; relativity of, 93–98; definition of complete, 281–283; unification of developing, 544–545.

L

LANGUAGE. *See* Philology.

Laplace, P. S., on nebulous ring development, 405, 462.

Latham, R. G., on inflexional language, 322.

Laughter, laws of motion exemplified by, 243.

Law: of continuity, 64, 70; uniformity of, 202; the author's belief in universality of, 336–337 note; increase in definiteness of evolving statutes, 371–372; developing systems, and the formula of evolution, 568–571.

Leibnitz, G. W., theory of matter, 65.

Leslie, T. E. Cliffe, on the formula of evolution, 561–571.

Liberty: general establishment of, 21; equilibration of, 507.

Life: and relativity of knowledge, 93–98; definition of, 95.

Light: transformed into other modes of force, 207; compound rhythm of interference, 257; like mode of production with sound, 324; segregation exemplified, 461.

Literature: integration of, 327; heterogeneity, 358; increasing truth of representation, 377; multiplied effects of, 451–452.

Liver, development of, 368.

Logic, definition of "*a priori*" and "necessary" truths, 184.

M

MAGNETISM: transformation into other modes of force, 206–208; illustrates laws of motion, 231; rhythm of variations, 261; consequent on added motion, 293; segregative power, 456; equilibration and the solar-spot cycle, 491.

Majorities, usually in error, 19.

Manifestations, the vivid and faint, 149–163, 176.

Manners and Fashion, essay on, 344 note.

Mansel, H. L.: on the first cause, the absolute, and the infinite, 53–56, 88–90, 98–104; conceptions of rational theology, 55; consciousness of self, 77; attributes being asserted of the absolute, 118.

Marriages, equilibration to means of subsistence, 501.

Marsupialia, integration of generative system in, 315.

Materialism and evolution, 547–550.

Mathematics: figures and mental development, 179–180; increase in definiteness, 373–374.

Matter: divisibility, 63; incomprehensibility, 63–67; solidity, 64; theories of Boscovich, 65–67, 72; Leibnitz, 65; and Newton, 65–67, 72; connection with force, 71–73; consciousness of, 171; indestructibility, 177–179, 182–183; creation and annihilation, unthinkable, 181–182; and space, 229; indestructibility of, a philosophical truth, 276–280; molecular motion and rearrangement of parts, 292–295; contained motion in organic, 300–302, 302–306; effect of uniform force on uniform, 427–430.

Maxwell, J. Clerk, on Thomson and Tait's *Treatise on Natural Philosophy,* 552.

Measurement, unable to prove persistence of force, 196–199.

Mechanics: progressive integration of machinery, 325; increase in indefiniteness of, 374–376; instability of the homogeneous illustrated, 399; multiplied effects of locomotive engine, 449; dependent moving equilibrium shown by steam engine, 481.

Metaphysics: sense of illusion after reading, 163; antagonism resulting from word real, 165.

Meteorology: laws of motion exemplified, 234–236; also rhythm of motion, 261–263; effect of heat on clouds, 286; visibility and audibility of objects preceding rain, 324; climatic effects of terrestrial irregularity, 333; definiteness of phenomena of, 366; molar originating in molecular motion, 380; redistributions of motion caused by earth's evolution, 384; instability of the homogeneous, 410; multiplied effects of solar action, 435; probable effects of Central American subsidence, 436–437; segregating effect of climate, 471.

Microscopes, great exactness of, 376.

Mill, J. S., on limit to industrial progress, 504.

Monotremata, integration of generative system in, 315.

Morbid growths, an increase in indefinite heterogeneity, 360–363.

Motion: incomprehensibility of, 67–70; relativity, 68; changing to rest, 70; conception derived from experiences of force, 172; continuity not self-evident, 184–185; Newton's first law, 186, 553; "latent" and "perceptible," 186–188, 188–191; of celestial bodies and pendulum, 187–188; continuity known in terms of force, 191; and involves its persistence, 192; transformed into heat, electricity, etc., 203–208; along line of least resistance, 230–232; general laws of direction, 233; laws supported by astronomy, 233–234; meteorology, 234–236; geology, 234–236; biology and botany, 236–240; psychology, 240–244; sociology, 244–250; spiral direction, 237; persistence of force underlies laws of direction, 250–254; universal rhythm of, 254–259; illustrated from astronomy, 259–261; magnetism, 261; meteorology, 261–263; geology, 261–265; biology with physiology and paleontology, 265–268, 385–388; psychology with the arts, 268–270, 353–357, 498; sociology, 270–273, 506; corollary from persistence of force, 273–275; final summary, 532; continuity of, a philosophical truth, 276; also law of direction, 277; facility of an aggregate to undergo rearrangement, 290–292; through space, and effects of incident forces, 290–292; amount in organic matter, 300–306; integration, heterogeneity, and distinctness of its evolution, 379–383; shown by geology, 380; meteorology, 381, 384; astron-